Growth Diagnosis

GROWTH DIAGNOSIS

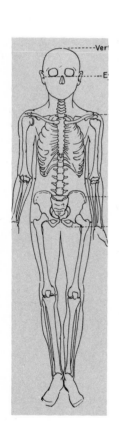

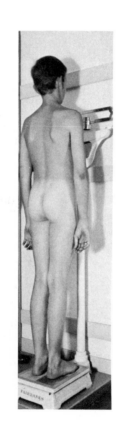

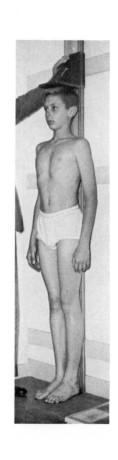

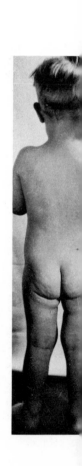

SELECTED METHODS FOR INTERPRETING AND PREDICTING PHYSICAL DEVELOPMENT FROM ONE YEAR TO MATURITY

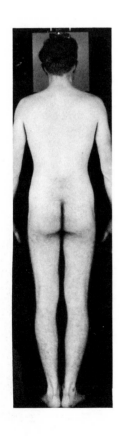

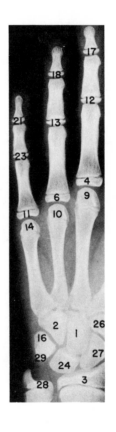

LEONA M. BAYER

NANCY BAYLEY

THE UNIVERSITY OF CHICAGO PRESS

*The University of Chicago
Committee on Publications
in Biology and Medicine*

EMMET B. BAY · LOWELL T. COGGESHALL
LESTER R. DRAGSTEDT · PETER P. H. DE BRUYN
THOMAS PARK · WILLIAM H. TALIAFERRO

Library of Congress Catalog Number: 59-11171

The University of Chicago Press, Chicago 37
Cambridge University Press, London, N.W. 1, England
The University of Toronto Press, Toronto 5, Canada

Preface

Physicians who deal with children and adolescents are well aware of the importance of evaluating growth; yet conclusive morphologic diagnoses are seldom made. Although developmental data are now available to define normalcy and deviation, the clinician rarely includes more than simple height and weight curves in his files on young patients. The most likely explanation is that a set of usable blueprints for more complete growth diagnosis has not been available in one place.

The past half-century has seen an impressive augmentation of knowledge in the field of human development, based on fairly standardized sets of measurements. If this knowledge is to be converted from research findings into practice, the physician needs a description of the measures and of the basic equipment used in their collection, along with instructions in their interpretation.

It is the intent of this book to convert selected segments of developmental data into simple techniques for appraising growth. The emphasis is on practical application, not on describing the research behind it. Attention is focused on the interrelatedness of different elements of growth, especially when these are meaningful over the whole span of childhood. A collection of various methods is presented, making it possible to select the ones most appropriate to a given situation. Sometimes a single device, properly used, will suffice to answer a specific question, such as "Is this child gaining weight too fast in his teens?" Multiple approaches best illuminate other problems and point up growth trends; they also serve as checks on one another.

While attention to the dynamics of growth has not always been a part of professional deliberations, current tendencies in medical practice are bringing morphologic concepts into greater prominence. In pediatrics the mastery of many acute diseases has been paralleled by increasing emphasis on continuous developmental supervision. Athletic coaches are turning more frequently to physicians for advice concerning the physical fitness and maturational status of their students. Mounting awareness of the difficult adjustments of adolescence inevitably calls attention to growth problems, a common source of worry at this critical age. Physicians are faced with deciding whether to reassure or to treat in view of the accumulating reports on hormonal treatment of children of all ages.

Often children or their parents are troubled by apparent deviations which have no pathological import but merely reflect individual variation in the tempo of development, differences which will disappear as the child matures. Nevertheless, at a given period, such deviations may have important effects on the child's image of himself, on his interpersonal relations, and on his social status. In such situations the value of correct **growth evaluations** may be enhanced by their demonstrated relation to **growth predictions.** Informed analysis may then serve as convincing reassurance to doctor, counselor, teacher, parent, and patient. The anxiety of a big girl who is "growing up" too fast can often be alleviated by indications that she will probably stop growing at an acceptable height. A small boy who is "growing up" too slowly may be similarly cheered upon finding that he will probably experience a satisfactory growth later. This kind of interpretation and prediction is quite different from the oft-heard, "There, there, it's just a stage and he'll outgrow it."

Just as diagnosis is the basis of all medical practice, so is growth diagnosis a valid basis for ruling out or identifying the presence of a significant growth deviation. **Growth diagnosis** is thus a first step toward reassurance or further investigation when a question is raised about an apparently unusual growth pattern.

If medical intervention is indicated and offers hope of success, evaluations of growth trends provide checks on the progress of treatment. The balance between growth and maturation is the crucial factor in the final outcome of any therapeutic effort.

To summarize, the substance of our book consists of instructions for collecting data on the individual patient; a limited number of generally accepted "normal" standards; techniques for interpretation of growth data in terms of these norms; and illustrations of all methods with appropriate case material. It is hoped that these collected items will give the physician a more confident basis for decisions regarding his patients with developmental problems.

Acknowledgments provide a pleasant opportunity to recall with appreciation the complex interdependence of workers in the contemporary scientific world. We could not have compiled our observations except as members of institutions with interested personnel and established machinery for the kind of co-operative studies here recorded. The Institute of Human De-

velopment at the University of California, where Dr. Bayley did most of her work toward this book, and the Stanford University School of Medicine, with which Dr. Bayer has long been associated, include on their staffs many valued co-workers.

At the Institute, we are happy to thank especially Drs. Harold E. Jones, Jean Walker MacFarlane, Herbert R. Stolz, Mary Cover Jones, and Marjorie P. Honzik; Mrs. Frances Baxter, Mrs. Dora A. Jensen, and Mrs. Katherine Eardley.

At Stanford, the clinical studies have had the steady support of the successive heads of the Department of Medicine: Drs. Arthur L. Bloomfield and David A. Rytand. Our special thanks go also to Drs. Horace Gray and William Walter Greulich, who provided not only material but encouragement for this book; to our photographer, Mr. Paul Tracy, and to Mrs. Estelle W. Rosenberg for her competent and devoted editorial assistance.

To safeguard the anonymity of patients, no physicians are mentioned in connection with specific referrals. The co-operation of colleagues is no less appreciated for this omission.

Our thanks go also to the publishers of our previous articles, who have permitted us to reprint reports and illustrative material, and to other authors and their publishers for similar releases. In every instance, specific acknowledgment is made in context.

LEONA M. BAYER
NANCY BAYLEY

Contents

List of Figures

CASE ILLUSTRATIONS: CLINICAL CASES

List of Tables

APPENDIX I. ANTHROPOMETRIC VALUES: MEANS AND STANDARD DEVIATIONS

APPENDIX II. HEIGHT-PREDICTION TABLES

APPENDIX III. CONVERTING AGE INTO THE DECIMAL SYSTEM

Purpose and Scope

Advances in our understanding of human growth patterns have come from various American research centers where the individual progress of hundreds of boys and girls has been documented from birth to maturity. Based on such studies, details of growth have been precisely delineated in regard to increases in individual parameters and changes in proportions, in indices, and in certain more superficial and subtle aspects of body contour and covering.

Simultaneous advances in our understanding of the physiology of growth emanate from biochemical, biological, cancer-research, and endocrine laboratories, where the intricacies of somatic growth have become increasingly subject to analysis. Comprehensive investigations have elucidated many basic metabolic and enzymatic processes which facilitate growth, even though they have not yet explained the essential mystery of the "steady state of imbalance" which is its foundation.

From this physiologic viewpoint normal growth, in its inception, maintenance, and termination, depends upon an orderly sequence of genetic, constitutional, environmental, nutritional, and endocrine influences.

The observable changes in size and proportion which constitute normal growth presumably reflect harmonious physiologic successions; conversely, deviations in growth patterns may reflect related physiologic abnormalities. Accurate recognition of deviations as such can therefore be an important diagnostic aid. An exact description of a growth deviation in terms of its morphologic and temporal aspects may give an excellent clue to its probable etiology.

In any case, it seems apparent that a combination of what is known about growth in both its topographic and its physiologic aspects can contribute more to clinical practice than can either alone. The phenomena and significance of these less familiar topographic aspects are the province of this volume. The emphasis is on precision in the evaluation of deviant growth and/or maturation per se, as a first step toward its further consideration.

In order to be clinically reliable, however, not only must growth assessments be precise, but also interpretation of those assessments must be circumspect. One result of the complexity of the growth process is the wide variability of its normal manifestations. Useful growth diagnosis requires an understanding of both central tendencies and normal variation. This brings us to a discussion of a pragmatic definition of normal.

THE CONCEPT OF NORMAL

To evaluate the development of a given child it is necessary to compare him with some generally acceptable standards. Such "norms" should satisfy at least two practical requirements: (1) They should be drawn from a population which is ethnically homogeneous, clearly described, and numerically adequate. (2) Within the framework of such a population, "norms" should be defined in statistically meaningful terms.

The anthropometric norms presented in this volume are adequate in regard to both these criteria. They are

1

derived largely from American children of European origin who have been nurtured under favorable conditions. They are, in most instances, expressed in terms of means and standard deviations.

Details concerning the population and the statistical units are presented in chapter 6, "Anthropometric Values and Deviation Charts."

SELECTION OF MATERIAL

Since this book is offered as a practical working guide rather than as a compendium, we have selected those procedures which seem to us most useful and informative.

Elaborations of anthropometric measures and indices are limited to five each. These have been chosen for their simplicity, for their usefulness over the whole span of childhood and adolescence, and for their special relevance to the degree and direction of sexual differentiation. We think any clinician will be willing to take three measures in addition to the conventional height and weight, whereas more measures might be prohibitive.

Only the hand and wrist are recommended for skeletal-maturation assessments. The hand has a tested usable relationship to growth in body size and build. Present awareness of the desirability of minimizing medical X-ray exposure is another potent practical argument in favor of taking one rather than many X-rays of joints. Other reasons for relying on exact readings in one proved area instead of approximate judgments in many areas are set forth in the chapter on X-ray of the hand and wrist.

In certain aspects the material selected for this volume is deliberately restricted. The age range covered is from one year to maturity. Material on children younger than one year has been omitted because its presentation would require somewhat different treatment, with separate charts and tables for measuring at three- or four-month intervals rather than annually. Furthermore, simple growth deviations, unassociated with other obvious pathology, rarely manifest themselves before the first birthday. Therefore, the descriptions and tables of growth which are incorporated in such standard texts as Holt and McIntosh (1953) and Nelson (1954) are adequate during the first year of life for most clinical purposes.

This volume is further restricted to those measurements which define the growth of the body and body segments in relation to age and rates of maturing. We have not presented certain popular indices, for instance, those derived from head measurements. The head has a growth pattern which differs from over-all

growth in that it shows little adolescent spurt. It would contradict our purpose to include specific areas of development which are not clearly integrated with the total picture. Again, standard pediatric books, such as the above-mentioned, plus endocrinology texts (e.g., Wilkins, 1957) are available; these give adequate descriptions of the growth of the head, the face, and other body parts as they figure in the diagnosis of recognized pathological syndromes.

TECHNIQUES AND ILLUSTRATIONS

The practicability and reliability of the techniques and standards collected in this volume have been amply tested in relation to ordinary office practice. Attention has been given to every step of the procedures involved. Tables, charts, and directions have been collected from sources which are widely scattered and often inaccessible. The deviation chart was adapted from Gray and Ayres (1931) and is published in its present form for the first time (see Fig. 15).

Selected material relevant to growth evaluation is brought together and explained. This includes normal standards, normal growth curves, and techniques for relating the data on a given child to these standards. Judicious combinations of methods for analyzing the tempo, degree, and direction of somatic growth and maturation permit inferences concerning the status of a child at any given moment as well as his progress over time.

Many of the graphs are essentially similar, with the abscissa ranging from birth to maturity so that young adult standards are included. An effort has been made to present charts which are clear, easy to understand, and easy to use, with a minimum of computational and interpretive work. Where computations are essential, they are specifically explained.

Finally, case studies show how various graphs and charts are used to interpret actual growth observations.

SOME IMPLICATIONS OF GROWTH ASSESSMENT

Modern research in the basic sciences is bringing to medicine a constantly enlarging and more diversified fund of specialized knowledge. Simultaneously there is an increasing awareness that before this knowledge can become clinically useful it must be refocused upon the individual patient. This effort to keep the patient in the center of his medical picture is the essence of the so-called "comprehensive viewpoint" in present-day medical teaching. Among the many medical disciplines, a few provide especially good vantage points for such a holistic view. Preventive medicine relates the patient particularly to his external environment. Psychosomatic research considers matters of both external and internal homeostasis. Concepts of growth and development, by emphasizing the importance of continuous change in the status of young patients, provide a good core for integration of the problems of children and adolescents, whether the main solutions be pediatric, medical, psychological, psychiatric, surgical, or social.

Like the theory of relativity, the concepts of growth and development bring the element of time into prominent relief. The implications of development extend throughout the life-span. Erikson (1950) has argued very well that, as growth proceeds from one stage to the next, each epoch of human life has its characteristic tasks and its characteristic disorders.

Finally, this consideration of the individual in terms of his own totality and his own tempo serves to reaffirm his unique personal value. As Gallagher and Gallagher (1953) point out, "It is as difficult as it is desirable . . . to promote the idea of the importance of the individual in people whose world, while protesting a belief in freedom, bombards them with talk about . . . average size, behavior, and attitudes, and [thus] unwittingly sets conformity on a pedestal."

Part I

Methodology

Section A
Collecting Data on the Individual Patient

Section B
Analyzing the Data—Current Status of Patient

Section C
Interpreting Successive Observations—Growth Trends

Section A

Collecting Data on the Individual Patient

Collecting adequate developmental data from the patient requires four simple operations: inspection, selected anthropometry, photography, and a special X-ray of the hand and wrist. These procedures bring to medical practice established anthropologic methods that have been extensively applied during the past quarter-century of research in American child-development centers. Thus the fruits of these comprehensive studies become immediately available to medicine as standards of comparison for individual data; evaluations can then be made which are of great diagnostic value.

Individual data provide the raw material for analytical methods described in later sections of this book. The present section summarizes certain general rules that apply to the collecting of individual growth data.

Although equipment and techniques are simple, they must be used with the same conscientious precision accorded any laboratory procedure. Birthdates and dates of measurement should always be noted exactly; parameters should be measured with attention given to the positioning of the patient, anatomical landmarks, and correct use of measuring apparatus. Special instructions for measurement and data-recording are included at appropriate points in the text, and conversion constants are inserted in context. For use here and in later sections, basic apparatus for simple calculations should be available—a good slide rule or a calculator which will add and subtract, multiply and divide. Also desirable is a twelve-inch, 30°–60° transparent triangle, a very helpful tool in reading tables and graphs.

Chapter 1

Inspection

"Observe, record, tabulate, communicate."

So Osler instructed his students, according to Thayer (1919). The quotation continues: "Use your five senses. The art of the practice of medicine is to be learned only by experience; 'tis not an inheritance; it can not be revealed. . . . See, and then reason and compare and control. But see first."

To look at a patient is an obvious step in any diagnosis. The first impression when a patient presents himself (or is presented by a parent) is itself a valuable guide as to what aspects of family background and past records may be worth pursuing. Observed reactions as the history is being taken give further clues as to what may be genetically significant or psychologically important. A "growth history" is thus an expansion of the conventional medical history, with emphasis on developmental aspects of familial and individual data.

Similarly, the conventional physical examination is expanded in the evaluation of problems of growth and development to include the collection of data particularly needed for such an evaluation. Here inspection is a crucial procedure. The physical examination should include a look at the child "from all sides," preferably standing and walking, and always in a situation which is physically comfortable and in which the examiner has taken considered pains to put the young patient at ease. Tact, incidentally, dictates that the observer make no thoughtless comments concern-

ing either his observations or his inferences. Children are very sensitive about their size and shape, especially during adolescence when even the most normal boy and girl experiences some anxiety about the outcome of the puberal metamorphosis. In this connection, Gallagher and Gallagher (1953) point out that in dealing with adolescents we should "avoid reinforcing their already unwarranted beliefs regarding standards, by ourselves avoiding careless or obsequious reference to them."

From careful inspection, educated eyes will observe much that can profitably be recorded; clues about size, maturity, and the degree, direction, and harmony of sexual differentiation are all apparent at first glance. Later these qualitative impressions are documented and interpreted. As experience in analysis increases, the observer will become more perceptive in recognizing essential aspects of growth and development.

In addition, during a first simple, courteous inspection under relatively standard conditions, much insight may be gained concerning a child's psychological relation to himself, to his body, and to his observer. For these reasons, it is urged that growth evaluation begin with a "look," a look which searches especially for the factors detailed in the following pages.

Chapter 2

Anthropometry

Besides **weight** and **stature,** three other reliable body measures are useful in the clinical evaluation of growth. These are **trunk length, bi-acromial diameter,** and **bi-cristal diameter.** On the basis of these five measures, many important questions can be answered regarding a child's absolute size, his build, his weight in relation to his build, and his proportions, especially as these reflect phases of sexual differentiation.

INSTRUMENTS

Weight is taken on a balance scale. A special support may be fastened to the floor of the scale for younger children to hold on to. This scale and other pieces of equipment are illustrated in Figures 2–7.

Heights—both total stature and trunk length—should be measured against a wall. Such positioning insures far greater standardization of posture than if the patient is measured against a free-standing pole of the sort often attached to scales. Materials include: a two-meter ruler and a six-foot ruler fastened flat against the wall and adjacent to each other; a triangle of wood for use with the measuring sticks to determine the distance from the floor to the crown of the head; and a box at convenient sitting height. If the sitting-box is stoutly constructed, with dimensions $20 \times 30 \times 40$ cm., it can be turned so as to serve subjects of all sizes.

Diameters are measured with large, sliding metal calipers of the Hrdlička type when these are available. Inexpensive adaptations are satisfactory for clinical purposes.

GENERAL PROCEDURES

Measurements are made essentially according to the classic methods detailed by Martin (1928). The child is measured with all his clothing removed. Unless otherwise indicated, he should be standing erect. All measures are repeated and read after fresh adjustments of the instruments. A number midway between the highest and the lowest reading is taken as the correct reading and recorded. Figure 1 shows the anatomical landmarks referred to in the following measurements.

Measuring Weight (W)

The child should be standing freely, as in Figure 2. If he jiggles unsteadily, show him how to hold the sides of his legs with his hands or how to hold onto a special support if it is available. Take the reading to the nearest unit on the scale.

Measuring Height or Stature (S)

The child stands with his back against a wall, resting firmly on both feet, heels touching the wall, hands at his sides (Fig. 3). Ask him to "stand tall," but make sure that his head is held so that the upper level of the earhole makes a horizontal line with the lower edge of the bony orbit. Bring down the triangle, held firmly against the measuring board, until it makes a firm contact with the crown of the head without pressure. Raise and lower the triangle several times, noting the reading, until you are sure it is representative when the child stands in the correct posture.

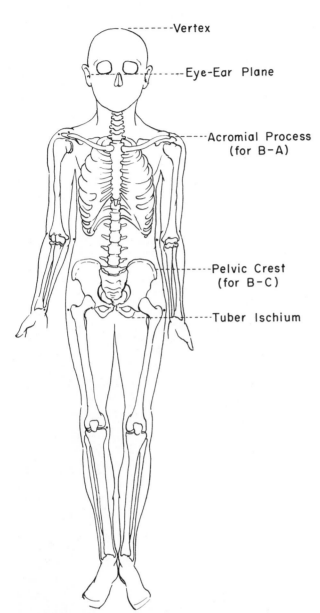

- - - - Vertex
- - - Eye-Ear Plane
- - - Acromial Process (for B-A)
- - - Pelvic Crest (for B-C)
- - - Tuber Ischium

FIG. 1.—Anatomical landmarks used in anthropometric measures. *V*, vertex; *E*, eye-ear plane; *A*, acromial process; *P*, pelvic crest; *T*, tuber ischium.

Measuring Trunk Length (Si or St)

When related to stature, **trunk length** gives more reliable information about leg length than any direct measure of the leg itself (Gray, 1922). Although it is not the measure generally used in medical circles, it could profitably be substituted for the present common practice of measuring "span." Two accepted measurements of trunk length were used in deriving the data in this book: **sitting height** (*Si*) and **stem length** (*St*). Both methods are described below. They differ only in the angle the leg makes with the trunk,

that is, the portion of the ischium on which the subject sits. *Si* is always very slightly larger than *St*.

To take **sitting height** (*Si*) the child is seated on the sitting-box with his back against a wall or against an upright measuring board which is attached to the seat (Fig. 4). The child should lean forward, slide far back, and then sit up straight. The box should be placed so that the child sits slightly lower than the knees, and his position should be such that the upper level of the thigh is perpendicular to the trunk, parallel with the floor. With his head in the same position as for measuring height, manipulate the triangle in the same

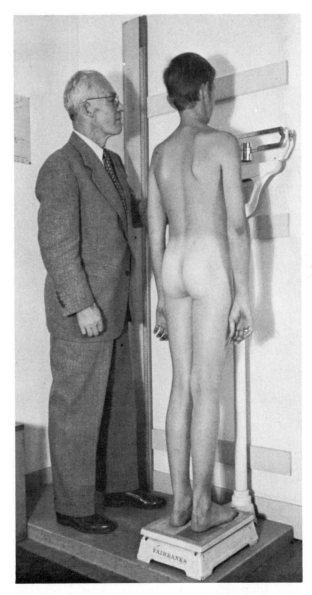

FIG. 2.—Weighing the child. From Stolz and Stolz, *Somatic Development of Adolescent Boys*, 1951. Photograph courtesy of the authors and the Macmillan Co., New York.

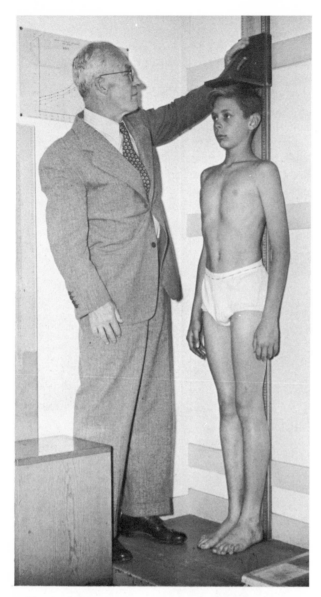

FIG. 3.—Measuring stature. From Stolz and Stolz, 1951. Photograph courtesy of the authors and the Macmillan Co., New York.

TABLE 1

SITTING HEIGHT $\rightleftharpoons$ STEM LENGTH: CONVERSION TABLE

Ages (Years)	Stem Length to Sitting Height	Sitting Height to Stem Length
Below 6.......	$Si = 1.02\ St$	$St = .98\ Si$
7–12..........	$Si = 1.01\ St$	$St = .99\ Si$
Above 13......	$Si = 1.03\ St$	$St = .97\ Si$

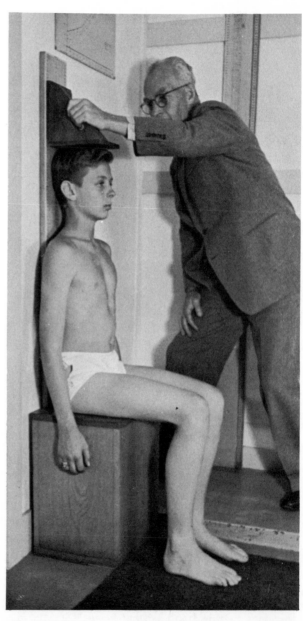

FIG. 4.—Measuring sitting height. The thighs are parallel to the floor. From Stolz and Stolz, 1951. Photograph courtesy of the authors and the Macmillan Co., New York.

manner as for measuring height. An alternative technique is to have the child sit on a paper towel on the floor, with legs straight out in front.

Stem length (St) is measured (Fig. 5) by having the child sit as for $Si;$ his feet, however, are so placed—either on the floor or on the rung of a nearby chair—that his upper leg makes a 45° angle with his trunk.

Values for sitting height and stem length, i.e., the trunk length with thighs at a right angle to the trunk or at a 45° angle, may be interchanged by the constants in Table 1 given by Gray (1922).

10

Measuring Bi-Acromial Diameter (BA)

The acromial processes may be located by palpation as the child stands relaxed with his back to the examiner (Fig. 6). The rigid end of the sliding calipers is placed just to the left of the left acromial process, and the free end is moved until it is just to the right of the right process. In doing this, the examiner holds the calipers so that the ends point upward and forward at an angle of about 45°. This measure is taken without pressure.

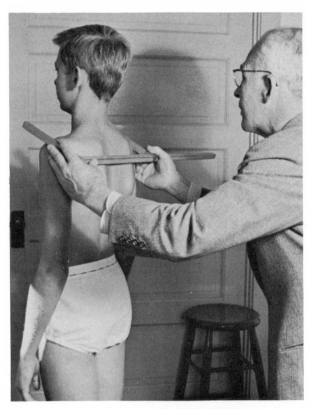

FIG. 6.—Measuring bi-acromial diameter. The shoulders are relaxed, and a light touch of the calipers is used. From Stolz and Stolz, 1951. Photograph courtesy of the authors and the Macmillan Co., New York.

Measuring Bi-Cristal Diameter (BC)

For this measurement (Fig. 7), also known as the **bi-iliac diameter,** the child stands either facing or with his back to the examiner, depending on which approach best avoids any fat pads. The iliac crests are located by palpation. The jaws of the sliding calipers are placed over the crests and pressed firmly (especially in fat children) in order to get, as nearly as possible, a measure of the bony diameter.

RECORDING

If measurements are being taken just as part of good pediatric supervision, it is convenient and sufficient to enter a set of measurements on a simple form, such as that of Table 2, rubber-stamped into the running record at semiannual or annual intervals. Either the English or the metric system may be used, with space provided for both. These are the same measures to be used on the deviation chart (Fig. 15), described in chapter 6.

Aside from weight, it is superfluous to collect routine measures more frequently than twice a year. But it is surprising how often a biannual record, col-

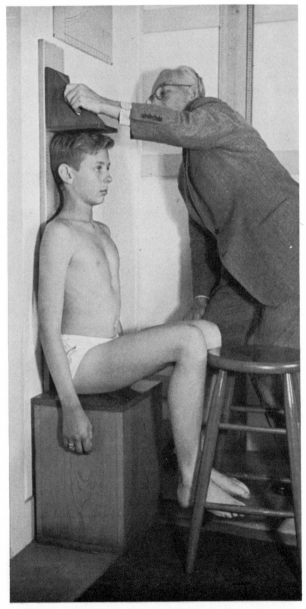

FIG. 5.—Measuring stem length. The knees are elevated, in contrast to the position in Fig. 4. From Stolz and Stolz, 1951. Photograph courtesy of the authors and the Macmillan Co., New York.

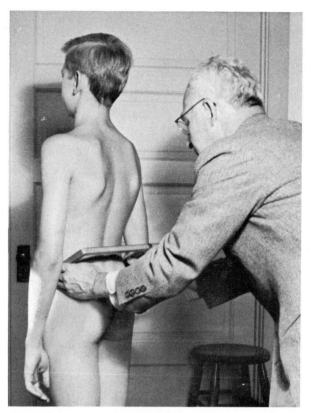

FIG. 7.—Measuring bi-cristal diameter. This measurement, also called the "bi-iliac," may be taken from the front or the back; firm pressure is applied to the pelvic crests. From Stolz and Stolz, 1951. Photograph courtesy of the authors and the Macmillan Co., New York.

lected casually over the years, proves invaluable in connection with later adolescent deviations in height and weight.

Measurements which are made specifically for the

evaluation of build are best recorded on a deviation chart, where space is provided also for the calculation or ratios and for their evaluation. Stature and weight readings to be used in a longitudinal study of these parameters might well be recorded directly on appropriate forms.

Indices

Two kinds of indices are helpful: those relating other absolute measures to stature and those relating certain absolute measures to one another. Either the English or the metric system is usable, except that data on the relation of weight to linear measures have all been published in the metric system. For uniformity, it is therefore usually better to convert all measures to metric before proceeding further. The necessary constants are included on the form (Fig. 15).

TABLE 2

CURRENT MEASURES
(Suggested Form for Rubber Stamp)

Date————Age————Wt.: lbs.————kg.————
Stature————in. ————cm.————
Sitting ht.————in. ————cm.————
  (or stem length, if this is the routine measure chosen)
Bi-acromial ————in.————cm.————
Bi-cristal ————in.————cm.————

Interpretation

In evaluating the growth status of a given child, his measures, both absolute and derived, must be compared with suitable norms. The use of deviation charts and other methods for analyzing growth data will be discussed in Section B.

Chapter 3

Photography

Photographs serve two purposes in growth diagnosis; they reveal the current status of an individual and they form a cumulative record over the years. Since photographs permit a number of leisurely comparisons—between an individual and a standard; between an individual and himself at another age; or among several individuals—they are most useful when they are taken under standard conditions, even though pictures of young patients may look very small in frames suitable for later adult size. The value of photography is emphasized by Stolz and Stolz (1951, p. 38):

"Seriatim photographic records, so taken and arranged that they present to the student of human development comparably scaled visual images of the bodily appearance of a boy or a girl at successive stages of growth, yield valuable information which cannot be brought to life from verbal descriptions or from recorded measurements.

"Each series shows not only the obvious developmental changes in height, shoulder breadth, hip width, body proportions, and postural alignment, but also changes in the amount and distribution of subcutaneous fat, changes in the muscular development, and changes in the development of primary sex-appropriate characteristics—all constantly related to each other and to the unique body configuration of the person in whom they occurred."

MINIMAL PHOTOGRAPHIC REQUIREMENTS

For practical clinical purposes it is important to have a regular setting and equipment, so that all photographs can be taken under the same conditions. The essential needs follow.

Lighting should be adequate and not too disturbing to the child.

A **distance** of at least 15-21 feet is desirable, to keep distortion at a minimum. In any case, the distance between camera and subject should always be the same. Although the distance can be constant only if both the posing stand and the camera tripod are fixed to the floor, this ideal can be approached if patient and camera are always placed in positions that are permanently marked on the floor.

The **camera lens** must be relatively non-distorting. Box cameras are preferable, though smaller cameras, even those using microfilms, may be considered. Distance must, of course, be adjusted for the focal length of the lens.

Standardized Procedures

Once trials with lighting arrangements have determined the best illumination for the setting, the same standard lighting should be used for all exposures. Aperture setting and exposure time will then also be constant, permitting uniform developing and printing procedures. Thus, good pictures of consistent quality and comparability can be achieved.

The subject is asked to stand on the designated spot for a given setup (Fig. 8). He is told to "stand tall," with feet in full contact with the floor and with head in the same position as for measuring height. Three views should be taken: front, rear, and left side. For the front and rear views, the arms should be just far enough away from the trunk so as not to obscure the body curves but no farther away than necessary, so that the picture is as compact as possible. For the front view, the hands should face forward to document the carrying angle; for the back view, the hands can take the most natural position, facing the trunk. In the side view, the arms should touch the sides and should be rotated until they do not conceal the anterior and posterior body contours. In this way, the lateral view reveals anterior and posterior body outlines, as well as giving some indication of posture.

FIXED PHOTOGRAPHIC INSTALLATIONS

One standardized photographic setup will be described here. This is essentially as outlined by Gavan, Washburn, and Lewis (1952) and may serve as a guide for a fixed installation in office, clinic, or hospital. Figure 9 is a reproduction of one of their prints.

"The *camera* was a Keith copying camera, 5×7. . . . This camera lacked 'swings' on the lens board

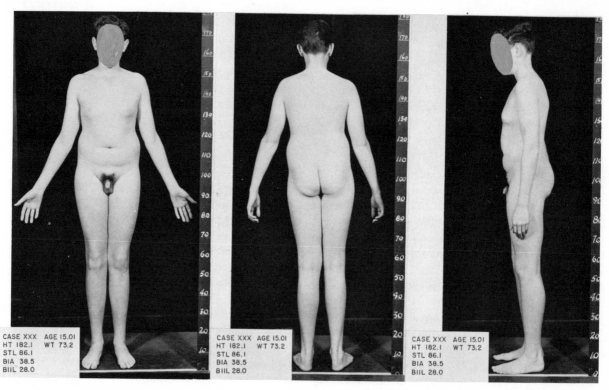

CASE XXX AGE 15.01
HT 182.1 WT 73.2
STL 86.1
BIA 38.5
BIIL 28.0

FIG. 8.—Positions of subject in the three views comprising a set of standardized photographs. Identifying data may be completely or partially incorporated into the pictures.

Identification

The best way to insure identification is to incorporate identifying data into the picture. Movable letters and figures mounted on a suitable board and photographed along with the subject may be used for this purpose. Figures should be at least an inch high, since they are greatly reduced in the photograph. Data should include either the child's name or, preferably, a case number, the date, and his age. It is often useful to include several of the measurements, such as height and weight, for ready reference and comparisons.

Interpretation

Special reference is made to the interpretation of photographs in the chapters "Androgyny" and "Secondary Sex Characters," where various somatic ratings are described.

and film holder so that the front and back of the camera were always parallel. It was mounted on an elevator type tripod equipped with a pan head; the camera could be raised or lowered without moving the tripod feet. Two spirit levels were used to make sure the head of the tripod was horizontal. Two perpendicular pencil lines intersecting at the center of the field were marked on the ground glass. These were used to align the camera [with lines on the platform].

"A 12-inch, Eastman Commercial Ektar *lens* was used. To it was synchronized a single, portable strobe unit which was mounted directly above the lens. This unit supplied all the *light* on the front of the subject.

"The *posing stand* was a light, wooden platform painted white. The vertical upright was a 2×4 inch on which was pasted a paper scale graduated in centimeters from 0 to 200.

14

"On the top of the platform three black lines were painted. The first extended across the platform from the base of the upright; the other two were perpendicular to the first. The subject was told to stand on the appropriate point of intersection at which the camera had previously been aligned. This was done by having the vertical line on the ground glass cover the line on the platform; the horizontal line on the ground glass was placed at the 100 cm. mark on the upright. . . .

"The *distance* from the lens to the upright was 21 feet.

"The *background* consisted of a heavy piece of white cloth suspended from the ceiling, three feet behind the platform. The bottom end of the background was attached to the back of the platform. Thus the background hung in a curve. It was *separately lighted*

by two No. 2 photofloods which were shielded from the subject.

"The *film* used was Eastman's Super Panchro-Press Type B. This is a high speed, fine grained pan film which is readily available as 5×7-inch cut film. The manufacturer recommends developer DK50 or DK60a, but as our light proved not to be as powerful as needed, special developing was used. This was only necessary because we did not realize at the time the light was purchased how long the lens-subject distance would have to be. The negatives were taken at *f16, 1/50 second*. This stop gives sufficient depth of field to cover the posing stand from front to back.

"The *negatives* were enlarged two diameters on 'Resisto Rapid' non-shrinkable base paper. Such *prints* have a reduction ratio of 10:1, and 1 mm. on the print

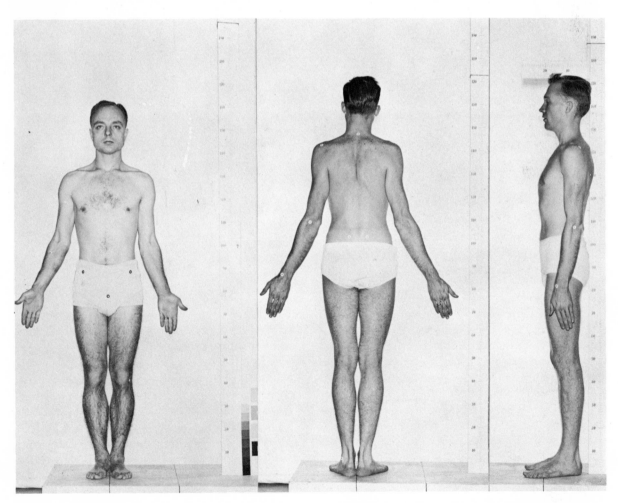

FIG. 9.—Three views of patient in the standardized photographic setup described by Gavan, Washburn, and Lewis in "Photography: An Anthropometric Tool," *Am. J. Phys. Anthrop.*, N.S., Vol. 10 (1952). Courtesy of the authors and the Wistar Institute of Anatomy and Biology, Philadelphia.

equals 1 cm. on the subject." (For most practical purposes, however, 5″×7″ contact prints are handier than such enlargements.)

Problems of positioning the subject, identification, and interpretation were handled by Gavan *et al.* much as we have already described. In addition to the above features, their paper presents refinements involving color scales and shading scales. Their method is sufficiently accurate so that, with the help of marking devices, anthropometric measures can be made directly from the photographs. However, if such color comparisons or direct measurements from photos are contemplated, the original article of Gavan *et al.* must be consulted for detailed presentation of procedures and rationale.

Slightly different methods are outlined by Stolz and Stolz (1951); the Berkeley photographs in this book were taken according to that setup. Sheldon's method of photography (Sheldon, Stevens, and Tucker, 1940) also insures good body photographs.

Chapter 4

X-Ray of the Hand and Wrist for Skeletal Age

A single X-ray of one hand and wrist can provide the basis for a critical evaluation of maturation to which many other indices, analyses, and predictions can be meaningfully related. The left hand is customarily chosen, since it is thought to be less subject to environmental influences. The X-ray should be taken with special attention to details of position and exposure to permit reliable matching with the age standards (Figs. 10*a* and 10*b*).

Many clinicians and radiologists are still somewhat uneasy about assessing skeletal age (SA) using the hand and wrist alone instead of a broad survey of bones and joints in which the presence of osseous centers and the closure of epiphyses are listed. It therefore seems relevant here to restate the adequacy of this area for determining skeletal maturation by matching with standard films.

T. Wingate Todd (1937) first developed the inspectional method of skeletal assessment by noting the shapes, contours, articular surfaces, and relative sizes of the diaphysial-epiphyseal region and other centers of ossification in six areas of the body. These areas were shoulder, elbow, hand (including the wrist), hip, knee, and foot. Todd selected for each area a series of X-rays of graduated maturational status, each representative of the normal stage of development for children of a given age. When he compared the skeletal ages arrived at by inspection of these different areas, he found that there was usually a high correlation— that is, as a rule a child was about equally mature in all parts of his skeleton. Furthermore, Todd was able to find in the hand and wrist, with its large number of

centers of ossification, a continuous series of identifiable changes throughout the period of growth. It was thus possible for him to make up two series of standards for the hand (one for each sex), using three-month intervals during infancy and six-month intervals from three years until growth was completed with closure of the distal radial epiphysis. These hand standards were published in 1937 in his *Atlas of Skeletal Maturation.*

Todd's next most useful set of standards were for the knee. A revision and refinement of the knee series has been published by Pyle and Hoerr (1955). Other standards, representing the other four bony areas, are being prepared by Pyle and associates for eventual publication.

However, the hand standards remain the most generally useful. The use of the single hand film has several additional advantages. It is inexpensive; it requires a minimal exposure to X-rays; it is easy to place a young child's hand in position for a correct exposure with little emotional disturbance to the child; the resulting image is likely to be clear and legible and to be in standard position for accurate assessment. These advantages combine to permit regular repetition of X-rays at intervals of a year or two.

There is an orderly sequence of patterning in the osseous invasion of cartilaginous areas in the diaphysial-epiphyseal regions of the metacarpals, phalanges, radius, and ulna and, to a lesser degree, in the carpal bones. It is this characteristic year-by-year progression in the appearance of bony shadows on the X-rays that makes it possible to use a set of standard films, with each film in a series representative of a given age (see Fig. 26, p. 44). Several investigators (Flory, 1936; Bayley, 1943; Macy and Kelly, 1957) have found the method highly accurate, and also a valid indicator of general physical maturity.

Macy and Kelly (1957) give an excellent review of the history of the various methods of assessing skeletal maturation by means of X-rays. The method most gen-

erally used has been to note two conditions (appearance of the bony centers and closure of the epiphyses at the ends of the long bones) in a large number of different joints of the body. This procedure requires that five or six X-rays be made (of the shoulder, elbow, hand and wrist, pelvis, knee, and foot). Most osseous centers appear in the first few years, and no epiphyses close (in normal growth) before 12 or 13 years. As a

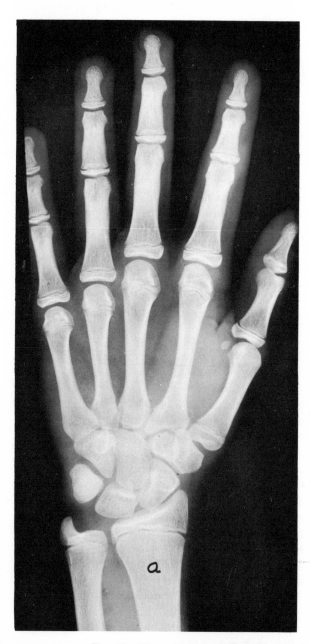 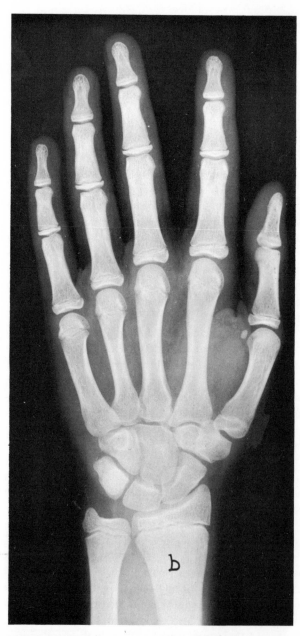

Fig. 10.—X-ray views of a girl's hand and wrist at two successive skeletal ages: *a*, 13 years; *b*, 13 years 6 months. Detecting the minute details of epiphyseal change depends on such technical refinements as correct centering of the X-ray tube. From Greulich and Pyle, *Radiographic Atlas of Skeletal Development of the Hand and Wrist*, 1959. Photographs courtesy of the authors and the Stanford University Press.

result, there are long periods during childhood when significant changes cannot be rated by this method. Accordingly, such bone-age readings are often only rough approximations.

Another, more rigorous, procedure—measures of the size of ossification centers (Cattell, 1934; Flory, 1936)—although exacting, yields equivocal results. Individual differences in children's sizes and differing rates of growth among the bones, with resulting changing proportions, render the measurements and the indices derived from them of little value.

The Todd method, however, makes use of the fact that, after an osseous center has appeared, it changes its size and shape in a systematic fashion as the ossification gradually spreads through the cartilaginous parts of the skeleton. Therefore, X-ray pictures of bones that are maturing at a normal rate show regularly increasing maturity in the configurations of these osseous centers and often, also, in the adjoining ends of the long bones. Thus it is possible to select a series of standard films of a single area that represent the characteristic bony patterns at successively mature ages. One can then readily compare a patient's film with these standards for its assessment.

Greulich and Pyle (1959) have well stated both Todd's original judgment and the results of research with the Todd method: "The skeleton of the healthy adequately nourished child develops as a unit, and its various parts tend to keep pace with each other in their maturation." Where disease leads to disharmonious development, this spread is also reflected in the hand, whose thirty bones represent well over 10 per cent of those in the entire body.

The Greulich-Pyle *Radiographic Atlas of Skeletal Development of the Hand and Wrist* (1959) first appeared in 1950 as a revision of the original Todd *Atlas* of 1937; it includes an excellent set of standards and clear directions for their use. These standards are the basis of the Bayley-Pinneau Height-Prediction Tables (1952), which will be described in chapter 10 and which are reprinted in Appendix II. If these tables are used for estimating future growth, there is greater assurance of accuracy when the SA's have been read from the Greulich-Pyle standards for the hand and wrist. The Height-Prediction Tables are also reprinted in the 1959 edition of the *Atlas* along with the original paper describing their use in combination with the standards (Bayley and Pinneau, 1952).

The knee, as assessed by the Pyle-Hoerr standards

(1955), is a second choice and may be useful as an additional area for appraisal. However, by itself the knee has been found to be a less reliable indicator of skeletal maturity and less accurate in predicting adult stature (Bayley, 1943).

Procedure

Position

The left hand should be placed palm down, flat on the film-holder, with fingers slightly separated and the axis of the hand, wrist, and forearm in a straight line. Center the tube halfway between the tips of the fingers and distal end of the radius. The radiograph should include the complete fingers and at least 1.5 inches of the radius, since all the hand epiphyses, as well as those of the distal end of the arm, are very important in the skeletal-age reading. Also, evidences of interrupted growth may be read from the appearance of cross-striations in the distal end of the radius.

X-Ray Technique

Films should be taken at a distance of 36 inches. Details of technique, involving the use or absence of screen, time, voltage, etc., will depend on the age of the patient, thickness of the part, variations in X-ray apparatus, and the preferences of the technician. Whatever the technique, fine details of the diaphysial-epiphyseal plane may be obscured by differences in relative position of the central ray; therefore, attention to centering is always important. For the additional assessment of the relative density of the bones, the physician may wish to use on each film a standard, graduated in density, against which the bones may be compared. This may be metal—a graded series of laminated thicknesses of aluminum as used by Todd—or bone with a similar series of graded densities.

Interpretation

Assessment of the X-ray for skeletal age and the use of SA for diagnosis of current status and for stature prediction are briefly described in chapters 9 and 10. We are not able here to supply the complete series of standards that must be used in accurate SA reading. Therefore, we recommend the use of the Greulich-Pyle *Atlas*, which also contains complete instructions for assessment (1959). This *Atlas* should be considered another important tool in the evaluation of growth in children.

Section B

Analyzing the Data—Current Status of Patient

Using the data collected by the techniques of Section A, this section describes methods for arriving at clinically valuable definitions of physical status. Devices are presented for comparing, rating, and assessing; directions for applying these devices and notes on their clinical significance are included. Fundamental to the construction of all such devices is the principle that the body undergoes orderly changes with age, changes both in absolute measurements and in proportions. So important are these shifts in proportion that the first chapter here is devoted to a portrayal of the changing body form of boys and girls as they grow to maturity.

Other chapters discuss anthropometric values and linear and lateral tendencies, dealing primarily with inferences that may be drawn from body measures and indices. Discussions of secondary sex characters and androgyny depend upon direct and photographic inspection. Skeletal assessment and height prediction are based, respectively, on the X-ray of the hand and wrist and on the X-ray plus height and age.

Whether a child is to be seen only once or is to be followed over time, there is always the first complete examination, at which many questions concerning his present growth status can be answered. How big is he for his age and sex? Are his proportions normal? How near optimal is his weight for his build? What level of maturity has he reached? If he is old enough for valid predicting (6–7 years), what will be his probable adult height? Definitive answers to such questions will often eliminate the need for further observations. For this purpose, in addition to the procedures which comprise this section, we will also use in reference some of the graphic material elaborated in Section C on growth trends.

Chapter 5

Changing Body Proportions

In evaluating children's growth, it is necessary to keep in mind that body proportions change with age in characteristic ways. The fact that different segments grow at different rates is well illustrated in Figure 11, in which photographs of the same boy, taken at ages 15 and 30 months, 6, 11, 14, and 18 years, are all equated to the same total stature. If this series were extended downward to early fetal ages, the change in proportions would be even more extreme. However, our present concern is with the evaluation of growth after one year of age.

GROWTH CHANGES IN PROPORTIONS

In general the sequence of regions showing the most rapid growth follows the cephalo-caudal, proximo-distal pattern. Early growth of the baby is most rapid in the head, later growth in the body stem. Only after the age of one do the legs start growing more rapidly than the body, a trend which continues until puberty. At that time trunk growth again surpasses leg growth, as will be seen in Figure 12.

At successive ages, in addition to differences in lengthwise proportions, there are differences in the

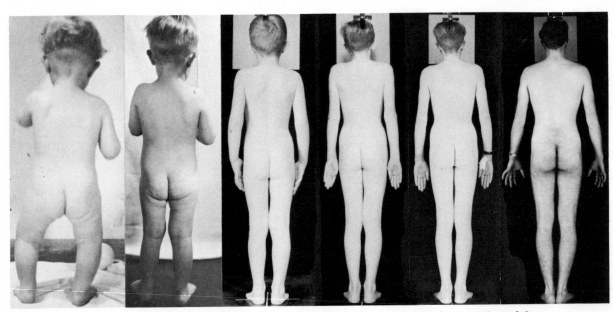

FIG. 11.—Photographs of a boy at various ages, equated to the same total stature. Ages, *left to right*, are 15 months, 30 months, and 6, 11, 14, and 18 years.

22

transverse dimensions, or body breadths. The large-headed, **newborn infant** seems all the more top-heavy because his body is thin, lacking in both muscle and fat as well as being generally small. Growth **during the first year** includes broadening and filling out; the child becomes plump and chubby. After one year, the rapidly growing extremities, together with the greater activity of the mobile runabout and the consequent loss of "baby fat," result in a general slendering-down. The **typical 6- to 9-year-old** is thus slender and long-legged. He may be described as "wiry" or "a beanpole."

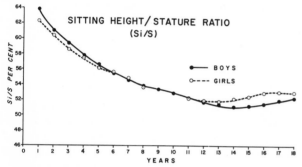

FIG. 12.—The ratio of sitting height to stature at ages 1–18 inclusive. As the legs grow relatively longer, the ratio falls, rising again after puberty.

Up to this point, the above descriptions fit boys and girls equally well. Boys average a little larger and heavier, but the differences are very slight. This is true even though the girls are slightly more mature, as may be seen in the ossification patterns of the skeletal structure. But in build and body proportions boys and girls are so similar that it is usually impossible to identify the sex of a child under 9 years of age from rear-view nude photographs when revealing haircuts are covered.

With the **prepubescent growth spurt,** which starts about two and one-half years earlier in girls than in boys, the broadening process starts again (Fig. 12). As we shall see in chapter 8, the boy fills out by developing muscle and by a general enlarging of the skeleton, particularly in the region of the shoulders. In the girl there is only a slight increase in muscle, but the pelvis rounds out and enlarges, and fat is deposited in characteristic patterns. This accounts for the gradually increasing ratio of bi-cristal diameter to bi-acromial diameter (**the trunk-breadth index**) in girls, the gradually decreasing ratio in boys (Fig. 13; see also Fig. 14).

At the beginning of the prepuberal period of rapid growth, many children put on an excess of fat, becoming quite plump, sometimes even obese. Stolz and Stolz

(1951), in a careful study of normal boys, found that two-thirds of their subjects showed some increase in subcutaneous tissue during this period; one-half became noticeably fat. These figures are probably about the same for girls. With sexual maturation this condition usually tapers off, lasting, as a rule, no more than a year or two. If the child was not fat during the mid-childhood years, then a period of prepuberal obesity is relatively easy to control, as it is not likely to persist.

After about **12 years of age in girls** and **14 years in boys,** the growth of the legs slows down while the body growth continues undiminished for a year or two longer. This change in the locus of growth contributes to the relative **laterality** of build, compared with the **linearity** of early childhood.

After **adult stature** is attained, girls tend to lose some weight. That is, starting at about 17 years, they often become less fat than they were at 15 or 16. Boys, however, continue to gain weight through 21 years of age. Their gains seem to be related primarily to increasing musculature, although there may be some fat accumulation as well.

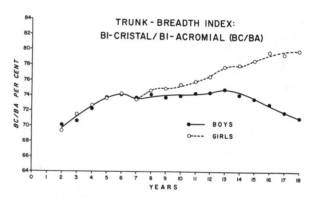

FIG. 13.—The ratio of bi-cristal diameter to bi-acromial diameter at ages 1–18 inclusive. As boys' shoulders grow relatively wider, their ratio falls. As girls' hips grow relatively broader, the *BC/BA* curve for girls rises.

GROWTH CHANGES IN POSTURE

As the body proportions of the growing child change, so do his stance and posture (Fig. 14). In part, posture is a function of body proportions. A large head and a long heavy body on short legs give **the one-year-old** a distinctive set of body mechanics. When the infant first starts to walk, he takes a wide stance for balance. As his feet get closer together, there is often a temporary stage in which he is bowlegged. In the normally healthy child, however, this bowleggedness is of no clinical significance. As his legs grow longer, they

Changing Body Proportions

become straight for a while. Then there frequently follows a knock-kneed period.

The typical two- to four-year-old may have a protruding abdomen, together with a lordosis, which seems to be primarily postural. With strengthening muscles, less fat, and longer legs, the healthy child soon stands straight and tall.

Another shift in leg alignment usually occurs **in adolescence** as adult body proportions develop. By this time, the boy characteristically has an open interspace as he stands with feet together, while the girl is more likely to become knock-kneed, with thighs closely approximated. Her leg alignment seems to result from the broadening of the pelvis, together with an increased deposit of fat over the pelvis and femur. These and other individual differences in build are discussed in chapter 8.

INTERPRETATION

The foregoing descriptions of growth changes in proportions and posture apply to the average child. Although most children go through these changes, there are, of course, wide individual differences which remain within healthy limits. Some children are consistently heavy-set, others are slender. Some go through the processes of maturing as much as a year or two ahead of the average, while others are retarded.

The charts we present take into account these normal variations in build and in speed of growth.

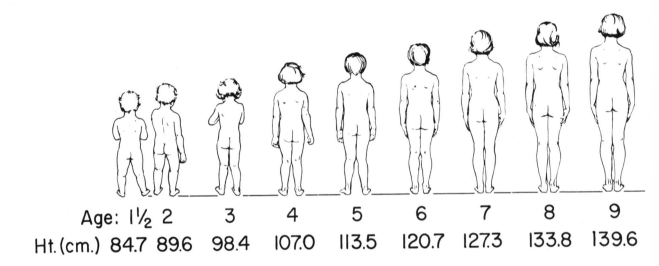

Age:	1½	2	3	4	5	6	7	8	9
Ht. (cm.)	84.7	89.6	98.4	107.0	113.5	120.7	127.3	133.8	139.6

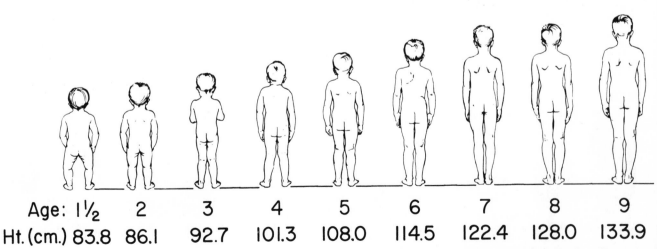

Age:	1½	2	3	4	5	6	7	8	9
Ht. (cm.)	83.8	86.1	92.7	101.3	108.0	114.5	122.4	128.0	133.9

FIG. 14.—OUTLINE DRAWINGS OF BOY AND GIRL, ILLUSTRATIN

When a child goes beyond normal limits, then further investigation is in order. In making evaluations, it becomes necessary to study each child, not only in terms of the norms for his age, but also in the light of his general physique and his rates of anatomic-physiologic maturing.

Changes in body proportions are closely allied to rates of maturation, and the two should therefore always be considered together. Diagnosis of over- or underweight can be made erroneously in children over 9 or 10 years of age if their relative maturity, and therefore their body proportions, do not match the averages from which the tables were constructed. Also, an exceptionally infantile or mature physique may serve

as the first visible indicator that a child's maturational status is out of line. More accurate diagnosis may then be made by skeletal X-rays and other tests of maturational status and by inquiries into the possible etiology of the deviant condition.

The child who becomes excessively fat during the prepuberal growth spurt often has emotional disturbances because of his condition. Fat boys, in particular those with some breast development, may be considered effeminate. Both boys and girls are upset over their deviation from the cultural ideal of slenderness. These children need help in understanding the temporary nature of their condition as well as in its control.

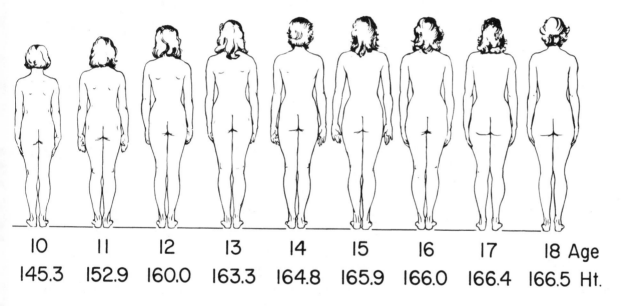

10	11	12	13	14	15	16	17	18 Age
145.3	152.9	160.0	163.3	164.8	165.9	166.0	166.4	166.5 Ht.

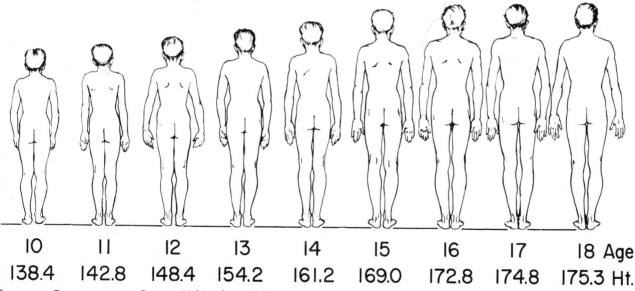

10	11	12	13	14	15	16	17	18 Age
138.4	142.8	148.4	154.2	161.2	169.0	172.8	174.8	175.3 Ht.

CHANGES IN PROPORTIONS AND STANCE (18 Months to 18 Years).

Chapter 6

Anthropometric Values and Deviation Charts

The source of our norms and their statistical definition are matters of relevance throughout this book, but this is perhaps the most logical chapter in which to summarize the essential information about them.

POPULATION

The anthropometric norms presented here were derived largely from American children of European ancestry who had been nurtured under favorable conditions. Some of the children were from private schools in various parts of the United States; others were middle-class children from California. Most samples contained at least one hundred individuals. It might be desirable for the physician to have a variety of ethnic standards derived from any other racial groups frequently encountered in his area. However, these selected norms can be useful if due consideration is given to individual racial patterns, insofar as these are known. For example, one expects the descendants of southern Europeans, of Japanese, and of some American Indians to be shorter; certain Negro tribes and people from northern China are on the average taller than the general population.

If one is not sure what to expect, it is wise to turn to a good sourcebook. For purposes of reference, Hathaway (1957) is excellent; it includes comparative norms and growth charts of height and weight for children in the United States, compiled according to state, geographic region, and date of study. It is available from the Superintendent of Documents, U.S. Printing Office, Washington, D.C.

Certain other factors must be considered when applying the norms to an individual case. While ecologic conditions which are less favorable than those which surround our norms do not prevent their use, such conditions must be taken into account. The comparisons may also be influenced by family patterns; the history-taking should include brief queries about the size and build of parents, siblings, and other relatives, particularly any who are recalled as being unusual.

STATISTICAL UNIT

Although the derivation of constants is not one of the tasks required of the readers of this book, an explanation is given here of the concept of the **standard deviation (S.D.),** or sigma (σ), which is the unit of variation that we use most frequently.

Mathematically the standard deviation is the figure which gives numerical expression to the extent of the deviation of the observed data from the mean of the data. Calculation involves finding the difference between each observation and the mean, squaring it, finding the mean of these squared differences, and again extracting the square root. A small S.D. reflects observations which cluster closely around the mean; a larger S.D. reflects a wider scatter.

The usual distribution of scores on any dimension is arranged about the arithmetic mean (or average) in

26

such a way that the middle two-thirds (roughly 67 per cent) fall within plus or minus one standard deviation of the mean. Individuals with measures within these limits may be considered normal in respect to the characteristic under consideration. Twice the S.D. (plus and minus) includes 96 per cent of the normal population; and almost everyone falls within plus or minus three S.D.'s. It is customary, in using S.D. as a unit, to express the patient's status relatively, as multiples and/or fractions of one standard deviation. Values with negative signs are smaller than the mean; those with positive signs are larger.

The arguments for using the standard deviation in the statistical definition of "normal" have been presented by Gray and Ayres (1931). "The premises which we assume are: 1. that normality may best be considered with regard to growth as a whole, and that normality is no longer considered a matter of striking the average, but rather of falling within certain zones. . . . 2. The unit used to limit these zones should be not centimeters, but one of the orthodox statistical units of deviation. 3. Among such units the basal one is the standard deviation, or sigma. 4. Definition in terms of sigma, of the border zones in which practical men are so keenly interested, should be further studied by empirical plotting of data from persons with recognizable disorders of growth."

For many variables, such as absolute measurements of body size and assessments of skeletal maturation, the value for the standard deviation in prepuberal children is close to the value of the difference between the means for that variable in two successive years. In other words, a 6-year-old child who is somewhere between the mean of 5-year-olds and 7-year-olds is apt to fall within this statistical definition of normal. In adolescence, the range of normal variability is greater.

TABLES OF MEANS AND STANDARD DEVIATIONS

The tables which appear in Appendix I are anthropometric values based on the techniques and data of Gray and Ayres (1931), with the exception that the values for a few of the sigmas in the younger ages represent points on a smoothed curve instead of the original published figures. To facilitate interpretation, both S.D. and percentile values are given. A table is presented for each sex at each age from 1 to 18 years inclusive.

Concerning the choice of the correct table, it should be noted that measurement-values apply to the *nearest* birthday, not necessarily the last birthday. For example, "age 14" includes children from 13.5 years old to 14.4 years old. Age expressed in years and

months may be converted to the decimal system by the use of the Pearl and Miner table (see Appendix III). When serial measures are planned, it is well to establish a schedule which includes an annual measurement within a week of the birthday. In any case, knowing the date of birth and the date of measurement permits the clinician to determine the child's nearest birthday.

DEVIATION CHARTS

The deviation chart (Fig. 15) is a graphic device for comparing the data from a given child with the set of norms which are appropriate for his age and sex. For all practical purposes the proper position for any given measure can be gauged by the two nearest sigma values in the table of means and standard deviations of anthropometric values (Appendix I). This information is plotted as a dot on the deviation chart. The dots are then connected to form a **profile.**

When such a standard comparison turns out to be very deviant, it is often useful to make other comparisons that may suggest themselves as relevant to the particular case under study. For instance, one may compare a child with his age peers of the opposite sex or with his height peers or skeletal age peers of the same sex. If different symbols are used, two separate comparisons may profitably be plotted on the same form. More than two are confusing.

Interpretation

In making any comparisons such as are offered by these tables and charts, the limitations of the norms must always be kept in mind, i.e., the suitability of the norms to the individual case and the meaning of the statistical evidence per se. With these reservations, it may be recalled that the exact average for each trait is indicated by the line M in the center of the deviation chart. Within the two central zones or columns lying on each side of this line (from -1σ on the left hand to $+1\sigma$ on the right) ordinarily fall 67 per cent of all normal observations. The area which includes also the adjacent zones, plus and minus (from -2σ on the left to $+2\sigma$ on the right) will ordinarily embrace 96 per cent of the observations. The two outside zones will usually receive only the remaining 4 per cent of the observations. Therefore, it seems legitimate to interpret any observations plotted in these two outside zones or beyond as being very exceptional. As Gray and Ayres (1931) point out: "The amount of importance to be attributed to results obtained by the foregoing mechanical procedure of measuring and plotting would, in most cases, be judged only after consideration of other factors than those apparent on the chart."

Four general types of profiles emerge from deviation charts:

1. Normal. (All measurements and indices fall within 1 S.D. of the mean.)

2. Unusual in size but normal in proportions. (Absolute measurements are consistently above or below 1 S.D. of the mean, but the indices fall within 1 S.D.)

3. Unusual in both size and proportions. (Most measures, both absolute and relative, fall outside the ± 1 S.D. range.)

The meaning of such a record may be tested by replotting the child's measures against the norms for his height peers. If the whole profile then moves closer to the mean, it is probable that the child's deviations in size and in maturation are parallel—that he is small or large because he is slow or fast in "growing up."

4. Disharmonious. (Profile points fall erratically outside ± 1 S.D. of the mean for his age and sex.)

The deviation is not lessened in such a case by replotting the measures against height peers. A plot of this sort suggests some unusual pattern of develop-

ment which calls for further exploration by additional comparisons.

The practical significance of variations in ratios can often be appreciated by a consideration of age changes in body proportions, described in chapter 5. For instance, relative broadening of the trunk occurs especially in the first year and again in early adolescence. Increased trunk ratios toward the end of the first decade may suggest early maturation—an approach toward adolescent growth. Conversely, a similar breadth excess in the runabout child, especially if coupled with shortness, may suggest slow maturation—a persistence of the infantile pattern.

The ratio of sitting height to stature (Si/S) requires similar judicious interpretation. Since plotting the means for Si/S against age gives a flattened U-shaped curve (see Fig. 12), short legs in the first decade of life often indicate slow maturation as well as slow growth, that is, retention of an infantile pattern. After puberty, short-leggedness might also indicate immaturity and a primary failure of leg growth; however, it might instead signify early closure of the epiphyses; in other words, accelerated maturation and a secondary

Name		Sex M F	Birth Date	Date	Age	Case #
Compared with Norms for:		Sex M F	Age	Other		

MEASURE		Pounds = Kilos x .454 / Inches = Cm x 2.54		STANDARD DEVIATION VALUES						
				-3σ	2% -2σ	16% -1σ	50% M	84% $+1\sigma$	98% $+2\sigma$	$+3\sigma$
Weight	W									
Stature	S									
Sitting height	Si									
Shoulder	BA									
Pelvis	BC									
Above measurements in per cent of stature.	W/S	*Ratios*								
	Si/S									
	BA/S									
	BC/S									
Index Trunkbreadth	BC/BA									

FIG. 15

28

failure of leg growth. The meaning of any single deviant finding, therefore, depends on other aspects of a given case.

Deviation Chart in Weight Assessment

The value of using the bi-cristal diameter as an index of breadth of frame and thus as a guide in the determination of optimal weight is discussed in chapter 12. It should be noted here, however, that on the deviation chart one would expect to find weight and bi-cristal diameter varying from the mean in similar direction and degree. Therefore, weight over stature and bi-cristal over stature would also tend to move together.

Chapter 7

Secondary Sex Characters

Indices of physiological and sexual maturity, originally described by many authors, were tested and related to one another in a report by Nicolson and Hanley (1953). Comparing the ages at which various physiological stages of development are reached during pubescence, they found "a high degree of relationship between measures as phenomenally different as pubic hair development and closure of certain epiphyses."

They also considered age at menarche, age at maximum growth, and stages of development of the breast and of the penis and scrotum. All such indicators of maturity were found to be closely associated

| I | II | III | IV | V |

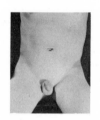   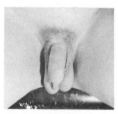 

FIG. 16.—Sexual maturity stages in boys, as shown by genital development. From Greulich *et al.*, *Somatic and Endocrine Studies of Puberal and Adolescent Boys*, 1942. ("Monographs of the Society for Research in Child Development," Vol. VII, Ser. 33, No. 3.) Photographs courtesy of the authors and the Society for Research in Child Development.

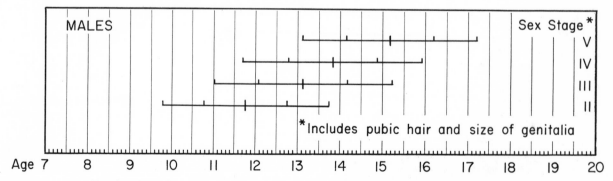

FIG. 17.—Maturity indices for boys, showing normal range of occurrence of sex stages. Adapted from Nicolson and Hanley, "Indices of Physiological Maturity: Derivation and Interrelationships," *Child Development*, Vol. 24, No. 1 (1953). Courtesy of the authors and the Society for Research in Child Development.

with the percentage of mature stature attained. We thus assume the operation of **a general factor of maturation during pubescence.** Hence a child's maturational status can be evaluated by a combination of several or all of these indicators.

The indices of sexual maturity presented in our charts (Figs. 17 and 19) are modifications of the physiological maturity indices published by Nicolson and Hanley; we have used only those portions which deal with secondary sex characters. Each index (or sex stage) is plotted independently against chronological age. The range of normal occurrence for each stage is

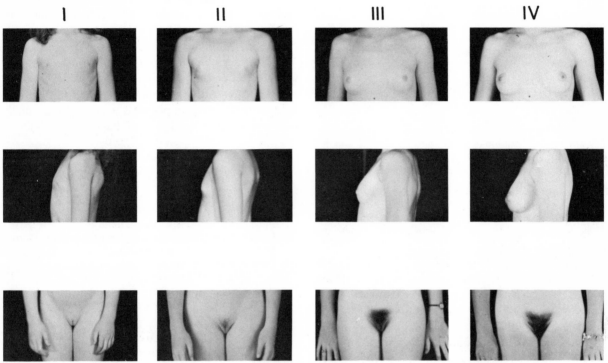

Fig. 18.—Sexual maturity stages in girls, as shown by breast development and pubic-hair growth. *Top row*, anterior views of the breasts at the four stages listed in Table 4; *center row*, corresponding side views of breast stages; *bottom row*, the stages of pubic-hair development.

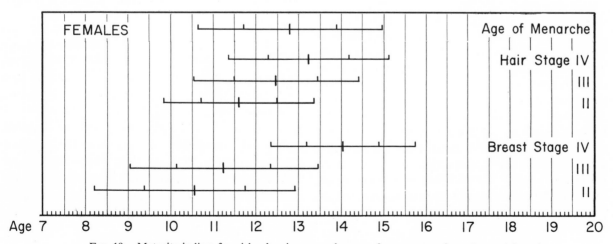

Fig. 19.—Maturity indices for girls, showing normal range of occurrence of sex stages. Adapted from Nicolson and Hanley, 1953; courtesy of the authors and the Society for Research in Child Development.

indicated by a horizontal line, with a point marking the mean and points at one and two standard deviations, plus and minus.

The clinician may compare these charts with the illustrations of sex stages (Figs. 16 and 18) and with Tables 3 and 4, which provide verbal descriptions.

TABLE 3

STAGES OF SEXUAL MATURITY, BOYS

I. Penis, testes, and scrotum are essentially the same as in early childhood.
II. Testes and penis have noticeably enlarged; lightly pigmented, downy hair has appeared. (Mean, 11.8 years; S.D. ± 1 year.)
III. The penis has appreciably lengthened; downy hair is interspersed with straight, coarse, pigmented hair. (Mean, 13.1 years; S.D. ± 1 year.)
IV. Larger testes and penis of increased diameter are apparent. Pubic hair looks adult, but its area is smaller. (Mean, 13.8 years; S.D. ± 1 year.)
V. Genitalia are adult in size and shape; pubic hair is adult.

Five sexual maturity stages for boys are listed in Table 3, as distinguished by Greulich *et al.* (1942); these are derived from combined consideration of the amount and patterning of pubic hair and the size of the genitalia. Four sexual maturity stages for girls (Table 4) have been derived, separately for the breast and the pubic-hair development. Our ratings are similar to Reynolds and Wines (1948).

It should be pointed out that size and shape per se are not considered in our descriptions of breast stages. Such constitutional variations will be discussed in chapter 8. Our purpose here is to chart differences which are meaningfully related to *general physiological development*.

In this connection, Stanley M. Garn (1956) has emphasized the fact that "areolar maturation is to some extent independent of breast size and form. In lean girls and in fat girls as well, the progress and pigmentation of the areola is a much more satisfactory index to estrogenic status, whereas the size and configurations of the breasts may have less clinical value."

Despite the high correlation, referred to earlier, between percentage of mature height attained at a given age and the stage of sexual maturity, curves for these percentages are not included among the indices in Figures 17 and 19. Since the per cent of mature height cannot be derived before growth is completed, the calculation is useful only retroactively rather than in clinical growth diagnosis.

INTERPRETATION

The simultaneous evaluation of several indices of sexual maturity provides both **a comparison between the individual and the norms** and an indication of **the degree of uniformity of development within the individual.** Each separate factor is thereby enhanced in value by becoming part of a more rounded picture. Since acceleration or retardation in the appearance of a single biological sign may reflect either a constitutional idiosyncrasy or a totally deviant growth pattern, such a check may be important.

The menarche, because it is so definite and unmistakable, is an event which receives special attention in any girl's developmental or endocrine history. But a delayed menarche in a girl who is otherwise normally differentiated for her age may have a very different

TABLE 4

STAGES OF SEXUAL MATURITY, GIRLS
(Age of Menarche: Mean, 12.8 years; S.D. ± 1.1 years)

BREAST STAGES

I. Prepuberal breast; elevated papilla only.
II. Elevated areola, or minimal breast swelling. (Mean, 10.6 years; S.D. ± 1.2 years.)
III. First swelling of the breast to a small mound formation. (Mean, 11.2 years; S.D. ± 1.1 years.)
IV. Final stage, after which no further *developmental changes* in breast contour appear. (Mean, 13.9 years; S.D. ± 0.9 years.)

PUBIC HAIR STAGES

I. Infantile; no pigmented pubic hair.
II. Hair is pigmented, straight or only slightly curled, sparse, and primarily along the labia. (Mean, 11.6 years; S.D. ± 0.9 years.)
III. Hair curled; slight spread on mons. (Mean, 12.5 years; S.D. ± 1.0 years.)
IV. Hair curled; moderate amount and spread. (Mean, 13.2 years; S.D. ± 0.9 years.)

basis than such a delay in a girl who is also physiologically immature in other ways. Thus, assembling a composite picture of somatic sexual maturation may help in deciding whether or not further clinical investigation of a single divergent phenomenon is in order.

Harmonious and consistent deviations probably reflect only physiological deviations in the tempo of maturation. In general, the child who matures at an average rate is apt to be better synchronized in the various phases of puberal development than is the child who is either very early-maturing or very late-maturing.

Chapter 8

Androgyny

Under the heading "The Mosaic of Androgyny," Draper (1941) discusses "maleness within the female, and femaleness within the male." The word **androgyny,** derived from the Greek roots meaning "man" (*andros*) and "woman" (*gyne*), has been chosen by Draper to designate "the divergent organismal aspects of man and woman."

In this chapter the concept of androgyny is applied to **variations in body build within and between the sexes.** Since sex differentiation in build varies more or less independently of other hereditary and environmental factors, it is a clinically useful standard for evaluating, by comparison, other characteristics of physique and personality. For example, knowing the androgynic variables of the two sexes has made it possible to classify certain physical and psychological traits as real sex differences while other traits are seen to vary without regard to sex. At the same time, androgyny emphasizes an accepted biological fact: that every individual is a composite of both masculine and feminine endowments. Sex-chromatin determinations will provide increasing opportunities to study the separate effects of genetic, gonadal, and endocrine factors on patterns of androgynic differentiation. This may be of special interest in studying the development of patients with various sorts of intersexuality.

The following discussion, modified slightly from our original article (Bayley and Bayer, 1946), is a working hypothesis of the method of androgynic rating, including descriptions of the devices and procedures used.

SEXUAL DIFFERENTIATION

In general, four factors seem recognizable in the topography of sexual differentiation: direction, degree, and tempo, and consistency within the same individual. When these factors were considered in studies of body build in women (Bayer, 1939) and in adolescent girls (Bayer, 1940) the following classifications emerged: *feminine, hypofeminine, hyperfeminine, virile,* and *mixed* (or *disharmonious*).

Considering these same factors expressly applied to manifestations of body form and covering, this classification has been largely confirmed for the female fig-

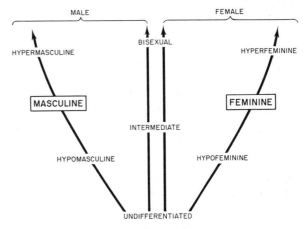

FIG. 20.—Diagrammatic representation of somatic sexual differentiation from relatively neutral childhood forms into masculine and feminine forms. Each of these adult forms varies in degree and direction of differentiation. An individual may be average, exaggerated, or muted in masculinity or femininity; may remain undifferentiated or may show a combination of masculine and feminine characteristics.

33

ure and further amplified and related to the male figure. It is possible, of course, to choose different factors, such as anthropometric ratios, as the critical basis of classification. Given individuals will then fall into somewhat different groups, depending on the basic criteria used.

But whatever the device, the same dynamic concept appears to hold: patterns of sexual differentiation can be visualized as a sort of fan, with **masculine** and **feminine** characteristics developing from an undifferentiated childhood form, and with **asexual** and **bisexual** variants falling in between the two normal radiations, as illustrated in Figure 20.

In adolescents, before growth is completed, androgyny ratings alone cannot determine whether a relatively undifferentiated individual is slow in maturing or whether his processes of differentiation are arrested so that he will never achieve the build characteristic of his sex. For this reason, even though intensity and speed of differentiation tend to be related, the ratings on still-growing adolescents should be applied in a limited way, with reservations about predicting the mature builds of undifferentiated cases. For adolescents younger than 18, the rating schemes described in the chapter on secondary sex characters are more specifically applicable.

ANDROGYNIC RATING: NECESSARY EQUIPMENT

Figure 21 is a copy of the standard form that is used in androgynic rating. Along with the photographic standards which illustrate the ratings, the scale is based on the androgynic variants in a group of boys and girls who had just approximated physical maturity. The purpose of this rating scale is to assess androgyny, not such variations of physique as the body types of Kretschmer (1925) or Sheldon (1940). We will have more to say about the relation of our rating and "somatotyping" somewhat later.

Figure 22 is a selection of photographs illustrating the five degrees of differentiation in regard to the various items on the rating scale (Fig. 21). To illustrate all the rating items of **1** and **5**, two cases are presented at each extreme; a single case rarely shows extreme development in all items. Although only one example is given for each sex in each of the two intermediate types, this same observation applies to them; a person who is totally asexual is as rare as one who carries an equal distribution of masculine and feminine traits. The ratings actually given to the standard cases are shown in Table 5. They should be used in combination with the standard photos and with the descriptions

which follow to determine the correct ratings for specific body areas.

The rating chart (Fig. 21), which may be used as an individual record form, gives abbreviated summaries of the descriptions to facilitate ratings once the directions are understood. It is hoped that, with the aid of these several devices, fairly objective ratings can be made.

The actual items to be rated are referred to in these descriptions by letters corresponding to letters on the chart. In general, the prejudice should be in favor of rating **2** or **4** for the appropriate sex, unless there are obvious indications to the contrary.

TABLE 5

RATINGS GIVEN IN TEN CASES USED AS STANDARDS IN FIGURE 22

ITEMS	RATINGS FOR STANDARD CASES									
	MH	*MH'*	*M*	*MB*	*MA*	*FB*	*FA*	*F*	*FH*	*FH'*
Surface modeling......	1	1	2	3b	2.5	4	4	4	5	5
Shoulder girdle.........	1.5	1	2	3b	3a	3b	3a	4	5	4.5
Waist line....	2	1	2	3b	3a	3b	3	4	5	5−
Hip flare.....	2	1	2	2	2−	3	3.5	4	5−	5+
Buttocks.....	1	2	2	4	3	3	3	4	4	5
Thigh form..	1	2	2	3	2	3	3	4	4	5
Interspace (whole leg).	1	1.5	2	4	3	3	4	4	5	5
Muscle bulge (lower leg).	1	1	2	4	3a	3b	3a	4	5	4.5

ANDROGYNIC RATING: THE ITEMS

Determining an individual androgynic rating involves evaluations of the surface modeling of the body, of four aspects of trunk contour, and of three items of leg pattern. Ratings in these eight items, assigned either by direct inspection of the patient or preferably by inspection of his rear-view photographs, provide an androgynic profile of his body form. The following directions are given in developmental perspective to facilitate rating along the "fan" of Figure 20, which consists essentially of two axes at right angles to each other: masculine-feminine ranging horizontally, with undifferentiated-differentiated on the vertical.

I. *Surface modeling*

Item *A* of Figure 21—surface modeling—is influenced by muscle, fat, bony protuberances, veins, and tendons.

The preadolescent is covered by a relatively uniform layer of subcutaneous fat, through which the contours of moderately developed muscles can be seen.

ANDROGYNIC PATTERNS OF BODY FORM: RATING PROFILE
Bayley-Bayer Standards
17–18 Year Norms

Name	Sex $\frac{M}{F}$	Date	Age	Skeletal Age	Case Number

ITEM	RATING				
(*A* through *H* from rear-view photographs)	Hypermasculine 1	Masculine 2	Intermediate, Asexual, or Bisexual 3, 3a, 3b	Feminine 4	Hyperfeminine 5
I. A. **Surface modeling**	Exaggerated hardness of relief. O	Strong muscle molding. Bone, vein and tendon prominences. O	b. Muscular and fat. O / a. Little muscle or fat. O	Smooth and soft, with little muscle. O	Very soft, fat, no muscle. O
II. **Trunk Contours** B. Shoulder girdle	Massive. O	Appears wide, heavy and muscular. O	b. Muscular and fat. O / a. Narrow, "bony." O	Slight, soft and narrow. O	Softly fat. O
C. Waist line	Marked torso narrowing to low waist: may have minimal indentation. O	Slight indentation due to narrowing of torso. O	b. Broad hip and shoulder; little O indentation. / a. Slight O symmetrical high concavity.	Definite line accentuated by hip widening. O	Marked indentation. O
D. Hip flare	No widening. O	Slight widening of hips from waist. O	Intermediate. O	Flares into wide hips laterally and posteriorly. O	Marked flare. O
E. Buttocks	Very flat. O	Flat and angular. O	Intermediate. O	Rounded and full. O	Very broad and rounded. O
III. **Leg Patterns** F. Thigh Form	Cylinder and/or bulging muscles. O	Approaches cylinder. Lateral outline convex. O	Intermediate. O	Funnel, fat and rounded. Lateral outline concave. O	Fat, wide-top funnel. O
G. Interspace (whole leg)	Very open. O	Open center above and below knees. O	Intermediate. O	Closed center except small space below knees. O	Thighs and knees together, feet apart. O
H. Muscle bulge (lower leg)	Strong bulge, no fat. O	Prominent inner bulge of gastrocnemius. O	b. Moderate muscle bulge. O / a. No muscle bulge; spindly. O	Slight inner bulge; shapely, smooth, outer curve. O	Very little muscle, but smoothly rounded and outer curve.
J. Penis size	1 Very O / 1.5 Large O	2 Average O	2.5 Small O / 3 Very O		
K. Breast size			3 Very O / 3.5 Small O	4 Average O	4.5 Large O / 5 Very O
L. Body hair density	1 O Heavy on thighs, etc.	2 O Easily discernible	2.5 O Sparse.	(3) O♂	O♀ Absent
M. Pubic pattern	Disperse O	Acuminate. O	Sagittal O	Horizontal O♂ O♀	
N. $\frac{\text{Bi-cristal}}{\text{Bi-acromial}}$ Index	−←68 69 O	73 O	74 76 O	77 82 O	83→+ O
P. Strength (Kg) Grip (R+L)+Thrust +Pull	+←244 243 O	186 O	185 148 O	147 110 O	109→− O
Grip (R+L)	+←126 125 O	95 O	94 80 O	79 59 O	58→− O
Androgyny Score (Sum of *A–H*)	8 12 O	13 19 O	20 B 25 O A	26 34 O	35 40 O
Characteristic Description (Circle one)	**Hypermasculine**	**Masculine**	**Intermediate Bisexual Asexual Disharmonious**	**Feminine**	**Hyperfeminine**

FIG. 21.—Form used in assessing an individual's pattern of sexual differentiation in body form. From Bayley and Bayer, "The Assessment of Somatic Androgyny," *Am. J. Phys. Anthrop.*, N.S., Vol. 4 (1946). Reproduced courtesy of the Wistar Institute of Anatomy and Biology, Philadelphia.

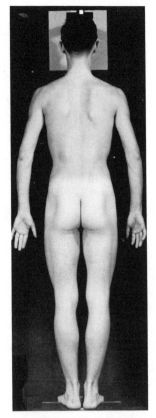

HYPERMASCULINE
(1)

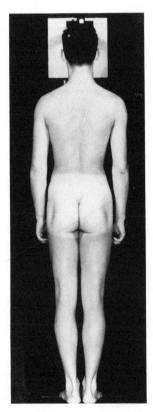

MASCULINE
(2)

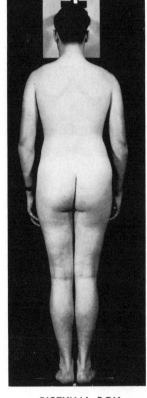

BISEXUAL BOY
(3B)

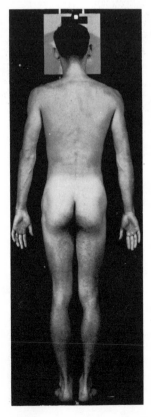

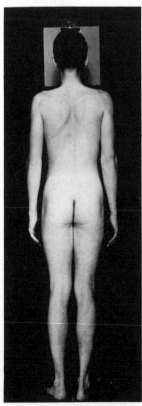

HYPOMASCULINE
(3A)

FIG. 22.—Standard photographs of the basic androgynic patterns, for use with the Rating Profile (Fig. 21). The rating **1** indicates hypermasculinity, as seen in two boys; **2,** typical masculine; **3a,** hypomasculine boy, hypofeminine girl; **3b,** bisexual boy, bisexual girl; **4,** typical feminine; and **5,** hyperfeminine, two examples. The various photographs are grouped to suggest the "fan" of Fig. 20. From Bayley and Bayer, 1946. Courtesy of the Wistar Institute of Anatomy and Biology, Philadelphia.

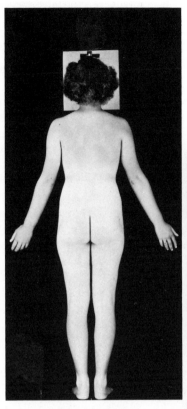

BISEXUAL GIRL
(3B)

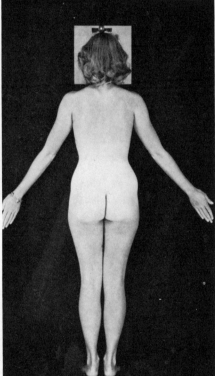

FEMININE
(4)

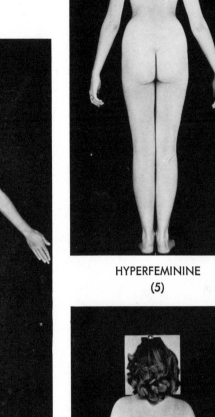

HYPERFEMININE
(5)

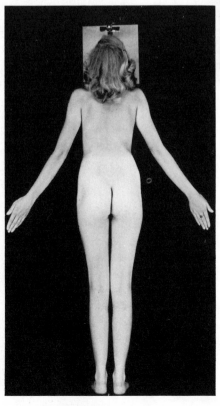

HYPOFEMININE
(3A)

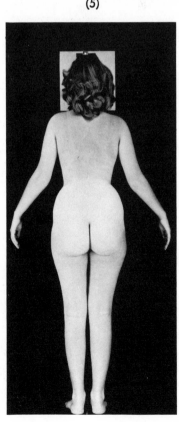

FIG. 22.—*Continued*

Androgyny

As maturity approaches, the **masculine modeling** is influenced especially by the development of larger muscle masses, the **feminine modeling,** by characteristic fat deposits (Fig. 23). Veins and tendons stand out strong and prominent on the masculine arm, whereas they disappear into the contours of a feminine arm, even if

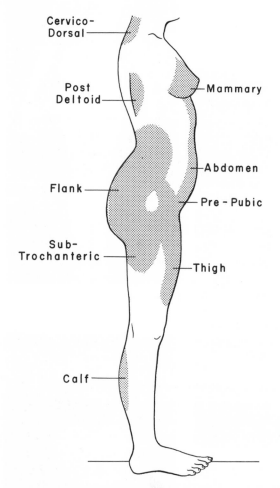

FIG. 23.—Normal distribution of subcutaneous fat in girls (*shaded areas*). From Bayer, "Weight and Menses in Adolescent Girls, with Special Reference to Build," *Journal of Pediatrics*, Vol. 17, No. 3 (1940). Courtesy of the C. V. Mosby Co. (Adapted from Wolff, 1933. Courtesy of the Macmillan Co.)

it is slender. Draper (1941) has described the sex differences in surface modeling as follows:

"In men such observable localized bosses or protuberances as may appear are chiefly due to the well-developed muscles, which are covered only by a thin layer of subcutaneous fat. . . . Woman's muscles are not large and knotty, and may be completely hidden beneath a fairly thick, smooth panniculus."

These differences show especially in the leg and in the arm and, to some extent, in the shoulders. When both the muscle masses and the fat covering are strongly developed, the surface modeling receives a bisexual rating.

II. *Trunk Contours*

Shoulder girdle (*B*).—In childhood the shoulder girdle is not much wider than the trunk and usually has a rather loose-knit appearance.

Maturity finds the **masculine shoulder** appearing wide, heavy, and muscular, in proportion to total size. In extreme cases it may be described as "massive." Although this appearance is usually emphasized by the narrowness of the hips, shoulders should be rated regardless of hip width. The **feminine shoulder** remains relatively slight and narrow with little muscle; it may look very frail, become rounded with soft fat, or even appear massive in a very fat subject. Ratings are made from a combination of factors: breadth, muscle, and fat.

Waistline (*C*).—In the childish torso the indentation of the waistline is slight and relatively high. The adult torso has more of an hourglass contour, broadening into the shoulder girdle above and the pelvic crest below. The individual waistline varies in depth, acuity, and position, depending on the development of the two trunk girdles. Since the greater trunk breadth of the male is in the shoulder and that of the female in the pelvis, the waistline reflects the sex differences.

The **masculine waistline** is low and less clearly demarcated, because there is no definite point at which the narrowing of the torso breaks into the widening of the hips. That is, it is typically lower than in childhood, appearing to be just above the pelvic crest. The **feminine waistline** is due less to a narrowing of the torso than to the wider hips; it is usually a marked indentation, dipping in below the ribs (except where excess fat prevails) and flaring out with the hips.

Hip flare (*D*).—Like the shoulder contour, the hips and buttocks in childhood are not much wider than the trunk. During adolescence, the masculine pelvic girdle changes relatively little; in this rating, it is the feminine differentiation which leads to the contrast between the sexes.

The **masculine hip** widens only a little and very gradually from the waist, giving a long-bodied, low-waisted effect. The **feminine hip** flares out from the waistline, with a fat pad superimposed on the wide iliac crest. This gives a high-waisted effect. In the pictures (Fig. 22) shading indicates an abrupt widening which extends somewhat toward the rear as well as laterally.

Buttocks (*E*).—The **masculine buttocks** are muscular with little fat and tend to have deep concavities or dimples near the median line. In cross-section at buttocks level, the body would appear to be almost triangular, with the apex of the triangle at the center rear. **Feminine buttocks** are rounded and soft, amply filled out with fat, and in cross-section curve out into a semicircle.

III. *Leg Patterns*

The legs in childhood also have only moderately developed fat and muscles, so that preadolescent boys and girls show rather knobby or spindly leg patterns. It is important to note that legs go through a characteristic development: bowlegs are typical at the earliest walking age; these often give way to knock-knees at ages 3–5; and thereafter legs straighten out again into the healthy, straight childhood contour. With adolescence, **masculine legs** undergo the changes resulting especially from greater muscle masses and larger bones; **feminine legs** become more rounded with fat and the thighs become closely approximated. As in the pelvic girdle, the masculine leg deviates less than the feminine from the preadolescent pattern. The typical masuline and feminine differentiations are described in these three items relating to leg pattern.

Thigh form (F).—Typically **masculine thighs** have little fat, tending to be almost cylindrical in form; some widening at crotch level is due to muscular development. The muscles bulge laterally, giving to the outline a characteristic convex curve. If a boy's muscles are tensed, this muscle bulge is somewhat set off by a longitudinal groove formed by the intermuscular space posterior to the iliotibial tract of the tensor fascia latae. **Feminine thighs** are funnel-shaped, widening smoothly at crotch level because of the fat; the lateral outline tends to be convex.

Interspace (G).—When the heels are approximated and the feet are parallel, the **space between masculine legs** is relatively wide. Because of little fat and in many instances a tendency to bow slightly at the knees, there is open space between the thighs as well as below the knees. **Feminine interspace** is very small, owing to fat and a tendency (because of the articulation of the femurs into a broad pelvis) for the knees to come together. The thighs are closely approximated and the knees press together; there is either a narrow space below the knees or the feet are forced apart by knock-knees and/or very fat thighs.

Lower-leg contours (H).—The inner outline of the masculine lower leg is knobby and uneven, owing primarily to the bulge of the inner belly of the gastrocnemius—a sharp bulge of muscle with little fat. Feminine lower legs are smooth, with moderate bulges or, in ex-

treme cases, no bulge on the inside. Smoothed out by a layer of fat, a "shapely" leg results, with the outer curve often more pronounced than the inner contour. Legs of **3a** subjects have little development of either muscle or fat.

ANDROGYNIC RATINGS: THE SCORE

The total score of androgyny is obtained by adding the numerical values of the eight ratings. For example, an individual who was 100 per cent **hypermasculine** would receive a score of 8; a completely **hyperfeminine** girl would have a score of 40—the sum of each of the eight items rated as **5,** the most feminine degree of differentiation.

Actually, **typical feminine** scores range from 28 through 34 inclusive; **typical masculine** scores range from 13 through 17. Intermediate scores, especially those between 19 and 26, should be considered **asexual** if there is a preponderance of **3a's**; **bisexual** if there is a preponderance of **3b's**.

SUPPLEMENTARY CRITERIA

The following items are additional physical characteristics which may be of value in assessing the androgyny of the individual. Note that the present assessments refer to *size* of penis and breast rather than *stage of development*, which is considered in the chapter on secondary sex characters. Similarly, *patterns of hair distribution* are described statically rather than developmentally.

Degree of Differentiation: Penis and Breasts

These ratings indicate degrees of sexual differentiation within the sex concerned; the values have been adjusted to fall into a bimodal distribution similar to those found for the androgyny ratings of body form.

Size of penis (J).—A five-point scale is developed in the masculine range of ratings by assigning the following numbers to penis size: **1,** very large; **1.5,** large; **2,** average; **2.5,** small; and **3,** extremely small (see photographic standards, Fig. 24). Size is determined in relation to the subject's total size, and judgment is based on consideration of a combination of length and width. It is necessary to try to take into account tumescence, when present, and to discount it. For this reason a series of several pictures taken at different times is helpful.

Size of breasts (K).—Numerical ratings have been assigned to the feminine range of distribution in breast size, as follows: **3,** very small; **3.5,** small; **4,** average; **4.5,** large; and **5,** extremely large (see photographic standards, Fig. 24).

Hair Distribution

The distribution of **body hair** (L) and **pubic hair** (M) does not show the same type of androgynic variation as is found for body form. Our findings are corroborated by Dupertuis *et al.* (1945), who classified pubic hair from photographs of over one thousand 18-year-olds and a smaller group of men and women, aged 30 and 40 years. They distinguished four patterns, using the criterion of the shape of the upper outline of the pubic shield. These are: *horizontal* (the classical feminine), *sagittal* (few hairs on the sagittal line),

linity in both sexes. The horizontal pubic pattern and the absence of coarse body hair are predominantly female characteristics and are given a rating of **4** when seen in women; but so many normal young men also have these patterns of hair distribution that a feminine rating for them would be unjustified. Such boys are therefore given a rating of **3** on this item.

THE BI-CRISTAL/BI-ACROMIAL INDEX

One of the items described in connection with the deviation chart in chapter 6—the *BC/BA* ratio—may be used as an objective supplement to the rating based

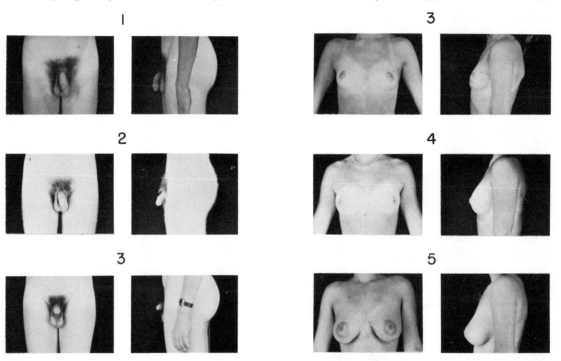

FIG. 24.—Standards for androgynic ratings. *Left, top to bottom*, standards in penis size from large, **1**, to very small, **3**. *Right, bottom to top*, standards in breast size from very small, **3**, to large, **5**. From Bayley and Bayer, 1946. Courtesy of the Wistar Institute of Anatomy and Biology, Philadelphia.

acuminate (the classical masculine with triangular upward extension), and *disperse* (hair distributed generally over abdomen). Approximately 90 per cent of 18-year-old women have the horizontal pattern, but so do about 40 per cent of the men, while the remainder have varying degrees of the more masculine patterns.

For the ages under consideration here, we can note only whether in the masculine-to-feminine order the pattern of pubic hair (M) is disperse, acuminate, sagittal, or horizontal, and whether body hair (L), primarily on the thighs, is conspicuous, moderate, sparse, or absent. The combined appearance of the acuminate pubic pattern and conspicuous thigh hair may have some significance as another factor indicating mascu-

on the standard photographs. These diameters are measured with sliding calipers, using the standard anthropometric technique. The measures on our standardization subjects at 17 years, 7 months, yielded indices with a mean of 72, S.D.3, for seventy-seven males; a mean of 78, S.D.5, for seventy-nine females. Deviation from the mean (for the same sex) of one S.D. or more would indicate an atypical ratio. Because there is considerable overlapping of the index between the sexes, the range was adjusted to fit the five-point rating scale of our profile as follows: rating **1** for an index of 68 or below; rating **2**, index 69–73; rating **3**, index 74–76; rating **4**, index 77–82; rating **5**, index 83 and above.

40

Strength

Another easily measured physical character with marked sex differences in adults is **strength** (*P*). It changes with age to such an extent that the norms presented here should apply only to the 17–18-year range. Scores may be based on right-plus-left grip only, or on a total of grips, thrust, and pull. A Collin-type hand dynamometer (Fig. 25) is used (Harold Jones, 1949).

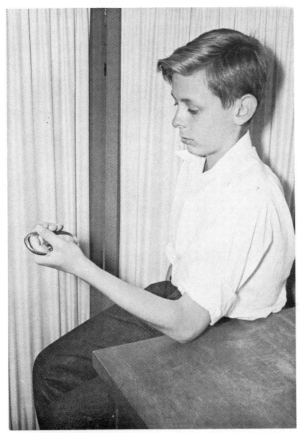

Fig. 25.—Strength test, using the hand dynamometer. From Stolz and Stolz, *Somatic Development of Adolescent Boys*, 1951. Photograph courtesy of the authors and the Macmillan Co., New York.

Three trials are given for each hand and the two best scores combined for the right-plus-left grip. For the more complete tests, three additional trials each are given for pull and for thrust, and the score is the sum of the best trials for right and left grip, thrust, and pull.

One other index should be mentioned. When examining post-adolescents for incomplete sexual differentiation or eunuchoidism, the clinician commonly seeks to demonstrate an *excess of limb length as related to total stature. Stem length* or *sitting height* in per cent of stature (chap. 6) provides a suitable index for this estimation.

In either sex, the presence of a relative excess in limb length suggests a deficiency in sexual and skeletal maturation. Since this deviation is a frequent finding in intermediate, asexual builds, its presence or absence should be noted in any case where hypogonadism is suspected. We have not provided for this measurement in the rating profile, since it has no value for androgynic differentiation.

ANDROGYNY AND SOMATOTYPES

A word may be said about the relation of the concept of androgyny as here developed to the somatotypes of Sheldon's (1940) system. In describing endomorphy, mesomorphy, and ectomorphy, Sheldon invokes certain theoretical relationships: for instance, that fat deposition goes with a large gastrointestinal tract. Whether or not such assumptions are valid, they have no immediate relation to our present concern with sexual development and differentiation.

Seen in the simplest terms, the form and covering of the body depends in large part on the absolute and relative amounts of fat, muscle, and bone. These are distributed, according to the scheme of somatotypes, into *endomorphs*, who have a predominance of fat, *mesomorphs*, who have a predominance of muscle (and a heavy skeletal frame), and *ectomorphs*, who have a relative absence of both fat and muscle, leaving a frame which is largely skin and bones.

If these same factors are now related to current theories of sexual differentiation, they take on a different meaning. Assuming healthy individuals with height, weight, and certain other basic elements equal, then fat predominance becomes a feminine trait and muscularity a masculine one, while their absence implies a lack of differentiation. In addition, large bones are characteristically masculine, while small bones are found in both feminine and undifferentiated builds. Since such a picture is readily related in a dynamic way both to our modern psychologies of personality development and to current work on metabolism and hormones, it seems to us that looking at the body in terms of androgyny, even though this is admittedly a limited view, gives one useful base from which somatic diagnosis can be made and psychosomatic relations sought.

CLINICAL SIGNIFICANCE

Androgyny appears to be truly a "mosaic," as Draper (1941) has so aptly labeled it. Valid sex differences, having little or no overlap between masculine and feminine scores, may vary quite independently within a sex. Specifically, the androgyny score, as derived from the first eight items (*A* through *H*), is not related to penis size but has a fair correlation with breast size; it is not related to amount or distribution of coarse body hair; it is related moderately to strength in boys, but not in girls; it is only slightly correlated with stature in either sex, or with weight in boys, but is strongly related to weight in girls. It thus becomes obvious that many individuals may deviate in a few characteristics; few will deviate in many. In general, however, there is some relation between the tempo and degree of sexual differentiation, just as there is a relation between the speed and intensity of linear growth.

With these standards for assessing somatic androgyny, it should be possible to determine its relationship to personality structure. Significant differences in personality may well be found by comparing those with normal builds, those with relatively immature builds, and those with build characteristics of the opposite sex. Androgyny scores may also prove useful in relating sex variations in physique to other aspects of body build, to physical fitness, to psychoses, and to hormone assays. Studies illustrating this approach have been reported by Bayer and Koets (1951) and by Bayer and Reichard (1951).

A recent comprehensive comparison of approximately 500 delinquent boys with 500 matched controls (Glueck and Glueck, 1956) has yielded rewarding information concerning significant contrasts between the physiques of the two groups. Although the build classification used by the Gluecks is a modification of the Sheldon somatotyping, the descriptions are such as to relate their findings also to our androgynic variants.

Chapter 9

Skeletal Age

Reading skeletal age from X-rays of the hand and wrist requires access to Greulich and Pyle's *Radiographic Atlas of Skeletal Development of the Hand and Wrist* (Stanford University Press, 1959). Since the technique of skeletal-age assessment is exhaustively presented in the *Atlas*, only a few notes of description and rationale are offered here for purposes of orientation.

THE TECHNIQUE

Determination of skeletal age involves two series of standard films, one for each sex, arranged in the order of increasing maturity. Directions for evaluating the individual patient's X-ray by use of the appropriate set of standards, along with interpretations, are included in the *Atlas*. Briefly, **this is a simple matching procedure.** The patient's hand and wrist is compared with the standard plates in twenty-nine critical areas until one plate is found which best approximates that of the patient. Since skeletal development in normally developing children tends to be harmonious and in an orderly sequence (Fig. 26), it is usually possible to select a matching standard plate, or two plates between which the patient's falls. Skeletal age (SA) may then be recorded in years and months, according to its estimated nearness to a given age standard.

For practical purposes, this matching process begins with the assumption of normality. Selecting the standard nearest to the chronological age of the patient, the clinician reads back and forth from that point. For cases where different areas suggest divergent SA's within the same hand, directions are offered for reading each joint area separately, a more tedious but not prohibitive process.

In any case, it is well worthwhile for the clinician who will be making repeated use of skeletal age ratings to make his own film evaluations rather than to rely on X-ray reports. Even when joint-by-joint readings are undertaken, the assay is not so time-consuming, for example, as a complete blood count, and each clinician soon develops his own manner of proceeding.

If hand films are repeated after an interval of several months or a year, they provide a means of determining the rate at which skeletal development is progressing, not only in general bone age, but in the amount of scatter in the maturity of different centers of ossification.

CLINICAL SIGNIFICANCE

At most ages, about two-thirds of the population of healthy children will have SA's that are no more than a year above or below their chronological ages. Acceleration or retardation of three years or more is considered very deviant. In infancy, and as the children approach maturity, the deviations are much less. Marked retardation in late adolescence is of clinical significance for evaluating aberrations in growth.

The skeleton of the healthy, adequately nourished child develops as a unit, and its various parts tend to keep pace with one another in their maturation. So intimate is the correspondence between maturation of the skeletal and reproductive systems that changes in the latter may be accurately predicted merely from X-ray films of the hand and wrist. For example, the skeletal status of the hand enables one to distinguish, some years before puberty, between children who will mature early and those in whom maturation will be longer delayed. Skeletal age has been found to be more highly correlated with menarcheal age and developmental status than is either height, weight, height-weight index, or annual increments in standing height.

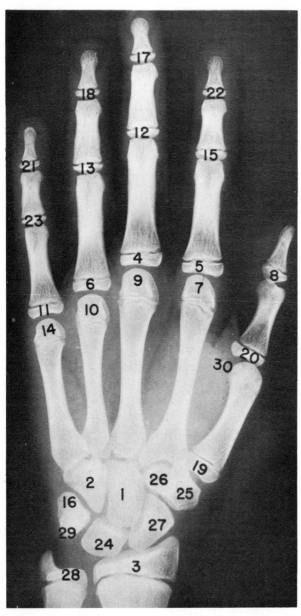

FIG. 26.—X-ray film showing the *sequence* of appearance of the ossification centers. From Greulich and Pyle, *Radiographic Atlas of Skeletal Development of the Hand and Wrist*, 1959. Photograph courtesy of the authors and the Stanford University Press.

It may be useful clinically to know that the first appearance of the sesamoid bone at the base of the thumb has been found to occur in most instances two years before the menarche and that the menarche occurs close to the time of closure of the epiphysis of distal phalanx II (Buehl and Pyle, 1942). In a similar way for the boy, stages of development of the external genitalia (see chap. 7) can be predicted more accurately from SA than from chronological age (CA). The same is true of the boy's period of rapid growth in stature, to be discussed in chapter 11.

These examples illustrate how a single X-ray film of a child's hand affords a measurement of the progress the child has made toward physical maturity. This same film also permits distinctions between the poorly and the adequately mineralized skeleton; it reveals developmental imbalances if such exist; it discloses scars of interrupted growth.

X-rays on the same child, repeated at appropriate intervals, can give an important indication of the **rate of maturation.** It is often helpful to plot a child's growth on the height and weight charts (Figs. 27–30 presented in chap. 11) using SA for the age axis. Such curves as height for CA and height for SA can each then be compared with the trend curves on the chart. Often a very deviant height-age curve becomes reasonable and consistent as a height–skeletal-age curve.

Furthermore, stage and rate of maturation tend to be closely associated with **behavior,** as well as with the physical aspects of development so frequently noted. For example, a series of studies relating rates of maturing to behavior (Jones and Bayley, 1950; Mussen and Jones, 1957) shows that children who mature at deviant rates (that may be well within the physically normal) have trouble in adjusting to their class- and age-mates in school and in other social situations. The difficulties are greatest for two deviant groups at opposite extremes. The early-maturing girls suddenly find themselves to be large and with mature feminine builds while their classmates are still just children; at the other end of the maturity continuum are the late-maturing boys, who remain immature little boys after most of the other boys and girls their age have grown and matured, with the accompanying changes in interests and abilities. It is often possible to reassure these children with information about the course of growth that they may expect.

Chapter 10

Height Prediction

The "Tables for Predicting Adult Height from Skeletal Age" (Bayley and Pinneau, 1952), reprinted in Appendix II, provide a simple clinical tool which combines skeletal age with the current understanding of its relation to growth. Sex, chronological age, skeletal age, and present height are the factors entering into a prediction. If skeletal maturation is within one year of the chronological age, the prediction may be read from one of the four tables pertaining to normal growth, depending on the age and sex of the child. Appendix II also includes other sets of tables for use when the skeletal age is retarded or accelerated by one year or more.

This system of prediction is based on the fact that a child's skeletal age (SA), as read by the Todd or Greulich-Pyle type of standard, is very closely related to the proportion of his adult stature achieved at the time of his X-ray. That is, SA shows a correlation of about .86 with per cent of mature height (PMH) at most ages after 9 years, if chronological age is held constant. The original 1946 tables were constructed by Bayley from height records and SA (assessed against the 1937 Todd standards) of 200 children from the Harvard Growth Study on whom annual records were available from 6 to 18 or 19 years. They were adapted by Bayley and Pinneau in 1952 from the original ones, utilizing assessments made on the Greulich-Pyle (1950) standards and data gathered at the University of California Institute of Human Development, using 192 normal Berkeley children (103 girls and 89 boys). These children were measured and X-rayed every six months from 8 years through 18 years, or until all epiphyses of the hand were closed. The tables were then validated by application to a different group of children (23 girls and 23 boys) on whom the same kinds of growth records were available. Since their construction in 1946 the Height-Prediction Tables have been tested in practice by data from many additional cases; the revised tables have been found to apply equally well using the 1950 Greulich-Pyle standards or the revised standards recently published in the 1959 edition of the *Atlas*. The tables reprinted as our Appendix II also appear in the new *Atlas* along with a reprint of the paper in which they were originally described (Bayley and Pinneau, 1952).

DIRECTIONS FOR USING THE TABLES

In using the tables it is necessary to have a proper X-ray of the hand and wrist, properly assessed for skeletal age (chap. 9); an accurate measurement of height (chap. 2); and a record of the child's age. Since girls mature more rapidly than boys—the difference during adolescence amounting to two years, on the average—it is also important that a child be assessed on standards and tables appropriate for his sex.

With the necessary data in hand, the correct table may be selected for the child's age, sex, and degree of maturation—normal (or average), accelerated, or retarded, depending on a comparison of SA with CA.

Height predictions may be read directly from the correct table, once it is selected. Find the column which represents the child's skeletal age and the horizontal row which represents his present height. The number at which the two columns intersect is the child's **predicted mature height.**

Height Prediction

For example, Boy X is 10 years 6 months old, 57 inches tall, and has a bone age of 11 years; according to the table, he may expect to reach a mature height of 70.9 inches.

Boy Y is also 57 inches tall and has a skeletal age of 11 years, but he is only 8 years 9 months old; therefore, his maturation is accelerated more than one year, and we may predict that his adult height will be 74.3 inches.

Boy Z provides an excellent example of the value in knowing skeletal age as well as chronological age. He is also 57 inches tall but 13 years 3 months of age. If we did not know his skeletal age but assumed it to correspond to his chronological age, the "average" table would lead us to predict a very short adult of 64.0 inches. However, when an X-ray of his hand and wrist shows his skeletal age to be 11 years—more than one year retarded—we turn to the correct table and find that he is more likely to reach an adult height of 69.3 inches.

In using the tables, approximate interpolations can be made by inspection for decimals of inches in height (vertical columns) and for intermediate skeletal ages in months or the corresponding PMH (horizontal columns). Another way to use the tables, especially when there are interpolations and when the child's

TABLE 6*

MEANS AND STANDARD DEVIATIONS OF PER CENT OF MATURE HEIGHT ACHIEVED AT SUCCESSIVE AGES, BIRTH TO 18 YEARS

CA	BOYS			GIRLS		
	N	Mean	S.D.	N	Mean	S.D.
Months:						
1	17	30.18	0.77	20	32.40	1.44
2	22	32.40	0.93	21	34.51	1.56
3	22	33.93	1.00	23	35.96	1.31
4	22	35.21	0.95	23	37.50	1.08
5	22	36.50	0.99	21	38.78	1.08
6	22	37.67	0.93	21	39.84	1.20
7	22	38.44	0.95	21	40.69	1.20
8	22	39.22	1.10	23	41.79	1.37
9	22	40.08	1.07	23	42.20	1.22
10	22	40.80	1.14	23	43.09	1.37
11	22	41.53	1.16	21	44.10	1.24
12	22	42.23	1.04	21	44.67	1.42
15	22	44.02	1.19	21	46.90	1.18
18	20	45.64	1.34	19	48.76	1.37
24	23	48.57	1.44	17	52.15	1.34
30	23	51.14	1.40	18	54.75	1.22
Years:						
3.0	23	53.53	1.34	22	57.16	1.20
4.0	22	57.72	1.38	22	61.84	1.45
5.0	23	61.60	1.49	23	66.24	1.45
6.0	23	65.31	1.58	23	70.29	1.60
7.0	23	69.08	1.60	22	74.28	1.61
8.0	22	72.40	1.68	23	77.57	1.87
9.0	22	75.61	1.68	21	81.19	2.00
9.5	21	77.21	1.66	20	83.03	2.13
10.0	22	78.40	1.76	23	84.76	2.42
10.5	23	79.82	1.77	22	86.85	2.71
11.0	23	81.30	1.94	21	88.65	2.88
11.5	23	82.54	2.00	21	90.81	3.06
12.0	20	84.00	2.23	22	92.61	3.27
12.5	21	85.43	2.49	21	94.72	2.61
13.0	23	87.32	3.02	18	95.96	2.15
13.5	21	89.22	3.57	18	97.17	1.70
14.0	20	91.00	3.96	19	98.27	1.24
14.5	20	92.60	3.85	19	98.74	0.93
15.0	20	94.60	3.74	21	99.31	0.68
15.5	21	96.00	3.31	21	99.54	0.48
16.0	22	97.09	2.71	21	99.62	0.35
16.5	20	97.95	2.12	20	99.75	0.34
17.0	20	98.79	1.43	22	99.95	0.25
17.5	20	99.28	1.01	19	99.91	0.25
18.0	21	99.55	0.58	18	99.96	0.11

* Data from Berkeley Growth Study cases (Bayley and Pinneau, 1952).

height is not included in the tables, is to make a slide-rule division of the present height by the per cent of mature height (as indicated in the line just below the SA), selected from the proper table. The dividend is the predicted mature height.

Prediction at younger ages is very subject to error, but there is sometimes a need to make an estimate of probable future growth. This may be done by computing, as suggested above, from the per cent of mature height achieved at successive ages (Table 6). In such instances, if the child is skeletally retarded to a significant extent, his actual future growth will probably exceed the prediction, while the converse might be expected of the accelerated child.

CLINICAL SIGNIFICANCE

It is obvious that for any child both chronological age and skeletal age move concurrently, if at different rates, toward the mature status. As he grows older and more mature he achieves with each year a greater per cent of his mature height. In other words, the greater the degree of maturity, either in years or in development, the less is the remaining growth potential.

It is important to remember that a height prediction is only a statement of potential, not a promise. It assumes a normal sequence of genetic, ecological, and hormonal influences on growth—just those factors which may be disturbed in cases where growth is deviant. Experience shows that where growth and/or maturation are excessively retarded or disturbed, this potential may never be realized. The growth impulse wears out, even though the theoretical potential exists.

Although extremely deviant children may thus grow wide of the prediction, these tables, by including so significant and personal a variable as skeletal age, score a higher accuracy than methods based on genetic or chronological expectations. The superiority of the skeletal-age prediction method, as applied to essentially normal children, was demonstrated by Gray as early as 1948.

Section C

Interpreting Successive Observations—Growth Trends

Serial observations over time eventually result in a longitudinal study. This applies to all the material which comprises the substance of this book. Repeated measurements at appropriate intervals of any of the basic items or any of the evaluations described in previous sections will permit the identification of growth trends.

Certain kinds of data, however, invite more formal charting. In medical practice, data on height and weight characteristically call for such treatment. In the following chapters various graphic methods are offered for long-time study of these parameters. Depending on the clinical purpose, the most useful devices can be selected.

Curves are offered for the study separately of height and weight, particularly as their patterns are related to tempo of maturation; standards for gauging annual increments are also provided (Figs. 27–30).

A graphic growth record is presented which permits simultaneous study of height, weight, and bi-cristal diameter. It is a method of choice for considering growth as a whole, especially in relation to body build and weight and changes in these during adolescence (Figs. 31, 32).

Finally, chapter 13 on growth rates offers a more detailed method for investigating changes in stature over short periods. Such analyses may be valuable when a patient is under treatment.

It should be noted that while the most desirable material for longitudinal study comes from the accumulated records of the interested clinician, many parents are already in possession of valuable records when they first bring the child for examination. Often they can secure such material from previous school and medical examinations. The more aware the parents are of a growth problem, the more likely are they to have, or to have access to, past observations. When the establishment of a trend as well as current status is immediately relevant, it is well worth seeking such prior notations for study.

Before plotting, it is wise to tabulate in one place the measurements that have been accumulated, from whatever source. The data sheets on the height and weight record forms may be used for this purpose.

Chapter 11

Height Curves and Weight Curves

The usual growth curves for height and weight are derived from averages, at each age, of large numbers of children. Even if allowance is made for percentile variations, the sample at any one age includes children who differ in physical maturity, that is, in the stage reached in their progress toward mature status.

The record forms presented here—Figures 27–30 —include curves which differ from the conventional in that the data have been grouped into a set of five curves for each of the charts; any point on any of the curves therefore represents the average for children of that age who are also alike in their skeletal maturity. The curves are based on the measurements of approximately three hundred healthy California children—an equal number of each sex—who were measured repeatedly from birth until between 18 and 21 years of age (Bayley, 1956).

Compared with the conventional curves, a given child may appear to lag behind others of his age and sex or to spurt ahead in an irregular fashion. The same data, plotted on these skeletally adjusted charts, often fall close to that curve which corresponds to the child's own particular "time table."

HEIGHT

Growth in height is closely related to the rate of physical maturing. This is true during adolescence in particular. Although most children mature and grow according to much the **same pattern,** normally healthy children may differ greatly in size, and they may also be as much as three years accelerated or retarded from the average in their **rates of maturing.** Girls, on the average, mature faster than boys. They thus attain their adult

height about two years earlier than boys and are also 5 or 6 inches shorter as adults. Therefore, separate record forms are required for boys (Fig. 27) and for girls (Fig. 28), with each chart including height curves for children maturing at different rates.

The Height Curves

The heavy central curve in each chart represents the growth in height of an average-sized boy (or girl) who is maturing at an average rate. Most children's curves of height for age, when plotted on this chart, will lie close to this central curve in pattern and in the timing of growth revealed; they will probably be not far above or below the curve in actual height.

Children who are accelerated in maturing will have growth curves more like one of the two upper lines. Children who mature slowly will grow more like one of the two lower lines. Those who are tall or short as children *only* because they are fast or slow in maturing, not because they are constitutionally large or small, will have growth curves similar to those immediately above or below the central curve.

Some children are large from a very early age, with a pattern of both accelerated bone age and rapid growth. Their growth is similar to that represented in the topmost broken line of each chart, which records the data from one such typical tall boy and one tall girl, respectively. They will be tall adults and will gain this height two or three years before the average for their sex.

Some children are small from an early age and grow and mature very slowly. Their growth will approximate the lowest curve on each chart, which again

Height and Weight Separately

PMH FOR BOYS
(Per cent of Mature
Height Achieved)

Age Years	Average	Accel-erated	Retarded
Birth	28.6		
1.0	42.2	44.5	40.4
2.0	49.5	51.3	47.0
3.0	53.8	55.6	51.6
4.0	58.0	60.0	58.0
5.0	61.8	64.0	59.7
6.0	65.2	67.8	63.8
7.0	69.0	70.5	66.8
8.0	72.0	73.5	69.8
9.0	75.0	76.5	73.2
10.0	78.0	79.7	76.4
11.0	81.1	83.4	79.5
12.0	84.2	87.2	82.2
13.0	87.3	91.3	84.6
14.0	91.5	95.8	87.6
15.0	96.1	98.3	91.6
16.0	98.3	99.4	95.7
17.0	99.3	99.9	98.2
17.5		100.0	
18.0	99.8		99.2
18.5	100.0		
19.0			99.8
20.0			100.0

Name_____ Birthdate_____

RECORD OF MEASURES

Date	Age Year	Month	Stature Inches	Cent.	Annual Gain	Skeletal XM	Rating Age Eq	Predict. of Adult Height

FIG. 27.—Form for plotting height by age for boys, showing patterns for boys maturing at average, accelerated, and retarded rates.

The Increment Curve (*lower right*) is a separate plot of annual gains in height. A normal curve is included plus points to indicate the maximum annual increments in early-maturing and in late-maturing patients. A table showing per cent of mature stature achieved in successive years is included on the form (*directly above*) plus a data sheet for recording measurements before plotting. From Bayley, "Growth Curves of Height and Weight by Age for Boys and Girls, Scaled According to Physical Maturity," *Journal of Pediatrics*, Vol. 48, No. 2 (1956). Courtesy of the C. V. Mosby Company and the University of California Institute of Human Development, Berkeley.

represents the data from one short boy and one short girl. They will probably attain a short adult stature, usually after 18 years for girls or 20 years for boys.

If a child's growth is unusual and does not approximate one of the central curves, his skeletal age should be determined from the Greulich-Pyle standards. A series of such SA readings, made at intervals of about a year, can be used for plotting a curve of growth that will show a child's height with respect to his own rate of development. Such assessments of SA may also be used for predicting adult height from the Bayley-Pinneau (1952) prediction tables. These two methods—

plotting of height by skeletal age and height prediction—may serve as mutual checks on height expectations.

Height-Increment Curves

Another way to evaluate a child's growth is from his **annual increments** in height. The increments for the average child, maturing at the average rate, are plotted as supplements to the height curves in Figures 27 and 28. If a series of heights by age is plotted for a child on the upper portion of the chart and a curve drawn through these points, his height can be read off at any

GROWTH CURVES OF HEIGHT BY AGE FOR BOYS
(Average, Accelerated, and Retarded Rates of Maturation)

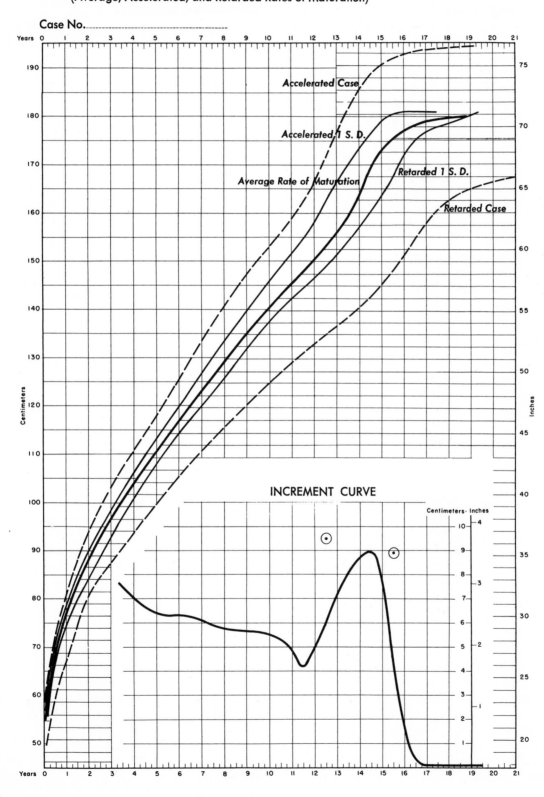

Height and Weight Separately

PMH FOR GIRLS

(Per cent of Mature Height Achieved)

Age Years	Average	Accel-erated	Retarded
Birth	30.9		
1.0	44.7	48.0	42.2
2.0	52.8	54.7	50.0
3.0	57.0	60.0	55.0
4.0	61.8	64.9	59.8
5.0	66.2	69.3	63.9
6.0	79.3	73.4	67.8
7.0	74.0	76.0	71.5
8.0	77.5	79.5	74.5
9.0	80.7	83.5	77.7
10.0	84.4	87.9	81.0
11.0	88.4	92.9	84.9
12.0	92.9	96.6	88.2
13.0	96.5	98.2	91.1
14.0	98.3	99.1	95.2
15.0	99.1	99.5	97.8
16.0	99.6	99.9	98.9
16.5		100.0	
17.0	100.0		99.6
18.0			100.0

Name_____ Birthdate_____

RECORD OF MEASURES

Date	Age Year	Month	Stature Inches	Cent.	Annual Gain	Skeletal XM	Rating Age Eq	Predict. of Adult Height

FIG. 28.—Form for plotting height by age for girls, showing patterns for girls maturing at average, accelerated, and retarded rates. For details, see Fig. 27 and text description, p. 49. From Bayley, 1956. Courtesy of the C. V. Mosby Company and the University of California Institute of Human Development, Berkeley.

point over the span of years included in his curve. The amount of growth from one year to the next can be determined and plotted on the lower chart. For example, if a child was 47 inches at 7 years and 51 inches at 8 years, his increment for that year was 4 inches; this should be plotted at the midpoint, or 7½ years). His increment curve will show whether his periods of slow and fast growth occur at the expected times. The maximum annual increments of the early- and late-maturers are represented on the increment charts by two dots. The early-maturing child's increment curve and growth curve of height should be compared with the accelerated curves; if he is late-maturing, comparison should be made with the retarded curves. Ordinarily, larger increments in height are found for physically accelerated children and smaller increments for the physically retarded. The degree of a child's acceleration or retardation will show in the age at which his maximum increment occurs.

Sometimes the point of inflection on the increment curve occurs sooner or later than would be expected from a child's previous record and skeletal development. Apparently in such cases the puberal phase of growth is accelerated or delayed. When this occurs, we find a shift in the pattern of growth. For example, when the spurt is delayed, the childhood growth continues slowly, and the eventual acceleration starts from a greater stature than if it had occurred sooner. For this reason, such children will turn out to be taller adults than their childhood measures would have indicated. The converse of this condition may be found in the child whose rapid growth and maturation start earlier than expected and result in shorter-than-expected adult stature.

Space is provided to the left of the chart on the individual record form for entering the measurements, calculated increments, skeletal ages, and predicted heights. Per cent of mature height attained is tabulated

GROWTH CURVES OF HEIGHT BY AGE FOR GIRLS
(Average, Accelerated, and Retarded Rates of Maturation)

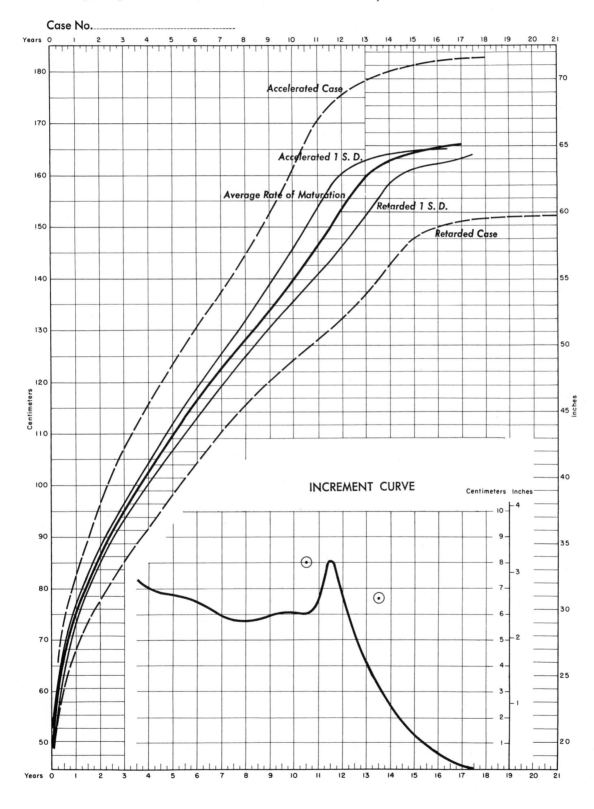

Case No._____

INCREMENT CURVE

MEAN WEIGHT FOR HEIGHT: BOYS

Name_____ Birthdate_____

Age Years	Average		Accelerated		Retarded	
	Height Inches	Weight Pounds	Height Inches	Weight Pounds	Height Inches	Weight Pounds
Birth	19.8	8.4	–	–	–	–
1.0	30.7	22.9	30.9	23.8	29.3	23.4
2.0	34.6	29.3	35.2	31.1	32.8	27.3
3.0	38.0	34.6	38.6	35.5	36.2	30.6
4.0	40.8	39.0	41.5	41.4	39.6	35.7
5.0	43.7	42.8	44.5	45.9	42.3	40.3
6.0	45.8	47.6	47.2	51.8	44.9	44.1
7.0	48.7	52.9	50.0	56.9	47.0	48.5
8.0	50.9	58.2	52.5	65.0	49.4	54.7
9.0	53.1	66.8	54.9	74.5	51.8	60.2
10.0	55.3	74.1	57.3	86.0	54.1	66.1
11.0	57.5	82.2	59.6	97.2	55.8	73.4
12.0	59.1	91.3	61.8	109.8	57.7	80.7
13.0	61.4	101.4	65.6	124.8	59.4	90.2
14.0	64.6	116.0	68.5	134.5	61.7	100.1
15.0	68.1	133.8	70.7	147.9	64.2	112.2
16.0	70.1	142.6	71.7	154.1	67.7	131.0
17.0	70.5	149.7	71.7	155.9	69.5	143.1
18.0	70.9	154.1	–	–	70.5	150.8
19.0	–	–	–	–	71.3	151.7

RECORD OF MEASURES

Date	Age		Weight		Annual Gain
	Years	Months	Pounds	Kilograms	

FIG. 29.—Form of plotting weight by age for boys, showing patterns for boys maturing at average, accelerated, and retarded rates. A separate chart (*lower right*) shows the annual increment in weight at the various rates. The table of mean weight for height at various ages and rates of maturation (*directly above*) permits additional comparisons. A data sheet is provided for recording measurements prior to plotting. From Bayley, "Growth Curves of Height and Weight by Age for Boys and Girls, Scaled According to Physical Maturity," *Journal of Pediatrics*, Vol. 48, No. 2 (1956). Courtesy of the C. V. Mosby Company and the University of California Institute of Human Development, Berkeley.

by age for children whose rates of maturation are average and for those who are accelerated or retarded by a year or two.

WEIGHT

The Weight Curves

In construction of the forms for recording and evaluating weight—Figure 29 for boys, Figure 30 for girls—the data were derived from the same children and in the same groupings as were used for the height charts. Thus, a point on the central curve represents the average weight of children of that age of the sex designated who are approaching physical maturity at an average rate. Children maturing at accelerated rates have weights represented by the two upper curves; the weights of children who are retarded in physical maturing are likely to fall in the region of the two lower curves.

GROWTH CURVES OF WEIGHT BY AGE FOR BOYS

(Average, Accelerated, and Retarded Rates of Maturation)

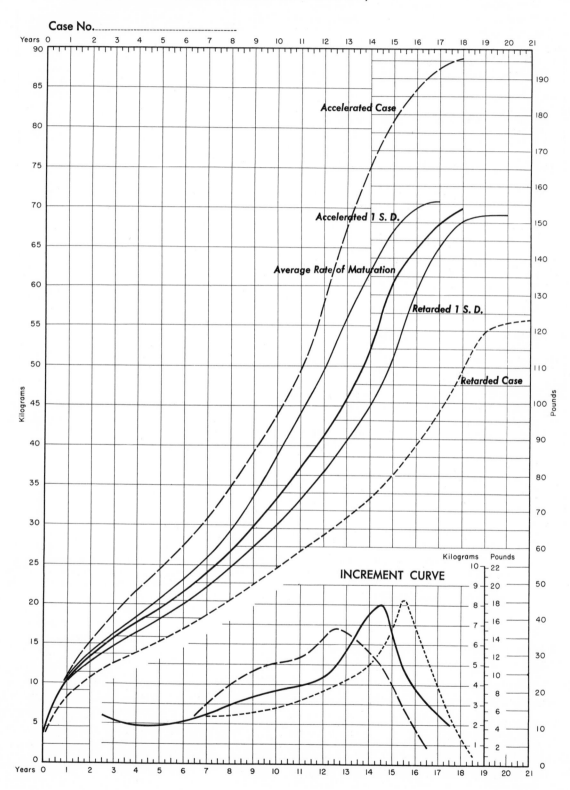

Name_____ Birthdate_____

MEAN WEIGHT FOR HEIGHT: GIRLS

Age Years	Average		Accelerated		Retarded	
	Height Inches	Weight Pounds	Height Inches	Weight Pounds	Height Inches	Weight Pounds
Birth	19.3	7.5	20.1	–	–	–
1.0	29.1	21.5	30.6	24.0	28.3	21.2
2.0	34.4	28.0	34.4	30.2	33.3	25.9
3.0	37.5	32.4	37.8	34.7	36.7	30.6
4.0	40.6	37.5	41.3	42.1	39.4	33.7
5.0	43.1	41.2	44.1	48.1	41.7	37.9
6.0	45.9	46.7	46.9	53.2	44.5	43.0
7.0	48.1	52.9	49.2	57.3	47.2	47.6
8.0	50.4	60.0	52.0	66.8	49.2	51.1
9.0	52.7	66.4	55.1	78.5	51.5	59.7
10.0	55.1	76.1	57.3	92.2	53.3	64.8
11.0	57.5	86.6	60.4	108.9	55.5	69.9
12.0	60.7	99.2	63.1	124.8	57.7	78.0
13.0	63.0	112.4	64.3	131.2	59.8	86.9
14.0	64.2	121.0	64.8	135.0	62.4	99.0
15.0	64.8	128.8	65.0	138.7	63.8	108.5
16.0	65.2	131.6	65.2	139.3	64.5	114.6
17.0	65.3	132.3	65.2	137.6	64.8	119.3
18.0	65.3	131.8	65.2	134.5	64.9	119.0

RECORD OF MEASURES

Date	Age		Weight		Annual Gain
	Years	Months	Pounds	Kilograms	

FIG. 30.—Form for plotting weight by age for girls, showing patterns for girls maturing at average, accelerated, and retarded rates. For details see Fig. 29 and text description, p. 54. From Bayley, 1956. Courtesy of the C. V. Mosby Company and the University of California Institute of Human Development, Berkeley.

Weight Increment Curves

Annual increases in weight may be entered in the section provided on the weight charts, using the method described for height. It should be noted that the greatest annual increment of weight is above average for early-maturing girls and below average for girls who are maturing slowly, corresponding to the height curves for girls. The pattern for physically accelerated boys, however, differs in having consistently large weight gains with no exceptional spurts. Retarded boys, on the other hand, remain slender with small gains in weight until they experience the sharp increase with puberty, at about 15 years.

Space is again provided to the left on the individual weight forms for entering the child's weight and annual increments. There is also provided a table of mean weight for height by age for each of the three maturity groups. It will be seen that the accelerated children are normally heavier than average for their height, while the retarded are correspondingly more slender.

GROWTH CURVES OF WEIGHT BY AGE FOR GIRLS
(Average, Accelerated, and Retarded Rates of Maturation)

Case No.

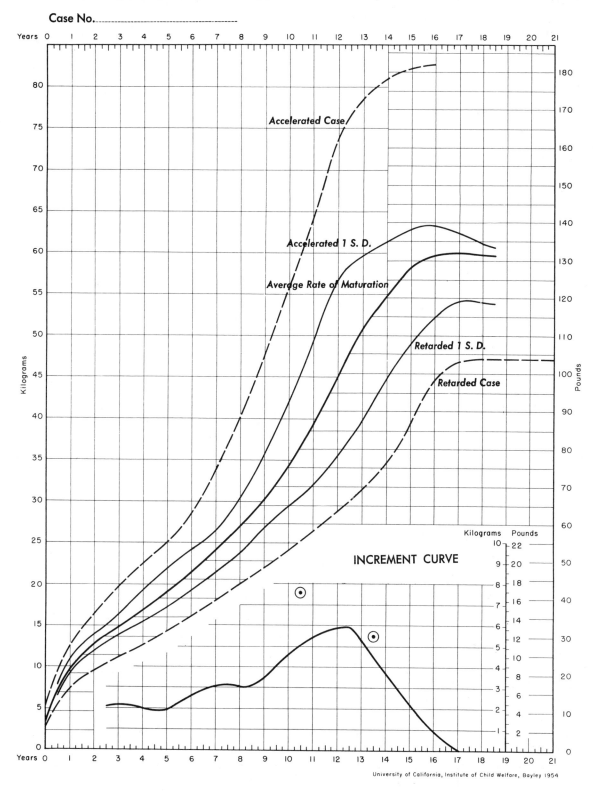

University of California, Institute of Child Welfare, Bayley 1954

Height and Weight Separately

CLINICAL SIGNIFICANCE

When a child's height or weight has been identified as an item in his development requiring special consideration, its individual study against standards set up specifically for these parameters allows more direct interpretations than do points plotted on a composite curve, such as the growth graph. However, especially in weight judgments, it is well, both initially and occasionally in its course, to assess weight expectation by the additional consideration of bi-cristal diameter instead of relying on channel progress alone.

Comparison between separate height and weight curves offers additional insights into the behavior of weight. Normally, a child's weight curve should be in the same channel as his height curve, and the two curves should follow the same pattern of annual increments. The extent and direction of disparity between channels for a child's weight and his height help to separate weight changes due to maturation from those due to nutrition. If weight deviations parallel height deviations, they probably reflect normal variations related to maturation rate; when weight deviates alone, it is more apt to signify a change in nutritional status.

Many children tend to put on extra weight during the prepuberal period, at about 10–12 years. This is when we are most likely to see childhood obesity. Such fat usually disappears as soon as puberal maturing and rapid growth in height are well started. The child's weight will return to the channel that is normal for him as he regains balance in his hormonal functioning.

Chapter 12

Graphic Growth Records

The **growth record graphs**—Figure 31 for boys, Figure 32 for girls—are designed to permit both current and longitudinal evaluations of growth in terms of height, weight, and bi-cristal diameter, with special reference to linear and lateral tendencies in body build, and the implications of bi-cristal breadth for weight prediction.

Stature is found on the vertical axis, **weight** and **bi-cristal** on the horizontal axis, with scales provided in both English and metric systems. In order to demonstrate the means for weight and bi-cristal at successive ages and the actual relation between bi-cristal and weight, it was necessary to graduate the bi-cristal scale in progressively longer intervals, a simple device that causes no difficulty in plotting.

The **solid dots** represent average values for height versus weight and for height versus bi-cristal at the indicated ages.

The **vertical bars** represent allowable normal variations of height for age—the average values plus and minus twice the standard deviation. This is the range which is expected by chance to include 96 per cent of the normal children with racial and environmental backgrounds similar to those of the children from whose measurements the diagrams were derived (Bayer and Gray, 1935).

The **horizontal** span of the **stream**—the space between the two curved lines—represents a similar range of plus and minus two standard deviations of weight for height and bi-cristal for height.

DIRECTIONS FOR USE

These graphs may be used either for casual reference at a single examination or for longitudinal study.

For quick reference, a pair of the charts may be kept on the desk or framed and hung upon the wall with a transparent triangle within easy reach.

For longitudinal study it is best to record measurements in the table before plotting. For any one set of observations, plot height against weight as a small **circle,** ◯, using a 30°–60° twelve-inch transparent triangle. Write age in years and months beside it. Evaluate the circle for height by its vertical position with respect to the bar bearing the child's age at the nearest birthday; for weight, by its position toward the right or left of the stream.

If bi-cristal diameter is also used, plot height against bi-cristal as a small **cross,** ✕. Weight can then be further judged by its nearness to bi-cristal. The circle and cross which belong together can easily be identified since they will be at the same height level.

When subsequent examinations are made, each new circle and each cross is joined to its predecessor by a line, thus showing direction of growth. Two different colors, or solid and dotted lines, will facilitate interpretation.

INTERPRETATION

Height may be evaluated from cross or from circle by noting the vertical position of either, relative to the appropriate vertical bar. For a single observation, it will probably be sufficient to note whether the child's position corresponds to the middle, upper, or lower third of the bar, i.e., whether his height is average, tall, or short compared to his age peers.

For successive sets of longitudinal observations, it may also be noted whether the vertical position relative

Height Combined with Weight and Bi-Cristal

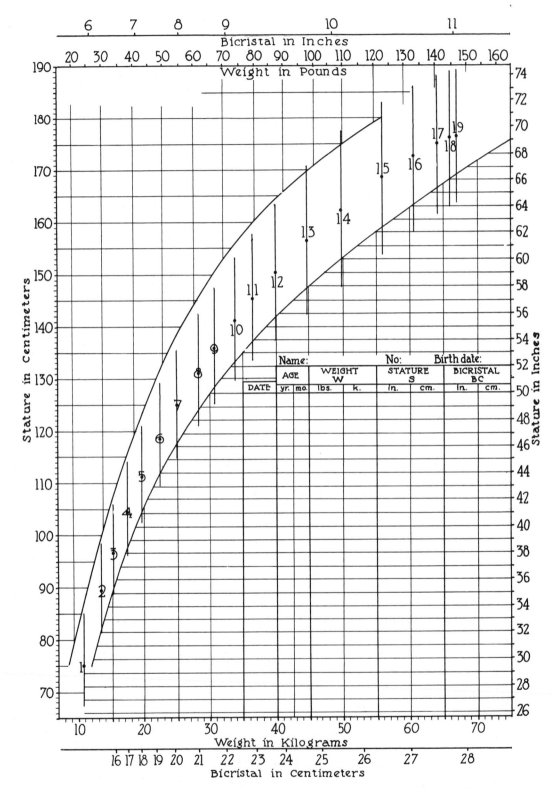

FIG. 31.—Graphic Growth Record chart for recording height, weight, and bi-cristal diameter of boys, ages 1–19. Normal range of *height for age* is shown by vertical bars. Normal range of *weight for height* is indicated by the open stream. See text for instructions in using. From Bayer and Gray, "Plotting of a Graphic Record of Growth for Children Aged One to Nineteen Years," *Am. J. Dis. Children*, Vol. 50 (1935). Courtesy Dr. Gray and the American Medical Association, Chicago.

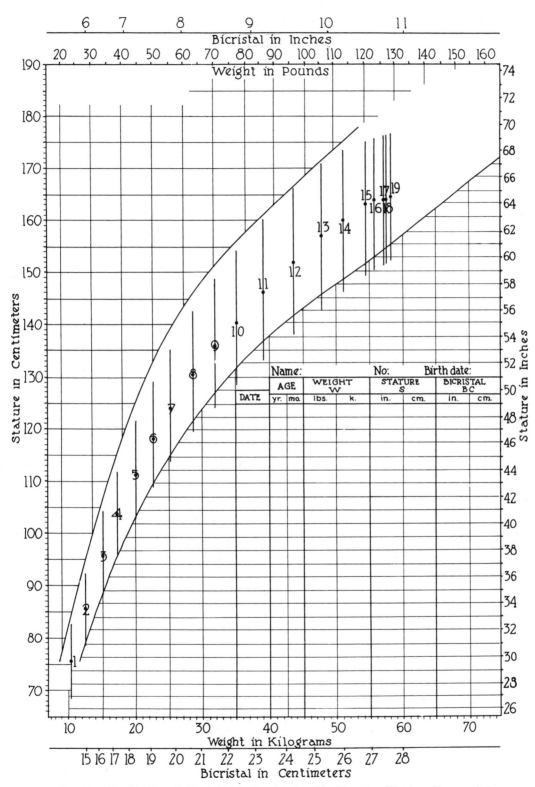

FIG. 32.—Graphic Growth Record chart for girls (see Fig. 31 and p. 59). From Bayer and Gray, "Plotting of a Graphic Record of Growth for Children Aged One to Nineteen Years," *Am. J. Dis. Children*, Vol. 50 (1935). Courtesy Dr. Gray and the American Medical Association, Chicago.

to the bar is stable, climbing, or sinking. The horizontal distance from the appropriate bar has no significance for height.

Weight and bi-cristal are each interpreted first by the horizontal position of circle or cross in the center, right, or left third of the stream. This tells whether the child is average, heavy, or light in weight; average, broad, or slender in build.

Bi-cristal here serves as an index of breadth of frame. Where it is average for the stature, the weight is expected to be average. Broader or narrower pelvic breadths are usually associated with relatively heavier or lighter weights. This observation is discussed in more detail in a later section, "Weight Assessment and Body Build."

Weight can thus be further judged as to its probable clinical normality by noting whether circle and cross are in the same channels of the stream. Identity is neither expected nor desired, but it is achieved with astonishing frequency in many children, i.e., weight often coincides closely with weight prediction on this graph.

LINEAR AND LATERAL BODY TYPES

The terms **linear** and **lateral types** were introduced by Stockard (1931) to characterize the two "normal adult types" which have been recognized, with variations, since ancient times. They are essentially the long, slender builds and the short, wide builds. Under a variety of names, countless implications of hormonal functioning and personality manifestations have been drawn from these two basic types and the gradations between them.

"Lateral" and "linear" suggest a simple dichotomy of body form, such as is suggested by "male" and "female." In chapter 8, on androgyny, however, it was shown that neither within each sex nor between the sexes does such a simple dichotomy exist, since build reflects the development of three fairly independent components, skeleton, muscle, and fat, each of which is acted upon by multiple influences. Similarly all body types do not fall easily into linear or lateral forms; they do not have dependable hormonal and personality implications. Nevertheless, there are observable tendencies toward linearity and laterality which are clinically useful.

Subjective assessment of linearity versus laterality of body form depends not only on the arrangement of skeleton, muscle, and fat but also on several variables within the skeleton itself, such as longheadedness versus roundheadedness, long-leggedness, and relative pelvic breadth. Earlier workers assumed that all these factors were related to maturation rate, and they even argued for a three-way relation between higher metabolic rate, increased thyroid activity, and linearity of build. Modern observations, however, tend to dispute this association.

Adolescent growth patterns, as noted by Bayley (1943) and others, indicate that **slow-maturing boys** tend to be long-legged and narrow-hipped at maturity, while **fast-maturing boys** tend to be of lateral build. **Fast-maturing girls** tend to be shorter-legged adults; furthermore, they tend to broaden earlier and thus to be broader-hipped during adolescence, a tendency that they may not show as adults.

We must therefore assume that, despite the known influence of metabolic rate on growth patterns, many other factors, including genetic inheritance and the sex steroids, are of equal or overriding importance in the total build picture.

Weight Assessment and Body Build

Even though the idea of linearity versus laterality has limited significance, it remains important for the homely task of evaluating normal weight. It is increasingly common practice to consider breadth of frame in this recurring clinical judgment. Newer life insurance tables for adults include this factor as one variable in weight expectation. After extensive review of the literature, Gray (1928) concluded that among the methods available for the assessment of optimal weight and nutritional status in children, weight prediction from stature and pelvic breadth is a superior one.

Recent support for the concept of referring weight to skeletal frame comes from the work of Captain A. R. Behnke and his associates (1957a and b) in which he demonstrates that **ideal weight,** or lean body mass, varies with "skeletal breadth" measures or diameters, whereas **actual weight** varies with "envelope" measures or circumferences.

CLINICAL SIGNIFICANCE

By introducing bi-cristal diameter, a simple and reliable bony measure, into the build constellation, an objective judgment of weight is provided to supplement its relation to itself over time. This is especially important during the adolescent growth spurt when dramatic changes occur in build as well as in size. The bi-cristal thus serves as a built-in "referee," so that the graphic growth record can indicate not only in which channel the child travels, as does the Wetzel Grid (1946), but also in which one he probably *ought* to travel.

The search for criteria other than stature and age as a clue to proper weight is a reaction against the overdogmatic application of early height-weight/age standards, as these were introduced into school health examinations and into pediatric practice. At that time overly strict interpretations of what was normal led to many wrong diagnoses of malnutrition in healthy children, resulting in unwarranted anxiety on the part of doctors, nurses, parents, and children. The introduction of bi-cristal as another parameter is intended to increase the flexibility, not the rigidity, of judgment.

Chapter 13

Growth Rates

Growth rates provide a sensitive index of acceleration or deceleration of growth **over short periods.** Although the height curve of chapter 11, giving absolute linear growth and its annual increments, adequately reflects growth trends in long-time observations, the evaluation of such trends during brief periods of treatment may require more precise analysis. Changes in growth rate can be combined with height prediction to obtain simultaneous evaluations of immediate and long-range tendencies. In this way normal spontaneous changes in the rate of growth will not be mistaken as effects of the therapy.

At least three months should elapse between successive growth-rate calculations. Intervals of six months or a year are of even greater value. Additional intermediate observations serve to validate the end points of such relatively short treatment or control periods.

CALCULATION OF GROWTH RATE

The method used to calculate growth rate was derived from Brody (1927) and Fisher (1936). Five items are required to assess growth during a given period of observation: birth date of the patient; the date on which treatment began; stature on that date; final date of the period; and stature at that time. The simple formula for calculation of growth rate is as follows:

$$\frac{S_2 - S_1}{S_{Av.}} \div \text{length of period} \times 100 \, .$$

where S_2 is stature at the end of the period of treatment, and S_1 is stature at the beginning of the period. The difference (increase in centimeters during the course of treatment) is divided by the average stature, since the gain has relatively more significance for a short child than for one who is tall. The result is then divided by the length of the observation period (expressed as per cent of a year) and multiplied by 100 to arrive at the **relative growth rate per annum,** or **per cent of stature gained per year.** To give an example, if a child grew from 99 cm. to 101 cm. in three months, growth rate would be calculated as follows:

$$\frac{101 - 99}{100} \div 0.25 \times 100$$

$$= \frac{2}{100} \times \frac{1}{0.25} \times 100$$

$$= 8 \text{ per cent per year} \, .$$

Actual computations are best done with the aid of a calculator, using a **calculation sheet** especially set up for the purpose. A form which has been found convenient is reproduced in Table 7. In the interest of simplified calculations, the order of procedure specified here differs somewhat from the conceptual formula, but it obviously includes the same steps. Special care is required to get decimal points in the right places, a process which can be checked by common-sense inspection of the growth rates finally derived. To demonstrate the calculation sheet in action, we have entered on Table 7 the numbers from the foregoing example.

Since growth-rate calculations are not usually undertaken until data from several successive observation periods are available, it is advantageous to proceed vertically down each column. The given data of the various sessions are entered on alternate horizontal lines of the first four columns. *Column 1* is for notations about the type and duration of treatment periods. In *column 3* "inches" must be changed to "centimeters" if the original heights were taken in the English system. In *column 4* "age" must be stated in years and decimals of a year; the necessary conversion is simple with the Pearl and Miner Table (1932), which is reprinted in Appendix III.

The remaining columns are for calculations as indicated, leading to the growth rate in *column 10*. These calculations are entered on the horizontal lines which fall between successive sets of observed data.

STANDARD GROWTH-RATE CURVES

Figure 33 illustrates the general congruence between the patterns for boys and for girls in the prepuberal years as well as the dramatic divergence which

reflects the earlier adolescent spurt in girls. The curves are derived from the same population and data (Gray and Ayres, 1931) that provided the material for our anthropometric values (see chap. 6 and Appendix I).

The kinds of curves that may result from the changing growth rate in individual children are illustrated in Figures 102, 109, 115, and 137. The heavy line in Figure 102 (p. 135) represents the results when values are pooled for longer periods as contrasted with the type of graph which results when shorter periods are plotted.

INTERPRETATION

The interpretation of each illustrative chart is incorporated into the context of the corresponding case. In general, it may be said that observation periods of three months or less—and many treatment periods in

TABLE 7

GROWTH RATE: CALCULATION SHEET

Name:——— Case No.:——— *Key:*

Birthdate:——— Sex:———

| A = age | M = mean |
| S = stature | d = difference |

(dS = difference in height)
(MS = average height)
(dA = elapsed time)

	OBSERVED DATA						CALCULATIONS		
1	2	3	4	5	6	7	8	9	10
Treatment	Date	Stature (In.) (Cm.)	Age	dS	MS	dA	dS/dA (5/7)	dS/dA/MS (8/6)	(9)×100 (Growth Rate, Per Cent per Year)
	2/25/59	99	4.00	2	100	.25	8	0.08	8
	5/27/59	101	4.25						

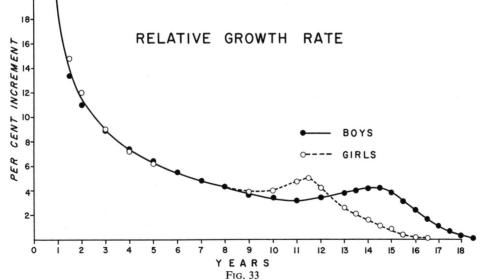

RELATIVE GROWTH RATE

● —— BOYS

○- - - - GIRLS

PER CENT INCREMENT

YEARS

FIG. 33

clinical practice are that brief—must be interpreted with caution.

Even so, curves from careful observations and shorter periods usually confirm the known tendency of the growth rate to fall from birth to adolescence and to show a spurt around puberty.

In using such a chart for the evaluation of a short treatment period, one must judge whether the treatment period shows a peak which is greater than, or at least equal to, normal variation. All favorable fluctuations must thus be viewed with reserve until they have been regularly repeated in the same or in several individuals.

CLINICAL SIGNIFICANCE

For evaluation of growth during brief periods, especially for comparing treatment periods with control periods, growth-rate calculations are superior to the derivation of simple semiannual or annual increments. By incorporating elapsed time into the formula, growth achieved during intervals of different duration may all be converted to annual rates and compared directly. As observations continue, several contiguous periods of treatment or of control may be grouped together for calculations toward a smoother or more reliable curve.

Furthermore, because the growth rate is also corrected for stature, groups of children can be directly compared and data pooled, for instance, as to results of treatment in a critical case study.

Particularly, by the critical use of growth-rate graphs, physicians may avoid misinterpreting a spontaneous, prepuberal growth acceleration as response to a growth stimulant or, conversely, a spontaneous, postpuberal growth deceleration as response to a growth inhibitor.

Part II

Case Illustrations

Part II

Case Illustrations

Previous sections of this book have described and demonstrated techniques for collecting and evaluating growth data. In this section methods will be exemplified in specific applications to individual cases. Each method of recording and studying is presented in connection with several individuals, but not every method is applied in each case. Status studies appear in all reports; longitudinal studies are added as the case requires and insofar as the material permits.

The twenty-two case studies include eight "normal" and fourteen "clinical" cases. The normals were observed in the Berkeley Longitudinal Growth Study. The clinical cases came under observation as patients in office or clinic.

Occasionally abnormalities were discovered in the normal group. Also occasionally, individuals in the clinical group, after observation, could be assured of their normality. These two groups are thus divided more by the route through which they came to attention and by their obvious relationship to the popular conception of the usual than by any rigid dividing line. Within the normal ("N") group, several cases therefore illustrate characteristic deviations from more common patterns. Within the clinical ("C") group, cases are presented that illustrate characteristic growth complaints (e.g., "too tall") or familiar clinical syndromes (e.g., "precocious menarche"). Explanatory headings are attached to such cases and to clinical subgroups of which they are a part.

Normal cases are each introduced by a characterization of the whole developmental pattern, which the longitudinal data then describe. They are further illuminated by status studies at one or two significant ages. These presentations are somewhat like a movie, with selected "close-ups."

Clinical cases, on the other hand, are introduced with a "close-up" of the status of the child at the age when the growth problem was presented and formulated, and when the first cross-sectional evaluation was made. This is the age posted in the heading. When earlier observations are available, they are included in the growth data tables. While there is only minimal reference to supporting clinical evidence, it should be noted that in the clinical group the diagnoses rest on the physical examinations and laboratory tests which are standard in up-to-date medical practice. Several of the patients have been subjects of more complete case reports published elsewhere, to which reference is made in the appropriate context.

In making a growth diagnosis it is assumed that the human body presents a composite record of all the forces—genetic, environmental, endocrine—which have created it and impinged on it. By seeking to decipher this record of the past, we add another dimension to the picture of current hormonal action, as this is reflected by modern laboratory assays.

Chapter 14

Eight Normal Cases

CASE N-I (AVERAGE BOY)

Characterization

Normal, healthy boy, average size and rate of maturing, studied from birth to maturity (Figs. 34, 35, 36). His medical history includes mumps at 2 years 6 months and a series of acute colds, with bronchitis between the ages of 5 and 6 years. There is, however, no evidence that these illnesses had any lasting effects on the course of growth.

Anthropometric Values and Deviation Chart

The deviation chart, described in chapter 6, gives information about body proportions. By comparing N-I's measurements at 4 years with the appropriate table of anthropometric values in Appendix I, the deviations from average have been obtained and plotted in Figure 37. N-I is seen to be average in weight, a little tall, but also somewhat short-stemmed, with a pelvic width just under average. The ratios of body proportions, accordingly, show him to be average in weight for stature, relatively short-bodied (long-legged), and rather slender in skeletal proportions. These proportions are illustrated by N-I's body photographs at 4 years (Figs. 34, 36).

Secondary Sex Characters

According to Greulich's standards of maturity of the genitals and pubic hair (see Fig. 16 and Table 3 in chap. 7), this boy is average. His pictures at 14 years show him to be intermediate between stages III and IV, which is average for 14 years.

Longitudinal Growth Data

This boy was measured repeatedly from the time he was born until he was 21 years old; his anthropometric values and skeletal ratings are tabulated in Table 8. These values are also plotted on the several

TABLE 8

GROWTH DATA

CASE N-I (Average Boy)

AGE (YR.-MO.)	WEIGHT		STATURE		BI-CRIS-TAL (CM.)	SA (YR.-MO.)	PRED. HT. (IN.)
	Lb.	Kg.	In.	Cm.			
Birth	8.6						
1	10.1	4.8	21.8	55.5			
3	13.3	6.0	24.0	61.0			
6	17.3	7.8	26.5	67.2			
9	21.8	9.9	28.7	72.8			
1–0	24.5	11.1	30.6	77.7		1–3	
1–6	26.0	11.8	33.3	84.6			
2–0	29.5	13.4	35.2	89.5		2–6	
2–6	31.0	14.1	37.2	94.6	14.6		
3–0	33.5	15.2	38.7	98.4	15.7	3–9	
4–0	38.8	17.6	41.4	105.3	16.8	4–3	
5–0	42.3	19.5	44.2	112.2	17.6		
6–0	49.5	22.4	46.9	119.0	18.6		
7–0	56.5	25.7	49.6	126.1	19.8		
8–0	58.5	26.5	51.5	130.7	20.3	8–6	69.7
9–0	64.4	29.2	53.6	136.1	21.1	9–6	69.5
10–0	66.4	30.1	55.5	141.0	21.7	10–6	69.8
11–0	74.7	33.9	57.2	145.3	22.6	11–6	69.9
12–0	80.2	36.4	59.0	149.9	23.0	12–3	70.4
13–0	87.8	39.8	61.3	155.6	23.9	13–0	69.8
14–0	102.1	46.3	63.6	161.6	25.0	14–0	68.6
15–0	123.7	56.1	67.6	171.8	26.7	14–8	70.9
16–0	141.5	64.2	69.7	177.0	27.8	15–6	71.3
17–0	142.0	64.4	70.4	178.8	28.5	17–0	71.0
17–6	145.1	65.8	70.6	179.2	28.5	17–6	71.0
18–0	147.3	66.8	70.6	179.3	28.7	17–9	71.0
18–6	......	......	70.9	180.2	......	18–0	71.3
19–0	155.4	70.5	70.9	180.0	28.7		
21–0	169.5	76.9	70.6	179.3	29.0		

Average Boy

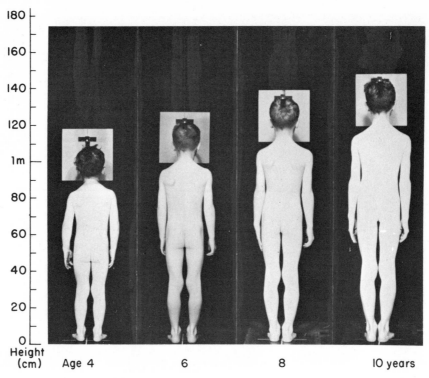

FIG. 34.—Views of N-I (Average Boy) at ages 4–10

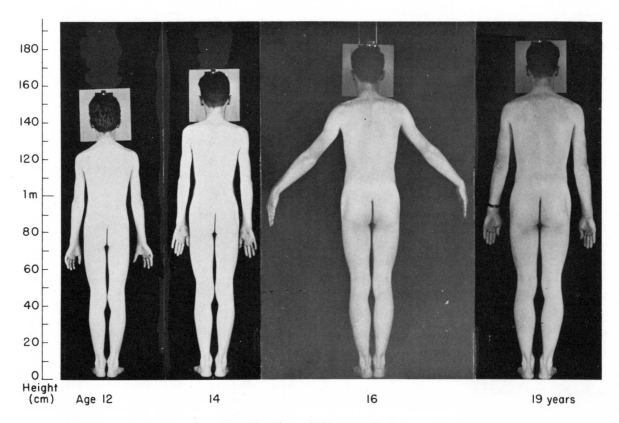

FIG. 35.—Views of N-I at ages 12–19

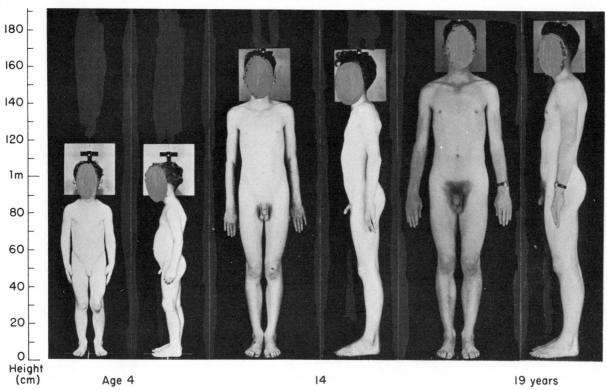

FIG. 36.—N-I as a young child, an adolescent, and a young adult

DEVIATION CHART FOR ANTHROPOMETRIC VALUES

Name		Sex Ⓜ F	Birth Date	Date		Age **4 y**	Case **N-I**

Norms for: Sex Ⓜ ⊙ F *Age* **4 y** *Other*

MEASURE		Pounds ÷ x .454 Inches ÷ x 2.54	Kilos Cm	STANDARD DEVIATION VALUES						
				-3σ	2% -2σ	16% -1σ	50% M	84% +1σ	98% +2σ	+3σ
Weight	W	38.8	17.6					⊙		
Stature	S	41.4	108.3					⊙		
Sitting height	Si		59.5				⊙			
Shoulder	BA		——							
Pelvis	BC		16.8				⊙			
Above-named measurements in per cent of stature.		*Ratios*								
	W/S		16.3				⊙			
	Si/S		54.9		⊙					
	BA/S		——							
	BC/S		15.5			⊙				

FIG. 37.—Deviation chart of N-I at the age of 4; measures compared with norms for 4-year-old boys.

Case N-I

Average Boy

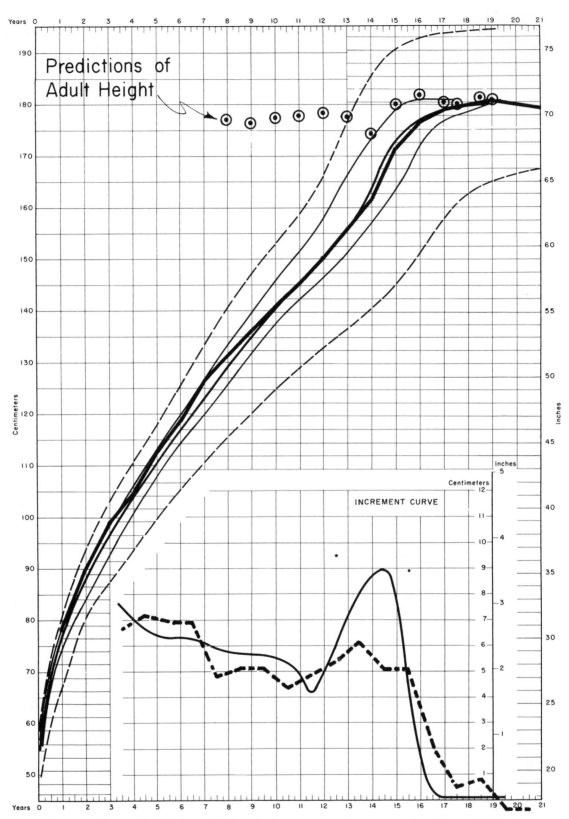

Predictions of Adult Height

INCREMENT CURVE

FIG. 38.—Curves of height by age for N-I: absolute measures, increments, and predicted adult height

72

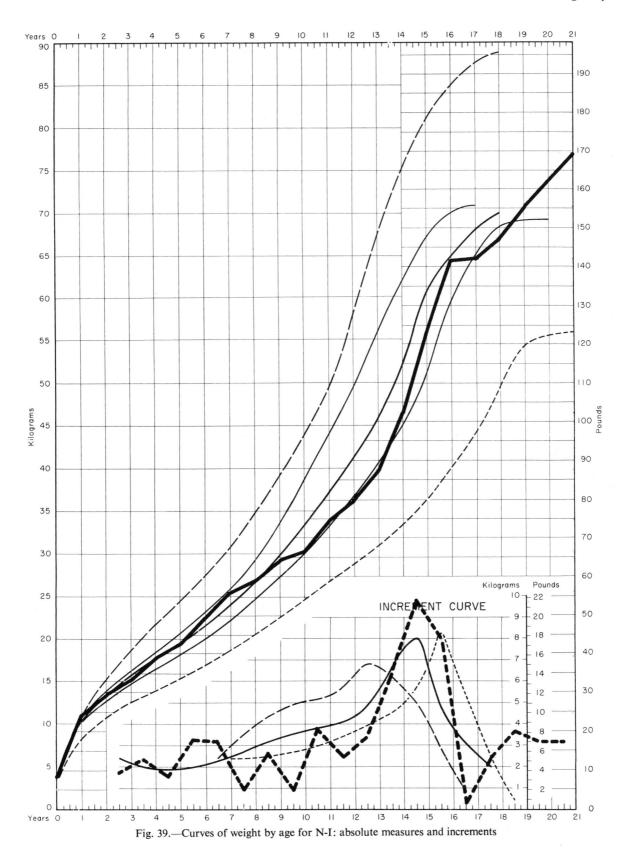

INCREMENT CURVE

Fig. 39.—Curves of weight by age for N-I: absolute measures and increments

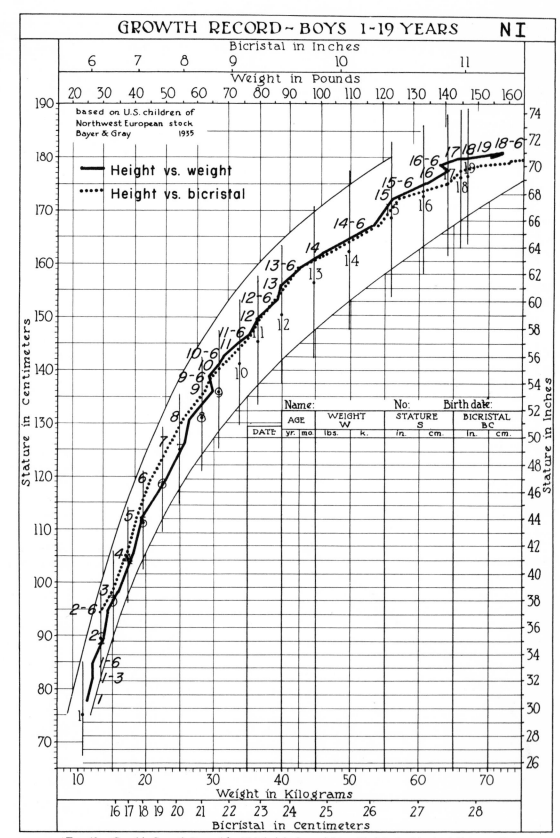

FIG. 40.—Graphic Growth Record for N-I: height for weight and height for bi-cristal diameter. See Fig. 31 for description of chart.

growth charts for evaluation and interpretation in relation to the norms for age, sex, and rate of maturing.

Growth Curves of Height by Age

This boy's stature is seen to be close to the Berkeley norms at all ages (Fig. 38). The annual gains, shown in the increment curve at the bottom of the same figure, follow the pattern of boys who mature at the average rate. See chapter 11 for interpretation.

Growth Curves of Weight by Age

Weight (Fig. 39) is average for the first nine years, then the gain is rather slow to 13 years, after which average status is regained. The period of rapid weight gain coincides with that of the average curve.

Graphic Growth Record of Height, Weight, and Bi-Cristal

The weight for height relationship is clarified in Figure 40. Case N-I's weight is consistently average for his height, except for a period of moderate slenderness between 9 and 15 years. During this period the curve deviates to the left of the center, but it is still well within the normal range or "stream" on this chart. Included here is another measure, stockiness or slenderness of build, or general frame, as indicated by the relation of bi-cristal diameter to stature (represented for Case N-I by the broken line). The two curves, for weight and bi-cristal, are closely approximated at all ages. Therefore we should say that weight for build (and probably nutritional status) is normal at all ages.

Skeletal Development

Skeletal ages (Table 8) are also plotted (Fig. 41) against chronological age to show the relative maturational progress, using the Greulich-Pyle norms. Skeletal age cannot be read with perfect accuracy, and the error in reading can account for three or four months of deviation. In general, this case shows skeletal pro-

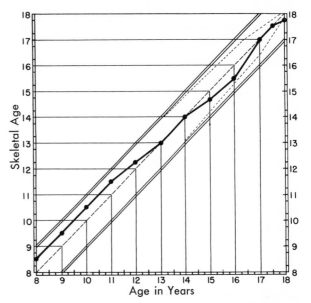

FIG. 41.—N-I's skeletal age plotted against chronological age. Mean skeletal age (*dashed line*) equals age in years on this form, with the double lines inclosing ± 1 S.D. for boys (also for girls to age 14; the dotted line incloses roughly ± 1 S.D. for girls after 14).

gression in keeping with the total picture of average growth.

Prediction of Adult Stature

The measures of height and the skeletal ages may be applied to the Bayley-Pinneau prediction tables for average boys (Appendix II). Prediction has become very accurate by 15 years, but before this age the ultimate adult height of 70.9 in. is underpredicted by about an inch. The greatest error—over 2 in. at 14 years—points up the fallibility of prediction from a single assessment and the need for verification by repetition at another age.

Comment

This is a representative, healthy boy, with normal physique and growth.

Early-Maturing Boy

CASE N-II (EARLY-MATURING BOY)

Characterization

Our second normal case, N-II, is a healthy, physically accelerated, broad-built boy (Figs. 42, 43). He suffered frequent respiratory infections during his first six years of life but has otherwise been in good health.

Anthropometric Values and Deviation Chart

His deviation chart (Fig. 44) shows that at 14 years N-II is two standard deviations above average (or at the 98 percentile) in weight, stature, and sitting height and more than one standard deviation above average in shoulder and pelvic widths. His exceptional size at this age is, in large part, attributable to his accelerated maturation. In body proportions he is at the 85 percentile in weight for height, is relatively long-bodied and broad-shouldered, and has narrow hips.

Secondary Sex Characters

At 14.5 years, Figure 43 shows that N-II has reached the adult stage in genital development. He is accelerated in this feature in accord with his general pattern of growth and maturation.

Growth Curves of Height By Age

For the first 2.5 years N-II is average in height (Table 9; Fig. 45). Then, in keeping with an accelerated rate of skeletal maturing, he grows rapidly and is tall for his age after 3 years. The curve of annual gains in stature is generally accelerated by one to two years, with a period of small gain (1.8 in.) between 10 and 11 years and the greatest puberal gain (3.7 in.) between 12 and 13 years.

Growth Curves of Weight by Age

Case N-II has been heavy for his age from the time of birth, deviating more at some ages than at

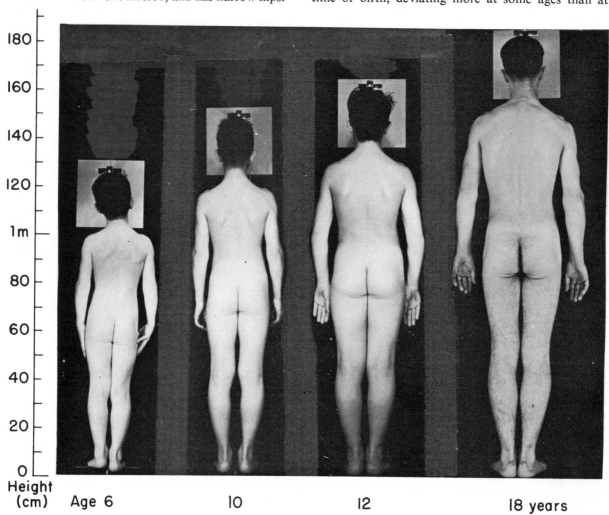

FIG. 42.—Views of N-II (Early-Maturing Boy)

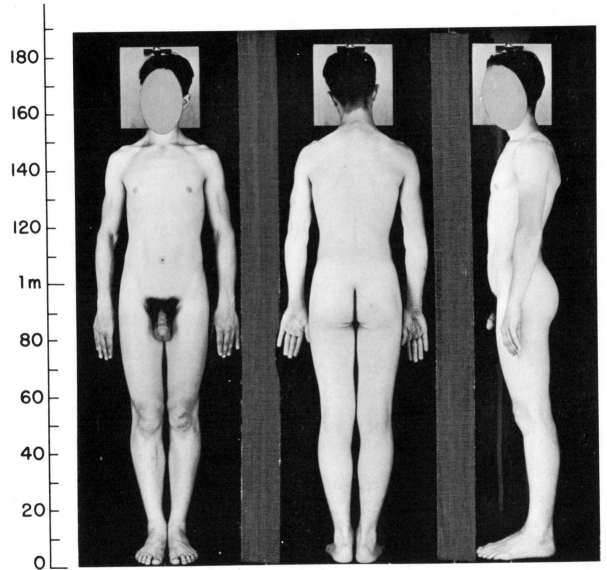

FIG. 43.—Three views of N-II at 14.5 years

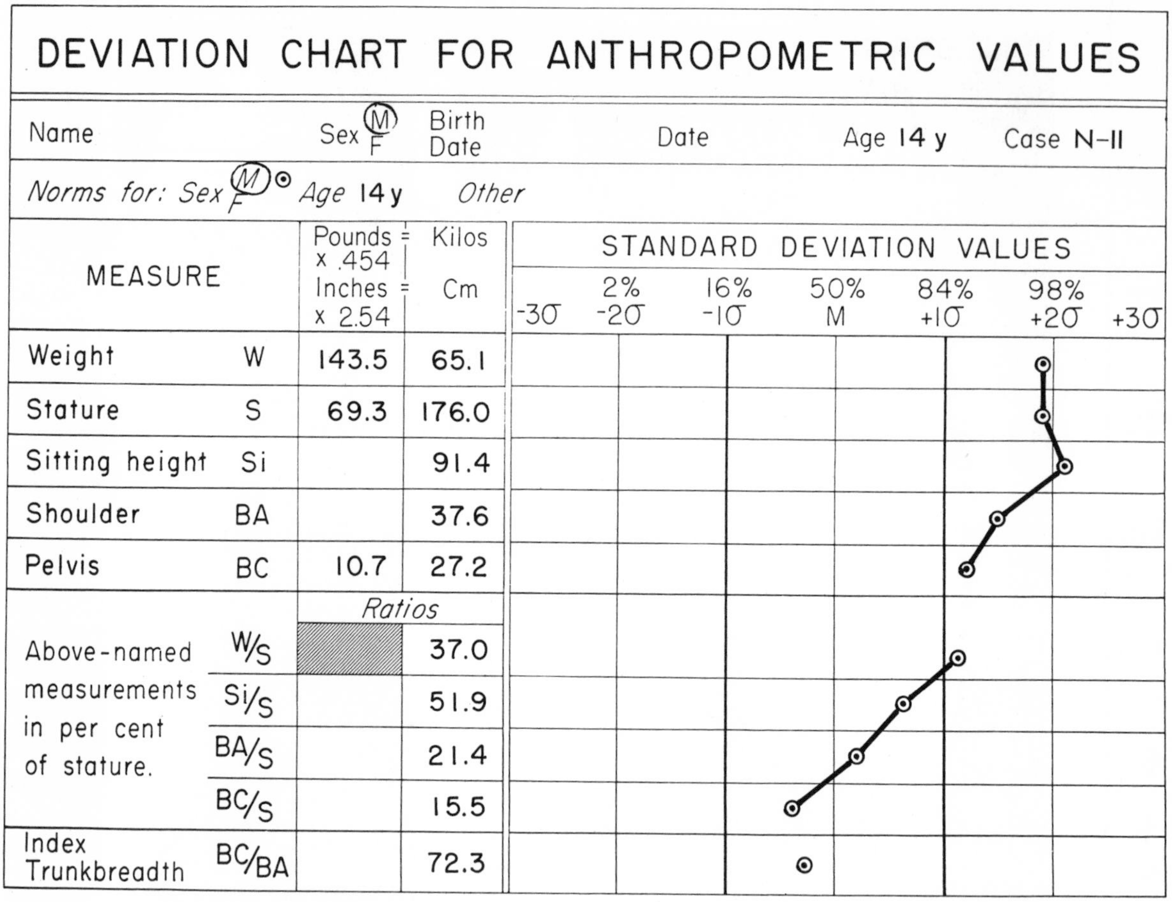

Case N-II

Early-Maturing Boy

FIG. 44.—Deviation chart for N-II at 14 years; measures compared with norms for 14-year-old boys.

others (Fig. 46); he was obese from about 5 to 7 months; then at 12–13 years he goes through the "fat period" characteristic of many children at this stage in their maturing. This shows clearly in his 12-year picture (Fig. 42). His greatest increment in weight is between 12 and 13 years, the age at which early-maturing boys gain most. Note that here, as in many individual curves for weight, the annual gains are often irregular, and actual decrements often follow periods of exceptional gain.

Graphic Growth Record of Height, Weight, and Bi-Cristal

Figure 47 shows boy N-II to be consistently heavy for his height, though he approaches the norms as he reaches adult status at about 15 years. His skeletal breadth, as represented in the bi-cristal diameter, tends to be average, except for a few broader readings in early childhood and in adolescence. In relation to this skeletal structure, he is heavy; from the general appear-

ance presented in his photographs, this greater weight for height is judged to be the result of both muscle and fat in above-average amounts. It is also true of this boy that though his pelvis is average, his long bones are generally wide relative to their length, thus contributing to an over-all sturdy build.

Skeletal Development

X-rays of the knee were available for this boy at four early ages. As read on the Todd knee standards (1930), by 2 years of age he is accelerated in skeletal maturation (Table 9). Starting at 8 years, a regular series of hand X-rays permitted assessments with the Greulich-Pyle Atlas. This series (Fig. 48) shows that N-II is consistently accelerated by from one to two years. Skeletal acceleration and the broad-built physique characteristically go together in boys. The patterns of growth in height and weight, as shown on the respective charts, are also characteristic of boys who are skeletally accelerated a year or more.

78

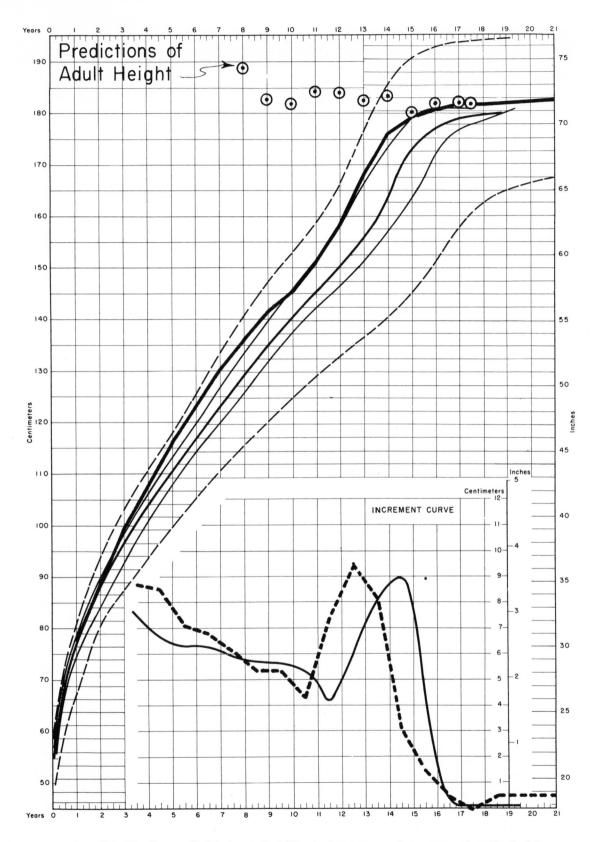

FIG. 45.—Curves of height by age for N-II: absolute measures, increments, and predicted adult height.

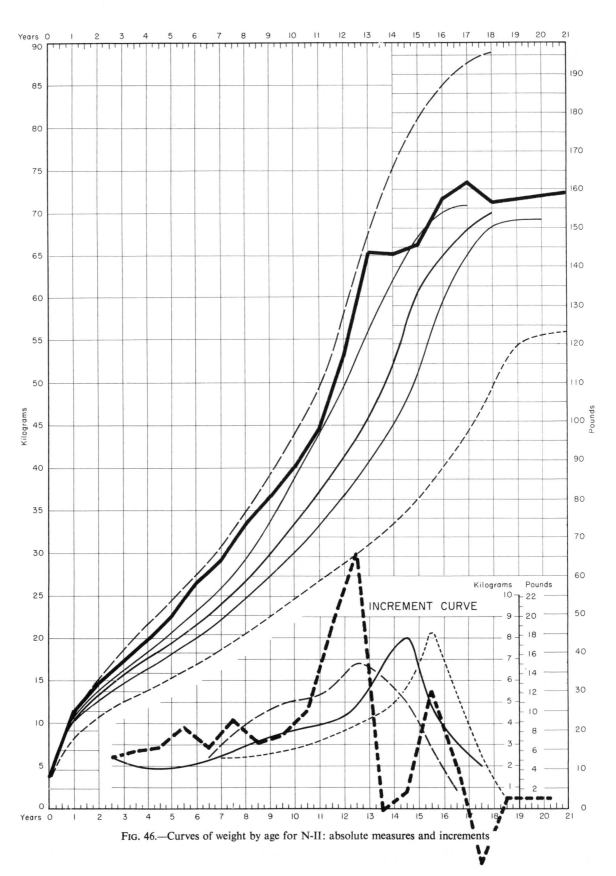

FIG. 46.—Curves of weight by age for N-II: absolute measures and increments

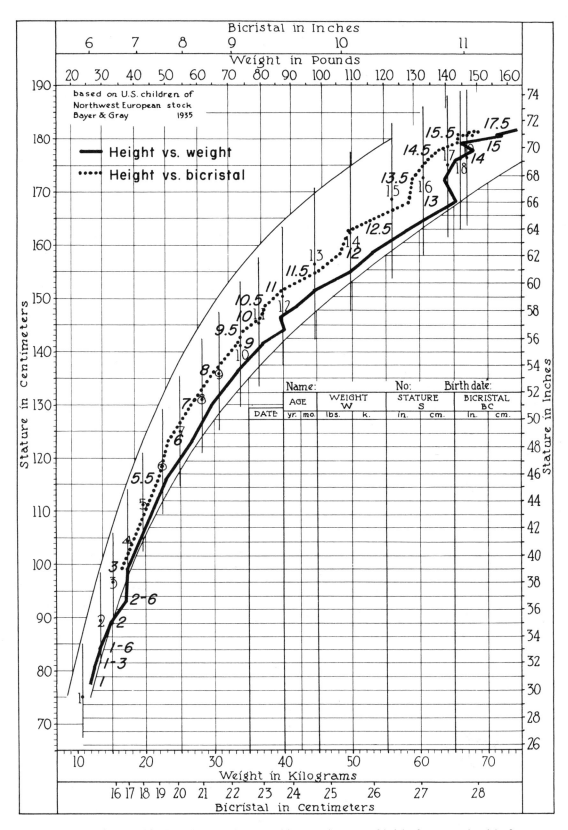

FIG. 47.—Graphic Growth Record, N-II, with normal ranges of height for age and weight for height for boys, ages 1–19. Height vs. weight and height vs. bi-cristal plotted for N-II.

Early-Maturing Boy

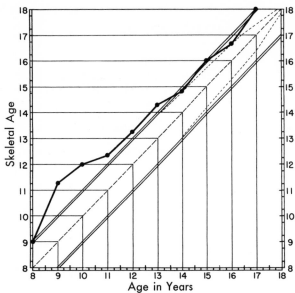

FIG. 48.—N-II, skeletal age plotted against chronological age

TABLE 9

GROWTH DATA
CASE N-II (Early-Maturing Boy)

AGE (YR.–MO.)	WEIGHT		STATURE		BI-CRIS-TAL (CM.)	SA (YR.–MO.)	PRED. HT. (IN.)
	Lb.	Kg.	In.	Cm.			
Birth	8.4						
1	11.5	5.2	21.1	53.5			
3	16.9	7.7	24.0	61.0			
6	22.0	10.0	26.8	68.1			
9	24.3	11.0	28.4	72.2			
1–0	25.0	11.3	30.4	77.3		1–0	
1–6	29.3	13.3	33.1	84.0			
2–0	32.0	14.5	35.0	88.9		2–9	
2–6	36.5	16.6	36.7	93.3			
3–0	37.3	16.9	39.0	99.1	16.5	4–3	
4–0	43.3	19.6	42.2	107.1	17.7	5–3*	
5–0	49.5	22.5	45.7	116.0	19.0		
6–0	58.0	26.3	48.5	123.2	19.5		
7–0	64.3	29.2	51.2	130.0	20.6		
8–0	73.4	33.3	53.6	136.2	21.4	9–0	74.4
9–0	80.3	36.4	55.7	141.4	22.2	11.3	71.8
10–0	88.0	39.9	57.8	146.7	23.0	12–0	71.5
11–0	98.1	44.5	59.6	151.3	23.7	12–4	72.5
12–0	117.1	53.1	62.4	158.6	25.3	13–3	72.3
13–0	143.7	65.2	66.1	167.9	26.8	14–4	71.7
14–0	143.5	65.1	69.3	176.0	27.2	14–10	72.1
15–0	145.3	65.9	70.5	179.1	27.7	16–0	70.9
16–0	157.4	71.4	71.0	180.4	27.9	17–8	71.5
17–0	161.8	73.4	71.2	180.9	27.7	18–0	71.6
17–6	163.4	74.1	71.5	181.6	28.1	18–6	71.5
18–0	156.1	70.8	71.3	181.1	28.1	19–0	
21–0	159.2	72.2	71.9	182.5	28.5		

* X-ray taken at CA 4 years 6 months.

Prediction of Adult Stature

From his accelerated skeletal ages, we should expect N-II to reach his adult stature sooner than the average. He is 71 in. at 16 years and has attained his adult stature of 71.5 in. at 17 years 6 months. Predictions from the Bayley-Pinneau tables (Appendix II) are too high at 8 years, but thereafter the predictions are usually within 0.5 in. of the measures obtained after 17 years. This difference is easily within the range of diurnal variations in height of an individual.

Androgyny Profile

Another characteristic of build that can be assessed in the young adult is that of sex appropriateness. Somatic androgyny can be read (1) from correctly posed photographs or (2) directly during the physical examination. Figure 49 is this boy's chart of androgyny, rated from his 18-year photographs. It shows him to be typically masculine, with a tendency toward hypermasculinity in some characters, such as surface-modeling and torso-narrowing.

Comment

This is a typically accelerated, heavy-set boy, large for his age after early childhood. He has a tendency to become fat; he is obese as an infant and again puts on fat during the preadolescent period when children often show this tendency. With a basically masculine physique, he quickly outgrows this period of fat, but remains a stocky, heavy-set adult. His acceleration in growth is commensurate with his accelerated maturation, so that his final height is achieved somewhat early and is not excessive.

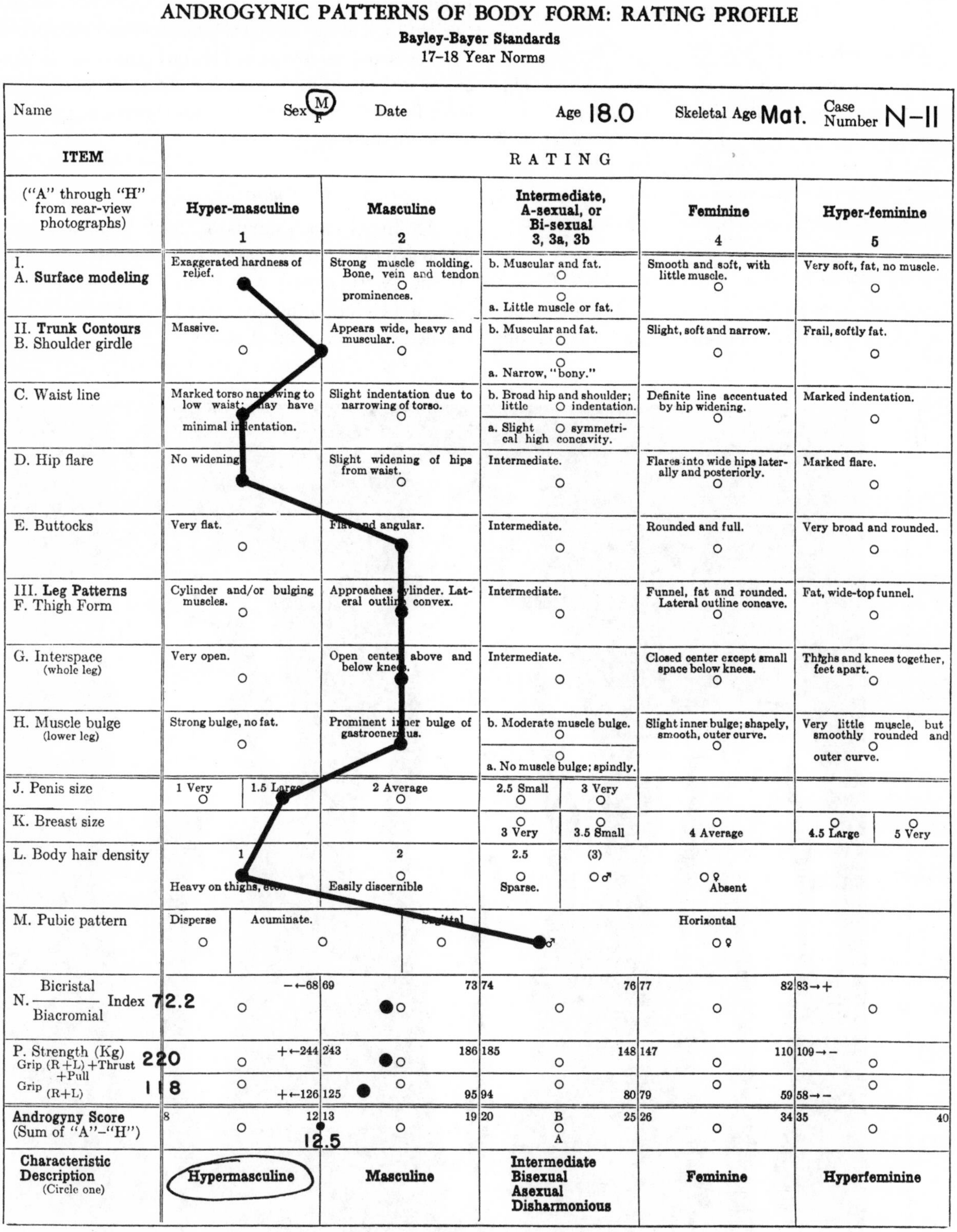

ANDROGYNIC PATTERNS OF BODY FORM: RATING PROFILE
Bayley-Bayer Standards
17–18 Year Norms

Name	Sex Ⓜ F	Date		Age 18.0	Skeletal Age Mat.	Case Number N-II

ITEM	R A T I N G				
("A" through "H" from rear-view photographs)	**Hyper-masculine** 1	**Masculine** 2	**Intermediate, A-sexual, or Bi-sexual** 3, 3a, 3b	**Feminine** 4	**Hyper-feminine** 5
I. A. **Surface modeling**	Exaggerated hardness of relief. ●	Strong muscle molding. Bone, vein and tendon prominences. ○	b. Muscular and fat. ○ — a. Little muscle or fat.	Smooth and soft, with little muscle. ○	Very soft, fat, no muscle. ○
II. **Trunk Contours** B. Shoulder girdle	Massive. ○	Appears wide, heavy and muscular. ●	b. Muscular and fat. ○ — a. Narrow, "bony."	Slight, soft and narrow. ○	Frail, softly fat. ○
C. Waist line	Marked torso narrowing to low waist; may have minimal indentation.	Slight indentation due to narrowing of torso. ○	b. Broad hip and shoulder; little ○ indentation. a. Slight ○ symmetrical high concavity.	Definite line accentuated by hip widening. ○	Marked indentation. ○
D. Hip flare	No widening. ●	Slight widening of hips from waist. ○	Intermediate. ○	Flares into wide hips laterally and posteriorly. ○	Marked flare. ○
E. Buttocks	Very flat. ○	Flat and angular. ●	Intermediate. ○	Rounded and full. ○	Very broad and rounded. ○
III. **Leg Patterns** F. Thigh Form	Cylinder and/or bulging muscles. ○	Approaches cylinder. Lateral outline convex. ●	Intermediate. ○	Funnel, fat and rounded. Lateral outline concave. ○	Fat, wide-top funnel. ○
G. Interspace (whole leg)	Very open. ○	Open center above and below knees. ●	Intermediate. ○	Closed center except small space below knees. ○	Thighs and knees together, feet apart. ○
H. Muscle bulge (lower leg)	Strong bulge, no fat. ○	Prominent inner bulge of gastrocnemius. ●	b. Moderate muscle bulge. ○ — a. No muscle bulge; spindly.	Slight inner bulge; shapely, smooth, outer curve. ○	Very little muscle, but smoothly rounded and outer curve. ○
J. Penis size	1 Very ○	1.5 Large ○	2 Average ○	2.5 Small ○	3 Very ○
K. Breast size			3 Very ○	3.5 Small ○	4 Average ○	4.5 Large ○	5 Very ○
L. Body hair density	1 Heavy on thighs, etc.	2 ○ Easily discernible	2.5 Sparse.	(3) ○ ♂	○ ♀ Absent	
M. Pubic pattern	Disperse ○	Acuminate. ○	Sagittal ○	♂	Horizontal ○ ♀	
N. Bicristal ──────── Index **72.2** Biacromial	— ←68 69 ○	73 ●○	74 76 ○	77 82 ○	83 → + ○
P. Strength (Kg) Grip (R+L)+Thrust +Pull **220** Grip (R+L) **118**	○ + ←244 243 ○ + ←126 125	●○ 186 ● ○	185 148 ○ 95 94 ○	147 110 ○ 80 79 ○	109 → — ○ 59 58 → — ○
Androgyny Score (Sum of "A"–"H")	8 ○ 12 **12.5**	13 19 ○	20 B ○ A 25	26 34 ○	35 40
Characteristic Description (Circle one)	(Hypermasculine)	Masculine	Intermediate Bisexual Asexual Disharmonious	Feminine	Hyperfeminine

FIG. 49.—Androgyny profile of N-II at 18 years

Case N-III (Late-Maturing Boy)

Characterization

This is a short, slender, slow-maturing boy (Fig. 50) with an average health history. He had colds, and his tonsils were reported infected from the ages of 3 through 6 years; he was ill with an ear infection at 4. He had chicken pox at 4 years 6 months and whooping cough at 5. After the age of 6, illnesses were infrequent.

Anthropometric Values and Deviation Chart

At 11 years N-III is consistently small in all dimensions, varying around minus-one standard deviation, or at the 16 percentile of boys for his age (Fig. 51). In build, or body proportions, he is definitely slender (weight for stature) but he is long-stemmed with broad shoulders and narrow hips. This boy is not exactly typical of late-maturing boys, who are more often long-legged and do not develop broad shoulders until they are more mature.

Secondary Sex Characters

On the Greulich standards, N-III is still at stage I at the age of 11; at 15 years this boy is between stages III and IV. (Compare with Case N-I at 14 and Case N-II at 14 years 6 months. Not until 18 years has he reached stage V, or adult status.

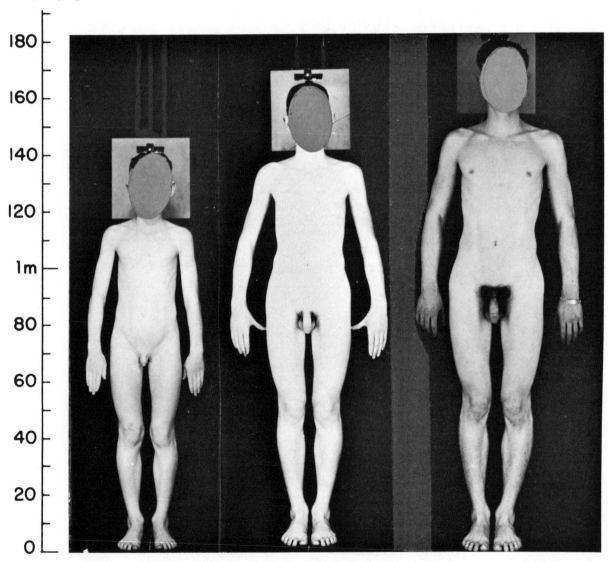

Fig. 50.—Views of N-III (Late-Maturing Boy) at ages 11, 15, and 18 years

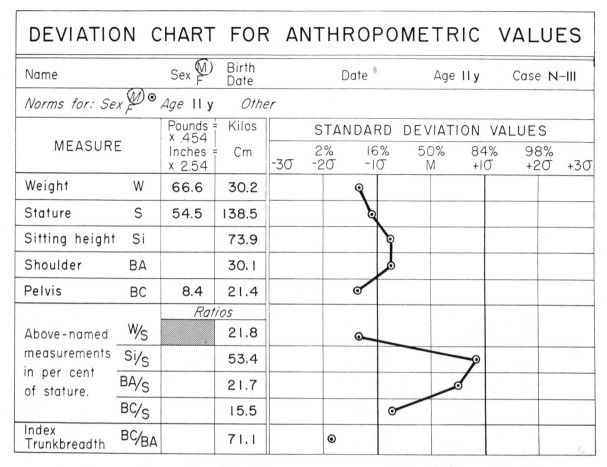

DEVIATION CHART FOR ANTHROPOMETRIC VALUES

| Name | Sex Ⓜ/F | Birth Date | | Date | | Age 11 y | | Case N-III |

Norms for: Sex Ⓜ/F ⊙ *Age* 11 y   *Other*

MEASURE		Pounds ÷ x .454 Inches ÷ x 2.54	Kilos Cm	STANDARD DEVIATION VALUES						
				-3σ	2% -2σ	16% -1σ	50% M	84% +1σ	98% +2σ	+3σ
Weight	W	66.6	30.2			⊙				
Stature	S	54.5	138.5			⊙				
Sitting height	Si		73.9			⊙				
Shoulder	BA		30.1			⊙				
Pelvis	BC	8.4	21.4			⊙				
		Ratios								
Above-named measurements in per cent of stature.	W/S	▨	21.8			⊙				
	Si/S		53.4					⊙		
	BA/S		21.7					⊙		
	BC/S		15.5				⊙			
Index Trunkbreadth	BC/BA		71.1		⊙					

Fig. 51.—Deviation chart for N-III at 11 years; measures compared with norms for 11-year-old boys.

Growth Curves of Height by Age

This boy is consistently short for his age (Fig. 52) until his last measurement at 18 years 6 months. He lags well behind his age group between the ages of 9 and 14, at which time his rapid growth begins to close the gap. The curve of annual increments shows that he has his most rapid gain earlier than would be expected in a skeletally retarded boy. That is, his spurt is between 14 and 15 years instead of the expected 15–16 years (Table 10).

Growth Curves of Weight by Age

Very small annual gains in weight are shown in Figure 53 up to 13 years. At this time N-III enters a three-year period of rapid weight gain which coincides with his period of rapid growth in height. The annual-increment curve resembles that of the late-maturer, except that the period of rapid growth is more extended.

Graphic Growth Record of Height, Weight, and Bi-Cristal

Both weight and bi-cristal, in relation to stature, show this boy to be of consistently slender build. This is very characteristic of late-maturing boys. The charts confirm the impression gained from the photographs. At 16 years the bi-cristal diameter approaches average for stature, but, with the exception of the measurement at 16 years, weight continues on the slender side of the stream (Fig. 54).

Skeletal Development

As a young child, N-III is shown by the Todd standards to be average or even accelerated in skeletal maturing (Table 10). On the Greulich-Pyle norms he becomes retarded a year or more after 10 years (Fig. 55).

Prediction of Adult Stature

Stature is underpredicted through the age of 15. This is characteristic for children who slow down in skeletal maturing in the prepuberal stage. The pro-

Late-Maturing Boy

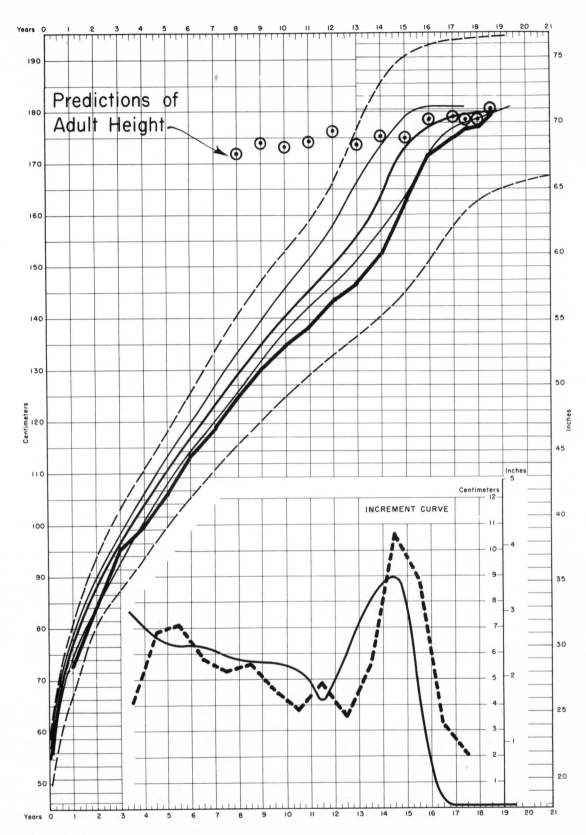

Predictions of Adult Height

INCREMENT CURVE

FIG. 52.—Curves of height by age for N-III: absolute measures, increments, and predicted adult height.

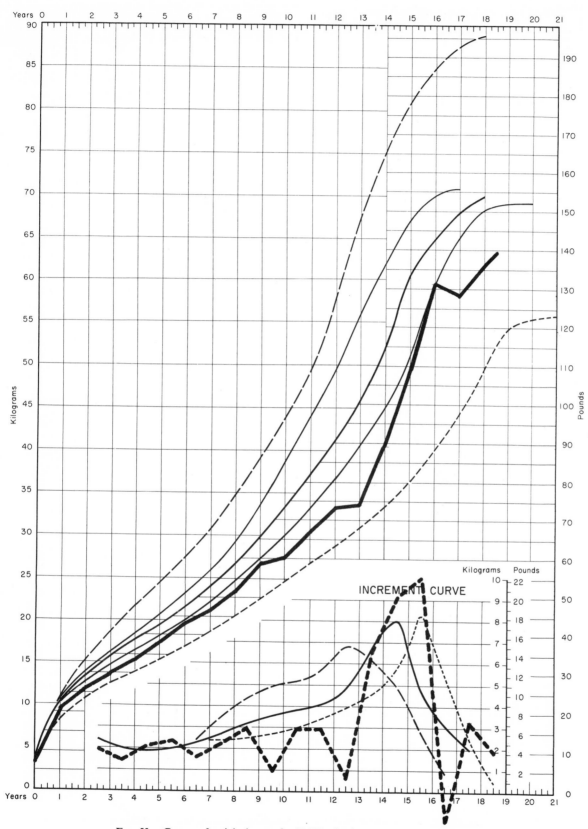

FIG. 53.—Curves of weight by age for N-III: absolute measures and increments

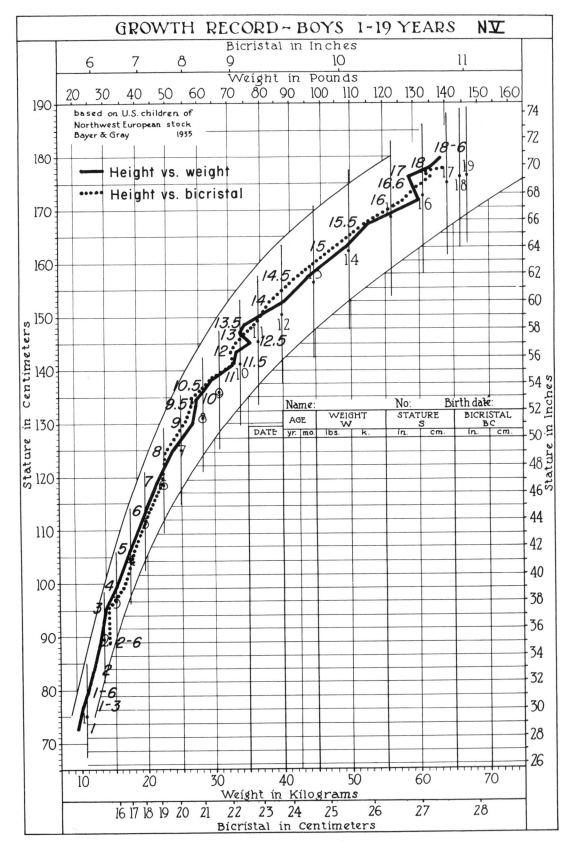

GROWTH RECORD ~ BOYS 1-19 YEARS NV

based on U.S. children of Northwest European stock
Bayer & Gray 1935

— Height vs. weight
···· Height vs. bicristal

FIG. 54.—Graphic Growth Record, N-III, with normal ranges of height for age and weight for height for boys, ages 1–19. Height vs. weight and height vs. bi-cristal plotted for N-III.

TABLE 10

GROWTH DATA

CASE N-III (Late-Maturing Boy)

AGE (YR.– MO.)	WEIGHT		STATURE		BI- CRIS- TAL (CM.)	SA (YR.– MO.)	PRED. HT. (IN.)
	Lb.	Kg.	In.	Cm.			
Birth	6.8						
1	8.9	4.0	21.5	54.6			
3	13.7	6.2	23.5	59.8			
6	17.8	8.1	25.9	65.8			
9	19.4	8.8	27.5	69.8			
1–0	20.6	9.3	28.5	72.5		1–0	
1–6	23.8	10.8	31.2	79.2			
2–0	25.5	11.6	33.0	83.7		2–6	
2–6	27.8	12.6	34.9	88.6	15.1		
3–0	29.8	13.5	37.5	95.2	15.1	3–9	
4–0	33.0	15.0	39.1	99.2	16.4	4–3	
5–0	37.5	17.0	41.8	106.3	17.2		
6–0	42.8	19.4	44.6	113.3	18.3		
7–0	46.4	21.0	46.9	119.1	19.1		
8–0	51.4	23.3	49.1	124.6	19.2	8–0	67.8
9–0	58.0	26.3	51.2	130.1	20.3	8–10	68.5
10–0	60.0	27.2	53.0	134.5	20.6	9–9	68.2
11–0	66.6	30.2	54.5	138.5	21.4	10–6	68.6
12–0	73.0	33.1	56.4	143.2	22.0	11–4	69.3
13–0	74.3	33.7	57.8	146.8	22.5	12–0	68.4
14–0	88.4	40.1	60.1	152.6	23.3	12–9	69.0
15–0	108.9	49.4	64.1	162.8	25.1	14–1	68.9
16–0	131.4	59.6	67.6	171.6	26.7	14–11	70.2
17–0	128.5	58.3	69.2	175.7	27.3	16–0	70.4
17–8	133.6	60.6	69.6	176.7	27.1	17–0	70.2
18–0	135.8	61.6	69.8	177.3	27.5	17–6	70.2
18–6	139.8	63.4	70.6	179.4		18–0	71.0

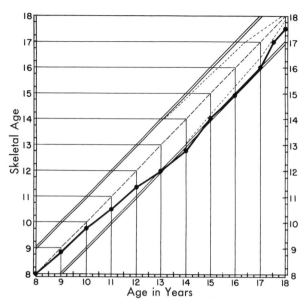

FIG. 55.—N-III, skeletal age plotted against chronological age.

longed period of open epiphyses appears to allow longer continued growth.

Comment

While this late-maturing boy is characteristic of this group in many ways, he is in several respects atypical. Many children normally show such deviations from their general class.

CASE N-IV (BOY WITH DEVIANT GROWTH PATTERN)

Characterization

N-IV shows a marked shift in rates of maturing (Fig. 56) and has a characteristic period of prepubescent transient obesity. According to Stolz and Stolz (1951) some tendency to put on fat occurs normally in at least 50 per cent of boys at this stage of maturing. This boy's health history is not unusual: some colds; a period of infected tonsils with one or two episodes of tonsilitis between 4 and 7 years; measles at 6 years.

Anthropometric Values and Deviation Chart

Figure 57 shows N-IV at his most obese period, 13.1 years, when he is large for his age and most deviant in weight. In body proportions, also, it is the weight/stature ratio that is most out of line. The deviation chart (Fig. 58) compares N-IV with the norms for 13-years-old girls as well as those for boys his age. Although N-IV is somewhat nearer the norms for girls in most respects, he remains relatively large and heavy and does not appear feminine in build. In the trunk-breadth index he remains masculine.

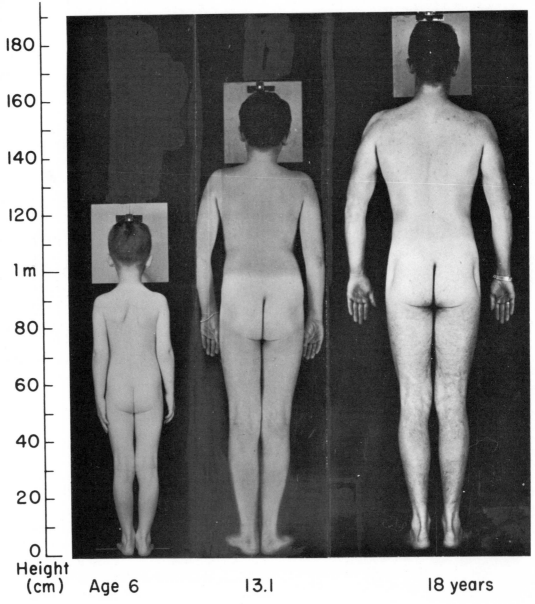

FIG. 56.—Views of N-IV (Boy with Deviant Growth Pattern)

90

Secondary Sex Characters

According to his 13.1-year photographs, this boy has reached sex stage III, which is the average degree of maturity for this age.

Growth Curves of Height by Age

N-IV is average in stature or slightly less for the first six years (Fig. 59). After this he tends to be somewhat above average, with a rather early spurt of adolescent growth and tall adult stature. The increment curve is a little erratic, reflecting the relatively early and prolonged acceleration.

Growth Curves of Weight by Age

As in stature, weight is below average before 7 years and becomes above average after 9 (Fig. 60).

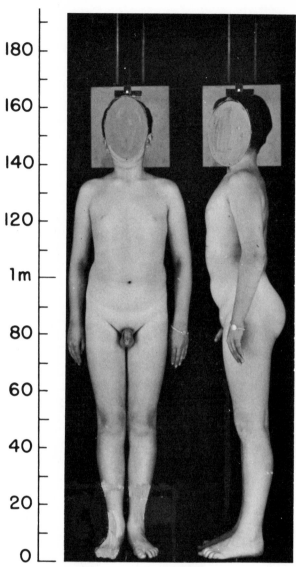

FIG. 57.—N-IV at 13.1 years

TABLE 11

GROWTH DATA

CASE N-IV (Boy with Deviant Growth Pattern)

AGE (YR.– MO.)	WEIGHT		STATURE		BI-CRIS-TAL (CM.)	SA (YR.– MO.)	PRED. HT. (IN.)
	Lb.	Kg.	In.	Cm.			
Birth	8.4						
1	9.8	4.4	22.1	56.1			
3	14.8	6.7	24.8	62.9			
6	18.6	8.4	27.2	69.2			
9	21.8	9.9	28.8	73.1			
1–0	21.8	9.9	30.3	76.9		1–0	
1–6	23.5	10.6	32.8	83.2			
2–0	26.5	12.0	34.0	86.4		1–9	
2–6	28.4	12.9	35.6	90.5	14.8		
3–0	31.3	14.2	37.2	94.6	15.7	3–0	
4–0	35.4	16.0	40.0	101.5	16.4	3–9	
5–0	39.0	17.7	42.9	109.0	17.7	4–3*	
6–0	44.5	20.2	45.7	116.1	19.0		
7–0	52.5	23.8	48.9	124.2	19.6		
8–0	55.6	25.2	51.1	129.9	20.5	7–6	72.2
9–0	67.2	30.5	53.6	136.2	21.4	8–3	73.3
10–0	81.1	36.8	55.8	141.8	22.2	9–3	73.3
11–0	93.5	42.4	58.2	147.9	23.9	10–3	73.7
12–4	108.0	49.0	61.1	155.2	25.1	12–0	72.6
13–1	120.6	54.7	63.3	160.9	25.9	13–0	72.4
14–0	122.3	55.5	67.7	171.9	26.6	14–0	73.1
15–1	139.8	63.4	70.5	179.1	27.7	15–6	72.2
16–0	156.2	70.9	71.3	181.0	27.9	17–0	71.9
17–1	158.7	72.0	71.6	181.9	27.7	17–9	72.1
18–0	172.0	78.0	71.6	181.9	28.1		
19–0	178.1	80.8	71.7	182.2	28.3	19–0	
21–0	167.6	76.0	71.8	182.3	29.0		

* X-ray taken at CA 4 years 6 months.

Annual gains tend to be like those of early-maturing boys, except that efforts to control weight actually resulted in temporary plateaus or weight losses.

Graphic Growth Record of Height, Weight, and Bi-Cristal

Weight for stature, and bi-cristal diameter for stature, are about average for the first 9 years (Fig. 61), after which rapid weight gains indicate increasing stockiness to 13 years. Loss of weight at this time shifted his curve temporarily toward the slender side of the stream. (Compare with his photographs.)

Boy with Deviant Growth Pattern

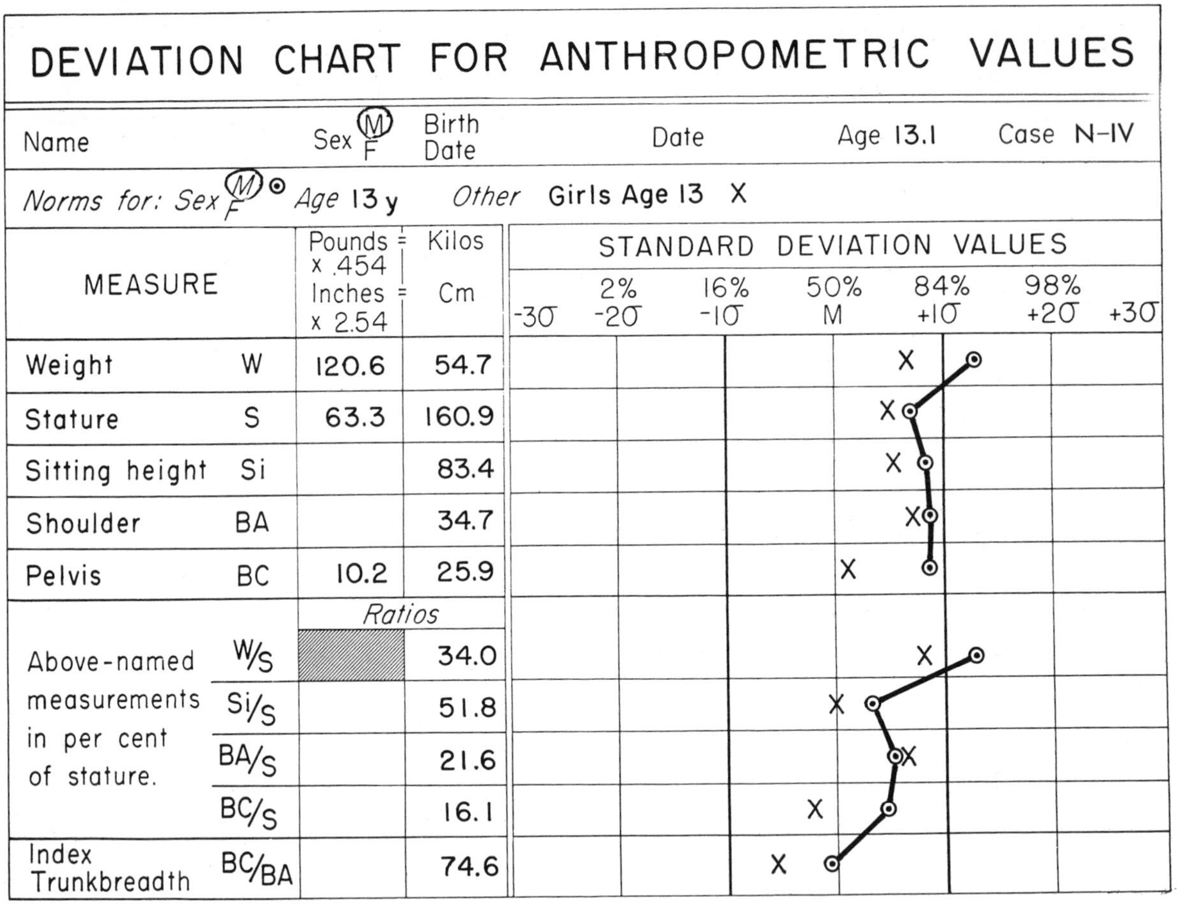

FIG. 58.—Deviation chart for N-IV at 13.1 years; measures compared with norms for 13-year-old boys and norms for 13-year-old girls.

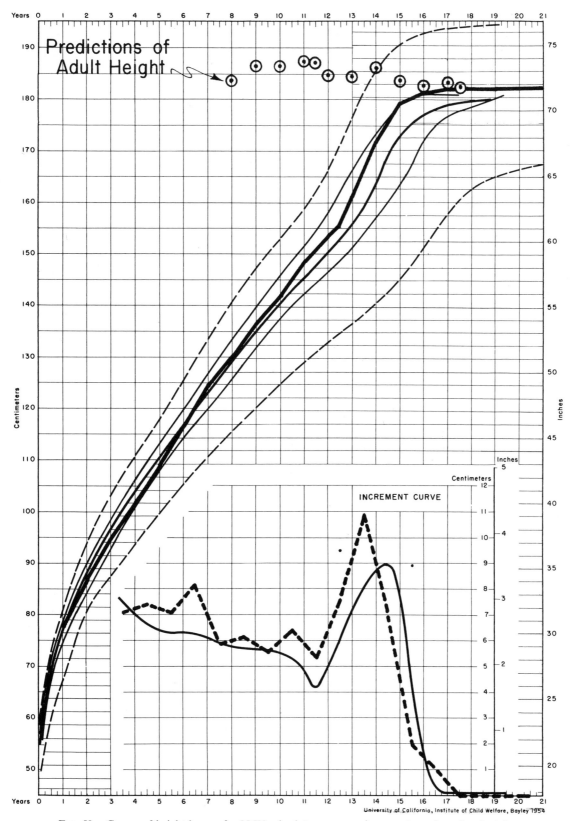

University of California, Institute of Child Welfare, Bayley 1954

FIG. 59.—Curves of height by age for N-IV: absolute measures, increments, and predicted adult height.

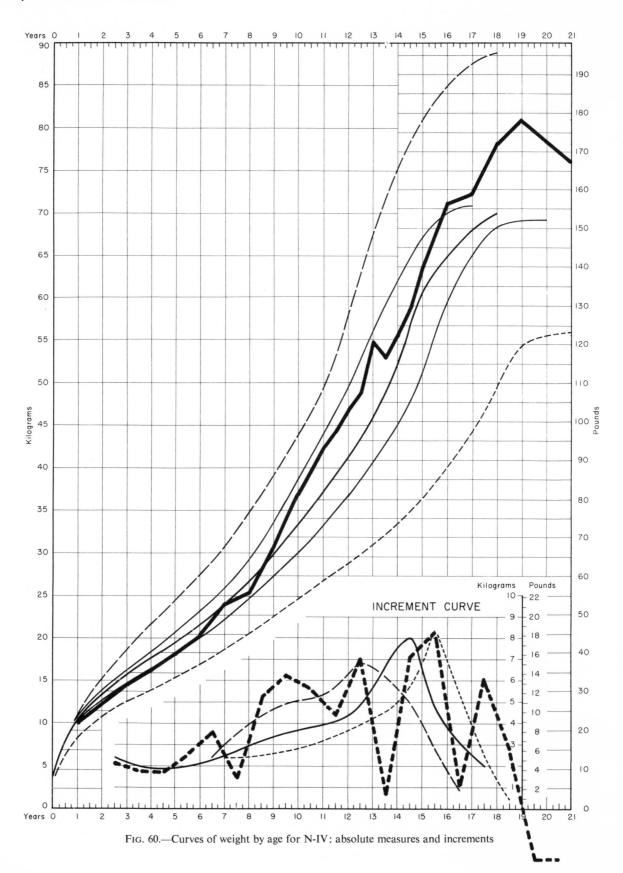

FIG. 60.—Curves of weight by age for N-IV: absolute measures and increments

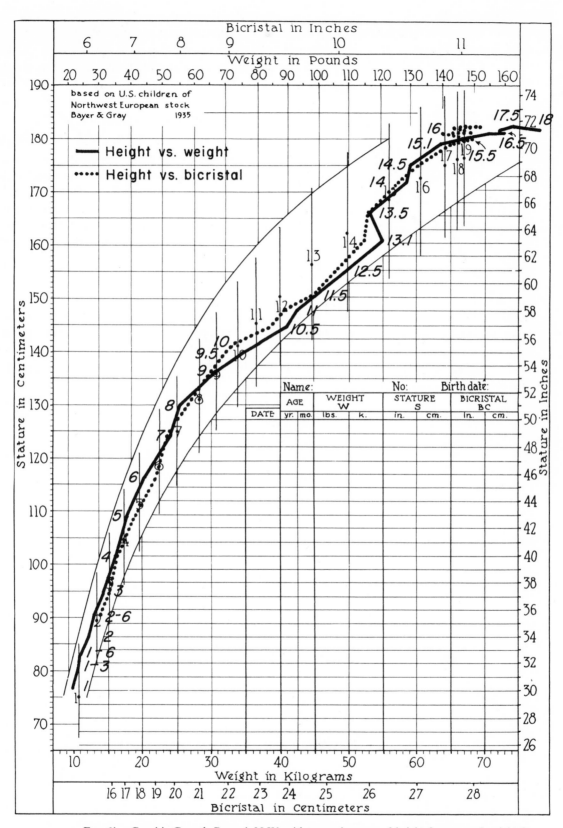

Fig. 61.—Graphic Growth Record, N-IV, with normal ranges of height for age and weight for height for boys, ages 1–19. Height vs. weight and height vs. bi-cristal plotted for N-IV.

Boy with Deviant Growth Pattern

Skeletal Development

Assessments at the early ages showed a slight tendency toward retardation in maturing (Table 11), though

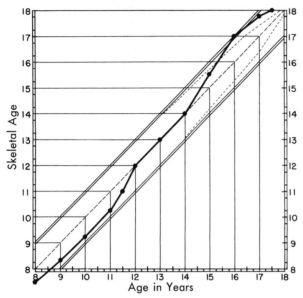

FIG. 62.—N-IV, skeletal age plotted against chronological age.

very close to age norms. By 13 years his SA has caught up to his CA (Fig. 62), and thereafter he matures rapidly. His steroid phase of growth appears to be accelerated in comparison with childhood growth. This is reflected in the pattern of growth in stature and weight.

Prediction of Adult Stature

The prediction at 8 years is very accurate (Table 11), but from 9 through 14 years there is a tendency to overpredict by about an inch. This is during the period when his growth is rapid while his skeletal status is still retarded, though becoming less retarded. It also covers the period of obesity. The growth and maturation processes of the organism seem to be in disequilibrium for a period of several years.

Comment

Although this boy's growth deviates in several respects from more consistent trends, he is never very far from average and is well within the limits of normal development. He was unhappy about his temporary obesity, but it was controlled with relative ease.

Case N-V (Average Girl)

Characterization

N-V is a healthy girl of average size, build, and rate of maturing. In addition to a skin infection at 10–13 months and occasional colds, she had chicken pox at 2 years, infected tonsils at 3 and 4 years, and a streptococcal throat infection at 6 years. General health was consistently rated good between episodes of illness.

Anthropometric Values and Deviation Chart

At 17.1 years, Case N-V has attained her adult stature and is almost at her heaviest weight. According to the deviation values (Fig. 64) she is less than 1 S.D. above the average in weight and slightly below in stature. She is a little short in stem length and a little broad in the shoulders. Body ratios put her at about 1 S.D. above average in weight for height. She is somewhat short-stemmed (long-legged) for the average girl, near average in other respects.

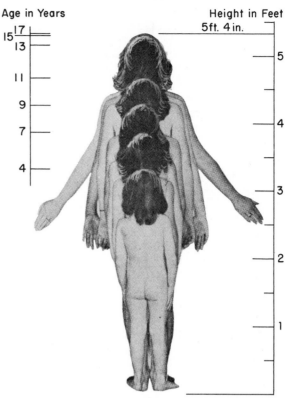

Age in Years / Height in Feet 5ft. 4 in.

Fig. 63.—Superimposed rear views of N-V (Average Girl) at ages from 4 to 17.

Name		Sex M (F)	Birth Date	Date	Age 17.1 y	Case N-V

Norms for: Sex M / (F) ⊙ *Age* 17 y   *Other*

MEASURE		Pounds = x .454 / Inches = x 2.54	Kilos / Cm	STANDARD DEVIATION VALUES						
				-3σ	2% -2σ	16% -1σ	50% M	84% $+1\sigma$	98% $+2\sigma$	$+3\sigma$
Weight	W	137.6	62.4					⊙		
Stature	S	64.3	163.3				⊙			
Sitting height	Si		84.9			⊙				
Shoulder	BA		35.3					⊙		
Pelvis	BC	11.0	27.9				⊙			
		Ratios								
Above-named measurements in per cent of stature.	W/S		38.2					⊙		
	Si/S		52.0			⊙				
	BA/S		21.6					⊙		
	BC/S		17.1				⊙			
Index Trunkbreadth	BC/BA		79.0			⊙				

Fig. 64.—Deviation chart for N-V at 17.1 years; measures compared with norms for 17-year-old girls

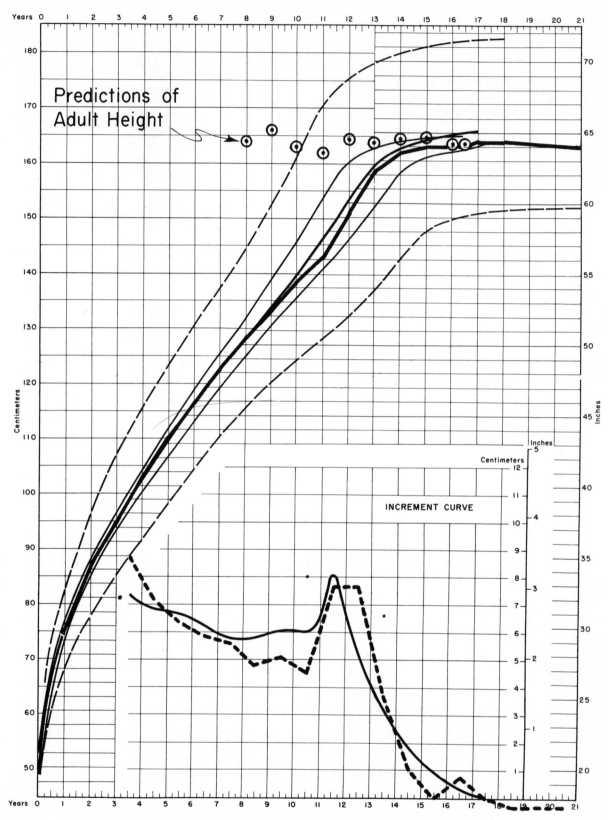

Predictions of Adult Height

INCREMENT CURVE

FIG. 65.—Curves of height by age for N-V: absolute measures, increments, and predictions of adult height. (See chap. 11 for interpretation of height curves and weight curves.)

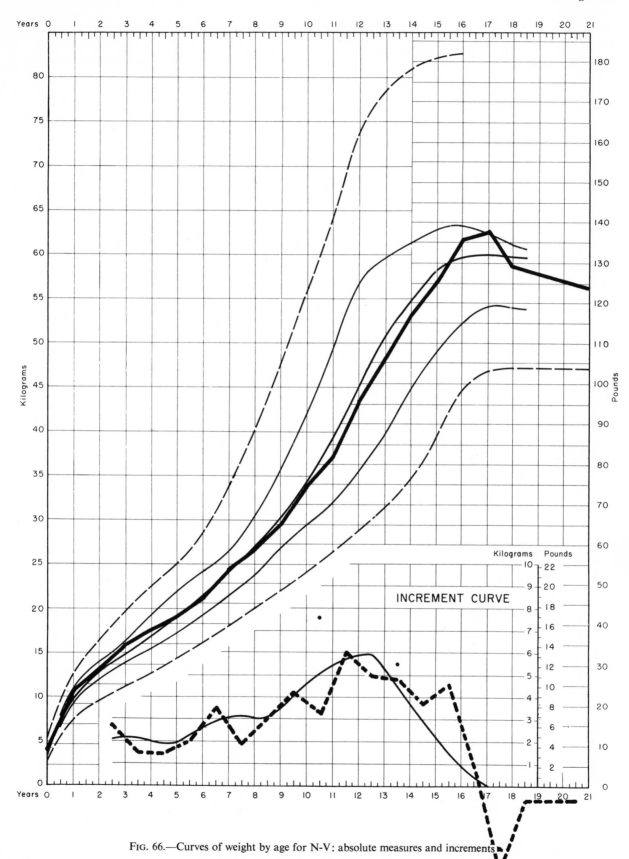

Fig. 66.—Curves of weight by age for N-V: absolute measures and increments

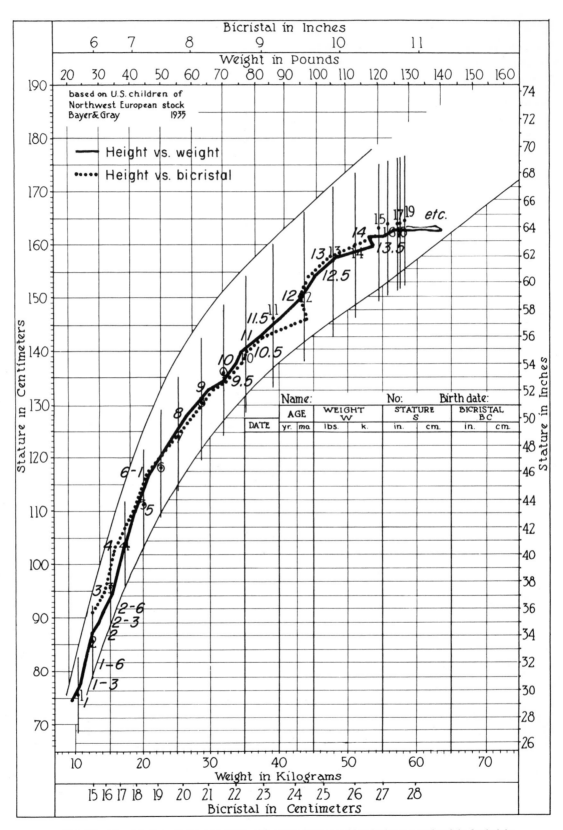

Fig. 67.—Graphic Growth Record, N-V, with normal ranges of height for age and weight for height for girls, ages 1–19. Height vs. weight and height vs. bi-cristal plotted for N-V.

Secondary Sex Characters

Menarche was at 13 years, which is close to the group norms. Breast development and pubic-hair development followed the average time table.

Growth Curves of Height by Age

This girl is average in stature (Fig. 65 and Table 12), except for a slight lag between 11 and 13 years. Her curve of annual gains closely follows the average curve in both amount and timing.

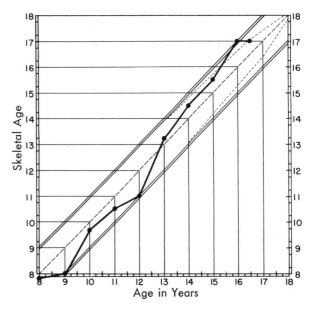

FIG. 68.—N-V, skeletal age plotted against chronological age. Mean SA is equal to CA, with one standard deviation plus-and-minus inclosed by the double lines, for boys at all ages and girls to the age of 14. The dotted lines inclose ± 1 S.D. for girls after the age of 14.

TABLE 12

GROWTH DATA

CASE N-V (Average Girl)

AGE (YR.– MO.)	WEIGHT		STATURE		BI-CRIS-TAL (CM.)	SA (YR.– MO.)	PRED. HT. (IN.)
	Lb.	Kg.	In.	Cm.			
Birth	9.2			57.3			
1	10.3	4.6	22.6	57.3			
3	13.7	6.2	24.7	62.8			
6	17.3	7.8	26.9	68.4			
9	20.5	9.3	28.2	71.6			
1–0	22.9	10.4	29.4	74.8		1–0	
1–6	25.5	11.6	32.0	81.2			
2–0	28.3	12.8	34.3	87.0		2–3	
2–6	31.0	14.1	35.8	90.8	15.0		
3–0	34.4	15.6	37.2	94.6	15.8	3.9	
4–0	38.0	17.2	40.6	103.1	16.7	4–3	
5–0	41.5	18.8	43.4	110.2	17.9		
6–1	46.0	20.9	45.9	117.0	18.6		
7–0	53.9	24.4	48.2	122.5	19.9		
8–0	58.2	26.4	50.4	127.9	20.4	7–10	64.4
9–0	65.0	29.5	52.3	132.8	21.2	8–0	65.1
10–0	74.5	33.8	54.3	137.9	22.3	9–8	63.9
11–0	81.8	37.1	56.1	142.6	23.0	10–6	63.4
12–0	95.2	43.2	59.1	150.1	24.2	11–0	64.4
13–0	106.3	48.2	62.1	157.7	25.2	13–3	64.2
14–0	117.1	53.1	63.6	161.5	26.8	14–6	64.5
15–0	125.4	56.9	64.0	162.5	27.4	15–6	64.4
16–0	135.6	61.5	64.0	162.5	28.2	17–0	64.1
16–6	140.2	63.6	64.0	162.6	27.9	17–0	64.1
17–0	137.6	62.4	64.3	163.3	27.9		
17–6	134.9	61.2	64.2	162.9	28.3		
18–0	129.0	58.5	64.3	163.3	27.9		
21–1	124.1	56.3	64.0	162.4	27.8		

Graphic Growth Record of Height, Weight, and Bi-Cristal

Weight for height is seen on Figure 67 as close to average, as is bi-cristal for height at most ages. Although N-V was briefly heavy for her stature at 17 years, she did not remain so and was never at any time obese. (The appearance of obesity on this chart at the upper ages may be compared with the deviation chart at the same age.)

Skeletal Development

Skeletal assessments (Table 12, Fig. 68) vary a little around average. Most of the deviations appear to be within the limits of errors in reading.

Prediction of Adult Stature

Height predictions are correct within small margins of error.

Comment

This girl has grown in a very steady, consistent manner, remaining close to the norms in all respects at most ages. At her heaviest she did not give the appearance of obesity.

Growth Curves of Weight by Age

Her weight curve (Fig. 66) is consistently average, except for a slightly high period at 16–17 years. Typically, the girls in the Berkeley Growth Study (Bayley, 1956b) gained weight through about 16 years and then lost weight, becoming more slender as young adults. N-V's increment curve is also consistently average.

CASE N-VI (EARLY-MATURING GIRL)

Characterization

A normal, healthy girl, N-VI shows somewhat accelerated maturation. Her health history includes abscessed ears at 14 months, infected tonsils from 18 to 36 months, and whooping cough at 4½ years. There was no further illness beyond the usual colds and minor respiratory infections.

Anthropometric Values and Deviation Chart

At 11 years this girl is large for her age in all dimensions considered, especially in bi-cristal diameter (Figs. 69, 70). Body proportions show her to be slightly heavy for her stature, long-legged and broad-hipped. These proportions, together with her generally above-average size, can be largely explained by her accelerated maturity. Compared with girls of the same skeletal age, N-VI would not be far out of line.

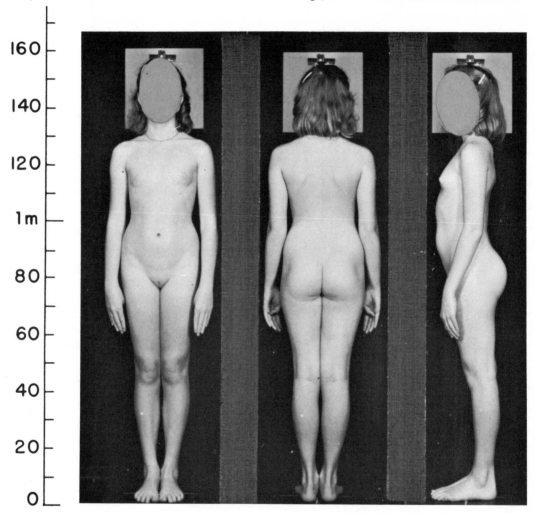

FIG. 69.—Three views of N-VI (Early-Maturing Girl) at 11 years

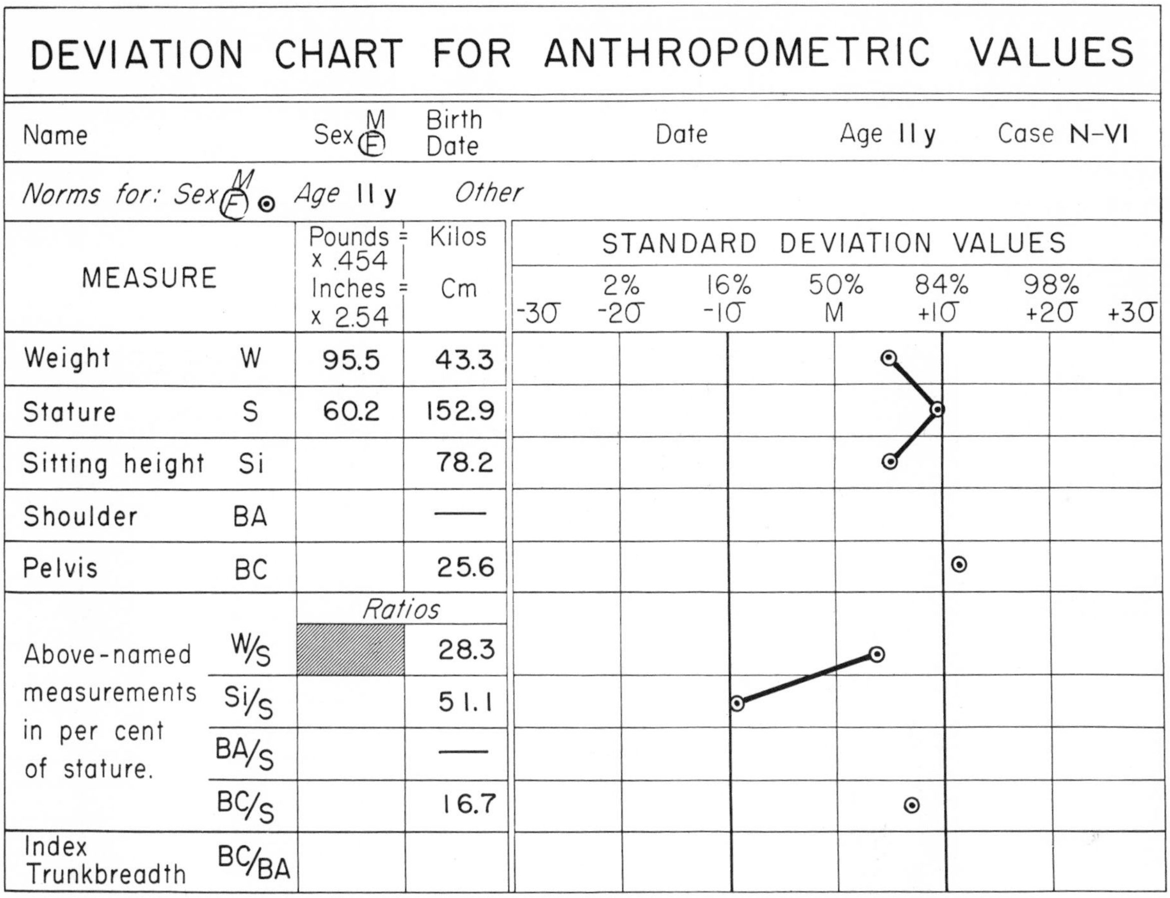

FIG. 70.—Deviation chart for N-VI at 11 years; measures compared with norms for 11-year-old girls.

Secondary Sex Characters

Menarche was at 11 years 6 months, accelerated 1.5 years. Breast and pubic hair had similarly, at 11 years, reached ratings more frequently achieved at age 13.

Growth Curves of Height by Age

This girl is consistently tall for her age, her curves for stature and stature increments falling closely along the mean curve for early-maturing girls (Fig. 71). She does, however, continue to grow to a somewhat above-average adult height.

Growth Curves of Weight by Age

N-VI tends to be heavy for her age; during the first nine years her curve (Fig. 72) approximates that for early-maturers, but then drops down somewhat. By 15 years she is just average or below. The indication is for a slender build for her stature.

Graphic Growth Record of Height, Weight, and Bi-Cristal

Before 2 years N-VI is heavy for her stature. After this, her curve (Fig. 73) is close to the center of the stream, though she is on the slender side from 11 years 6 months through 12 years 6 months. Her bi-cristal stature curve, however, indicates a broad skeletal frame. For these proportions, her weight is relatively low at all ages after 5 years.

Skeletal Development

Skeletal-age assessments (in Table 13 and Fig. 74) are advanced about one year at most ages between 1 and 16.5 years.

Case N-VI

Early-Maturing Girl

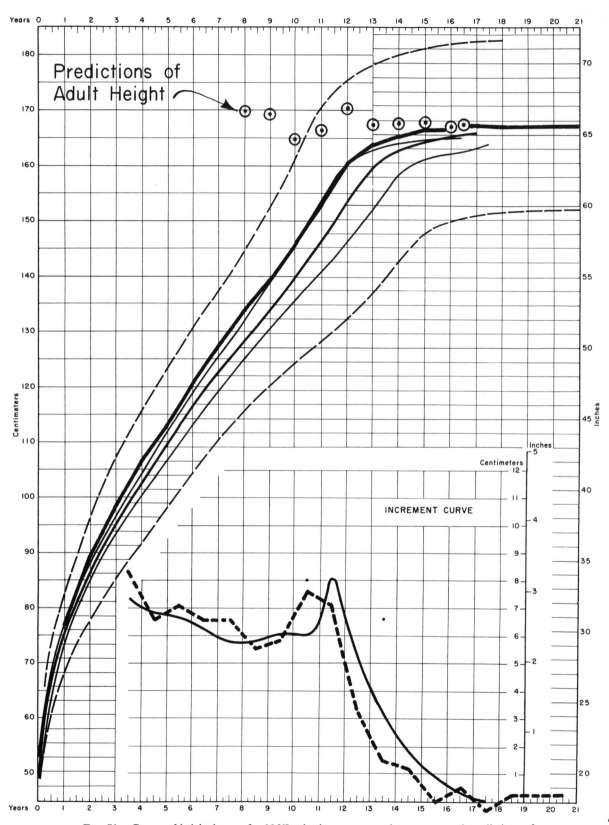

FIG. 71.—Curves of height by age for N-VI: absolute measures, increments, and predictions of adult height.

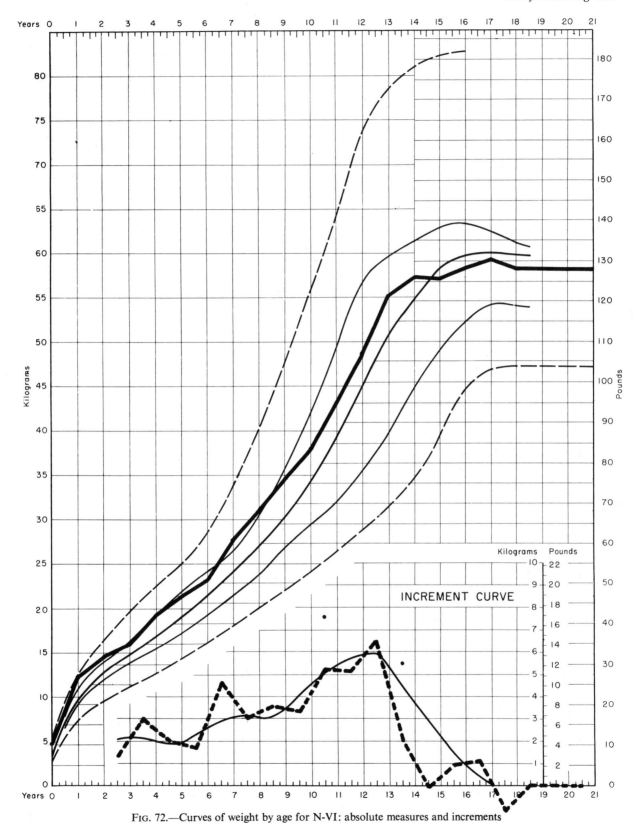

Fig. 72.—Curves of weight by age for N-VI: absolute measures and increments

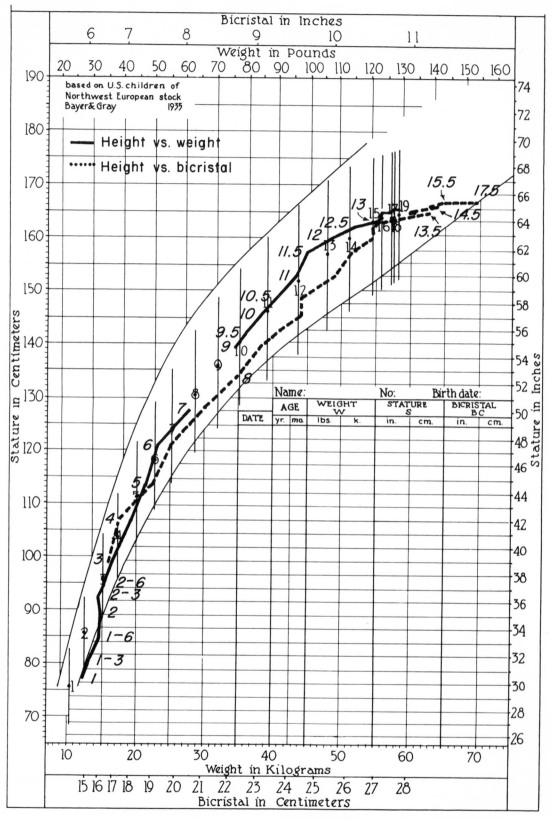

FIG. 73.—Graphic Growth Record, N-VI, with normal ranges of height for age and weight for height for girls, ages 1–19. Height vs. weight and height vs. bi-cristal plotted for N-VI.

Prediction of Adult Stature

Stature was somewhat overpredicted with the Greulich-Pyle standards at 8, 9, and 12 years. At other ages the predictions were very close to the achieved height of 65.7 in. (Table 13).

TABLE 13

GROWTH DATA
CASE N-VI (Early-Maturing Girl)

AGE (YR.-MO.)	WEIGHT		STATURE		BI-CRIS-TAL (CM.)	SA (YR.-MO.)	PRED. HT. (IN.)
	Lb.	Kg.	In.	Cm.			
Birth	10.1						
1	10.1	4.6	22.1	56.2			
3	12.4	5.6	24.0	61.0			
6	18.9	8.6	27.1	68.9			
9	24.8	11.2	28.8	73.2			
1–0	27.3	12.4	30.4	77.2		1–8	
1–6	32.0	14.5	33.3	84.7			
2–0	32.5	14.7	35.3	89.6		2–8	
2–6	33.3	15.1	37.2	94.6			
3–0	35.5	16.1	38.7	98.4	16.8	4–3	
4–0	42.3	19.2	42.1	107.0	17.4	5–3	
5–0	47.0	21.3	44.7	113.5	19.0	5–9*	
6–0	51.0	23.1	47.5	120.7	19.8		
7–0	61.4	27.8	50.1	127.3	21.0		
8–1	68.3	31.0	52.7	133.8	22.3	8–0	66.7
9–0	76.3	34.6	55.0	139.6	23.1	9–0	66.4
10–0	83.8	38.0	57.2	145.3	24.5	10–6	64.7
11–0	95.5	43.3	60.2	152.9	25.6	12–0	65.3
12–0	106.9	48.5	63.0	160.0	26.9	13–0	66.8
13–0	121.5	55.1	64.3	163.3	27.0	13–9	65.7
14–0	125.9	57.1	64.9	164.8	28.0	14–6	65.8
15–0	125.7	57.0	65.4	165.9	28.5	15–6	65.9
16–0	127.9	58.0	65.4	165.9	28.8	17–0	65.5
16–6	127.4	57.8	65.6	166.5	28.8	18–0	65.6
17–0	130.5	59.2	65.5	166.4	29.0		
17–6	126.3	57.3	65.6	166.6	29.6		
18–0	127.9	58.0	65.5	166.3	28.8		
21–1	127.9	58.0	65.7	166.8	29.8		

* X-ray taken at CA 4 years 6 months.

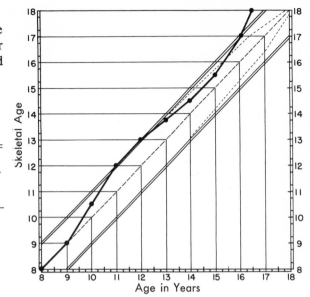

FIG. 74.—N-VI, skeletal age plotted against chronological age.

Androgyny Profile

N-VI was selected as the standard for the typical feminine build in our studies of somatic androgyny (see Fig. 22 in chap. 8). Her rating profile is presented here (Fig. 75).

Comment

Generally about one year accelerated in physical maturing, N-VI has a typically feminine build and is close to the norms for accelerated girls. Whereas acceleration in tempo of differentiation often occurs together with exaggeration in degree, such "hyperdifferentiation" did not ensue in this instance.

ANDROGYNIC PATTERNS OF BODY FORM: RATING PROFILE
Bayley-Bayer Standards
17–18 Year Norms

Name		Sex M/Ⓔ	Date		Age 18.0		Skeletal Age Mat.	Case Number N-VI

ITEM	RATING				
("A" through "H" from rear-view photographs)	**Hyper-masculine** 1	**Masculine** 2	**Intermediate, A-sexual, or Bi-sexual** 3, 3a, 3b	**Feminine** 4	**Hyper-feminine** 5
I. A. **Surface modeling**	Exaggerated hardness of relief. ○	Strong muscle molding. Bone, vein and tendon prominences. ○	b. Muscular and fat. ○ a. Little muscle or fat.	Smooth and soft, with little muscle. ●	Very soft, fat, no muscle. ○
II. **Trunk Contours** B. Shoulder girdle	Massive. ○	Appears wide, heavy and muscular. ○	b. Muscular and fat. ○ a. Narrow, "bony."	Slight, soft and narrow.	Frail, softly fat. ○
C. Waist line	Marked torso narrowing to low waist: may have ○ minimal indentation.	Slight indentation due to narrowing of torso.	b. Broad hip and shoulder; little ○ indentation. a. Slight ○ symmetrical high concavity.	Definite line accentuated by hip widening.	Marked indentation. ○
D. Hip flare	No widening. ○	Slight widening of hips from waist.	Intermediate. ○	Flares into wide hips laterally and posteriorly.	Marked flare. ○
E. Buttocks	Very flat. ○	Flat and angular. ○	Intermediate. ○	Rounded and full. ●	Very broad and rounded. ○
III. **Leg Patterns** F. Thigh Form	Cylinder and/or bulging muscles. ○	Approaches cylinder. Lateral outline convex. ○	Intermediate. ○	Funnel, fat and rounded. Lateral outline concave.	Fat, wide-top funnel. ○
G. Interspace (whole leg)	Very open. ○	Open center above and below knees. ○	Intermediate. ○	Closed center except small space below knees.	Thighs and knees together, feet apart. ○
H. Muscle bulge (lower leg)	Strong bulge, no fat. ○	Prominent inner bulge of gastrocnemius. ○	b. Moderate muscle bulge. ○ a. No muscle bulge; spindly.	Slight inner bulge; shapely, smooth, outer curve. ●	Very little muscle, but smoothly rounded and outer curve.
J. Penis size	1 Very ○ | 1.5 Large ○	2 Average ○	2.5 Small ○ | 3 Very ○		
K. Breast size			3 Very ○ | 3.5 Small ○	4 Average ○	4.5 Large ○ | 5 Very ○
L. Body hair density	1 ○ Heavy on thighs, etc.	2 ○ Easily discernible	2.5 ○ Sparse. | (3) ○♂	●♀ Absent	
M. Pubic pattern	Disperse ○ | Acuminate. ○	Sagittal ○	○♂	Horizontal ●♀	
N. Bicristal / Biacromial Index **77.8**	− ←68 |69 ○	73|74 ○	76|77 ● ○	82|83 →＋ ○	
P. Strength (Kg) Grip (R+L)+Thrust **115** +Pull	＋←244|243 ○	186|185 ○	148|147 ○	●110|109 → −	○
Grip (R+L) **59**	＋←126|125 ○	95|94 ○	80|79 ○	59|58 → − ●	○
Androgyny Score (Sum of "A"–"H")	8 ○ |12|13 ○	19|20 ○	B ○ A 25|26 ○	**32** ● |34|35 ○	40
Characteristic Description (Circle one)	**Hypermasculine**	**Masculine**	**Intermediate Bisexual Asexual Disharmonious**	(**Feminine**)	**Hyperfeminine**

FIG. 75.—Androgyny profile of N-VI at 18 years

CASE N-VII (LATE-MATURING GIRL)

Characterization

A tall, slender, normally healthy girl, N-VII shows

somewhat retarded maturation. The only childhood illnesses recorded are chicken pox at 2 years and occasional colds.

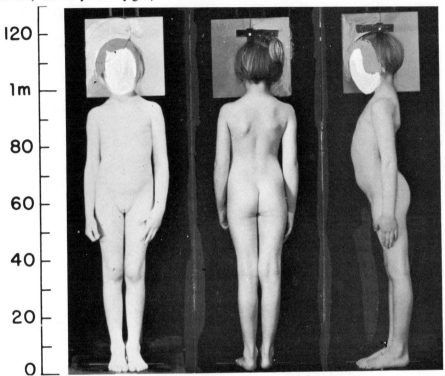

FIG. 76.—N-VII (Late-Maturing Girl) at 6 years

Name			Sex Ⓜ/Ⓕ	Birth Date	Date		Age **6 y**	Case **N-VII**

Norms for: Sex Ⓜ/Ⓕ⊙ *Age* **6 y** *Other*

MEASURE		Pounds = x .454 Inches = x 2.54	Kilos Cm	STANDARD DEVIATION VALUES						
				-3σ	2% -2σ	16% -1σ	50% M	84% +1σ	98% +2σ	+3σ
Weight	W	44.0	20.0				⊙			
Stature	S	46.2	117.2					⊙		
Sitting height	Si		60.7		⊙					
Shoulder	BA		—							
Pelvis	BC		18.2		⊙					
Above-named measurements in per cent of stature.	W/S	*Ratios*	17.1				⊙			
	Si/S		51.8	⊙						
	BA/S		—							
	BC/S		15.5				⊙			

FIG. 77.—Deviation chart for N-VII at 6 years; measures compared with norms for 6-year-old girls

FIG. 78.—VIEWS OF N-VII AT ANNUAL

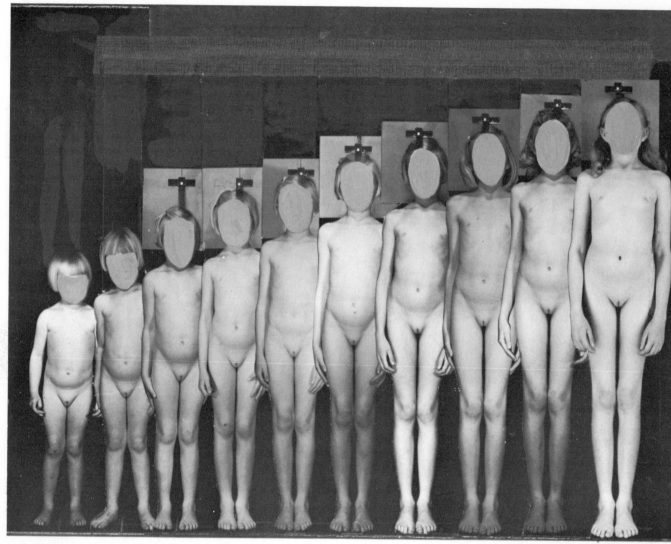

Age	3.0	4.0	5.0	6.0	7.0	8.0	9.0	10.0	11.0	12.0
Ht.	94.6	103.0	111.0	117.2	123.0	128.1	133.7	139.0	144.0	152.2

Anthropometric Values and Deviation Chart

At 6 years (Fig. 76) she is almost average in stature, rather light, and very short-stemmed with a narrow pelvis. The ratios show her to be slender and long-legged (Fig. 77).

Secondary Sex Characters

Menarche was at 14 years 2 months, in keeping with her generally slow maturation tempo.

Breast and pubic hair were also slow in development and remained somewhat undifferentiated even at maturity.

Growth Curves of Height by Age

Height is average for her age, with a very slight lag around 10 and 11 years; after 13, however, she becomes tall, attaining an adult stature of 68.3 in. (Figs. 78, 79). Annual increments in height are normal, reaching their highest point a year later than average.

INTERVALS, AGES 3 THROUGH 18 YEARS

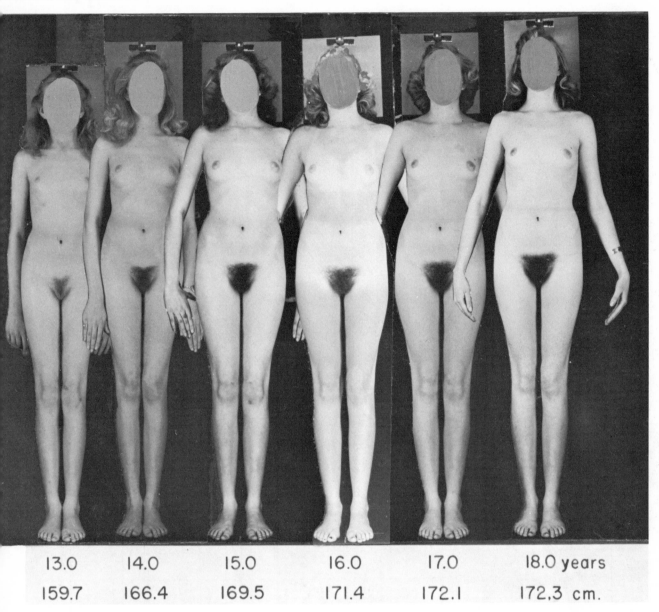

13.0	14.0	15.0	16.0	17.0	18.0 years
159.7	166.4	169.5	171.4	172.1	172.3 cm.

Growth Curves of Weight by Age

Weight follows the curve in Figure 80 that is characteristic of girls with a slow rate of maturation. Since she has been of average-to-tall stature during most of childhood, it follows that N-VII is slender. Annual increments are somewhat below average, the period of greatest gain occurring at the expected age for a late-maturer. She shows a typical decrease in weight after her 16-year high.

Graphic Growth Record of Height, Weight, and Bi-Cristal

Both weight and bi-cristal, in relation to stature, show a very slender girl. Before 6 she tends to be on the plump side for her build; after this, she is lightweight for her build but not excessively so (Fig. 81).

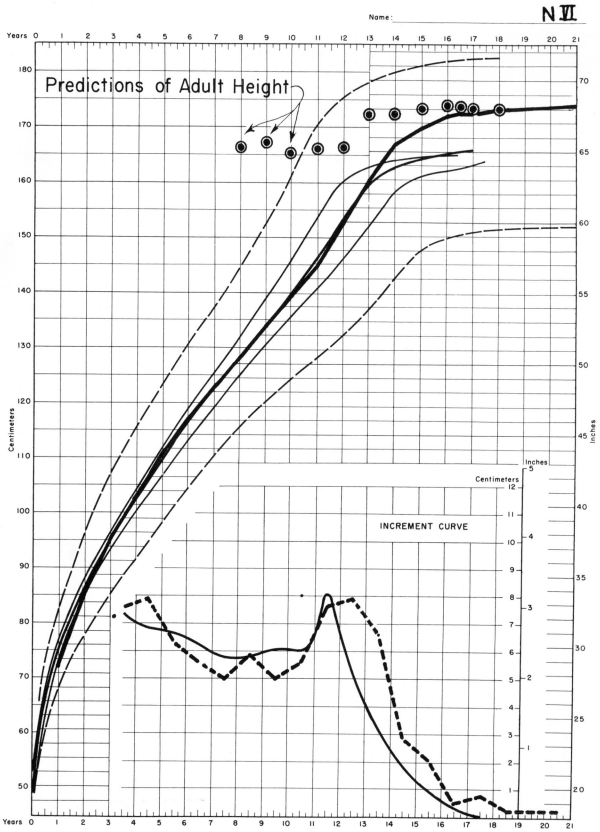

Name: _____   N VII

Predictions of Adult Height

INCREMENT CURVE

FIG. 79.—Curves of height by age for N-VII: absolute measures, increments, and predictions of adult height.

Name: _____ N VII

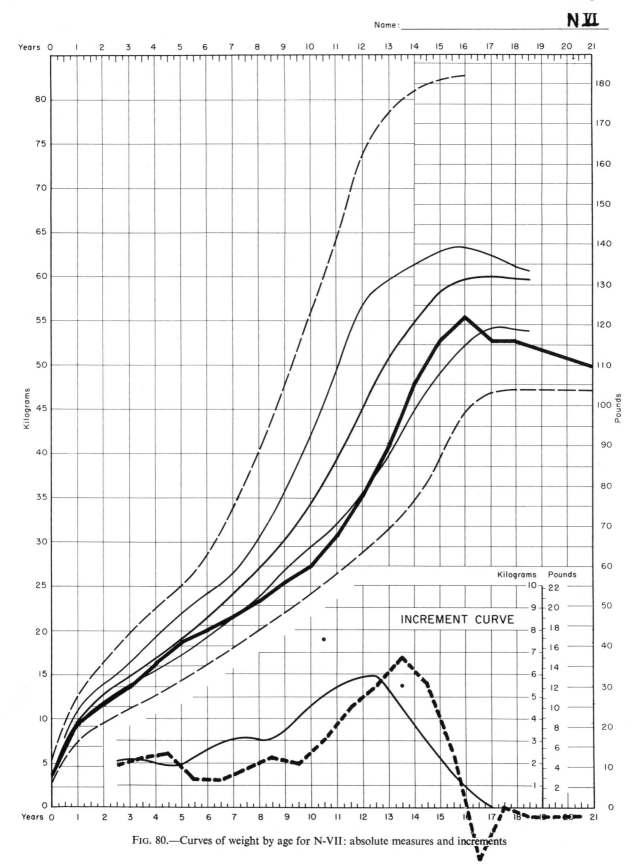

INCREMENT CURVE

FIG. 80.—Curves of weight by age for N-VII: absolute measures and increments

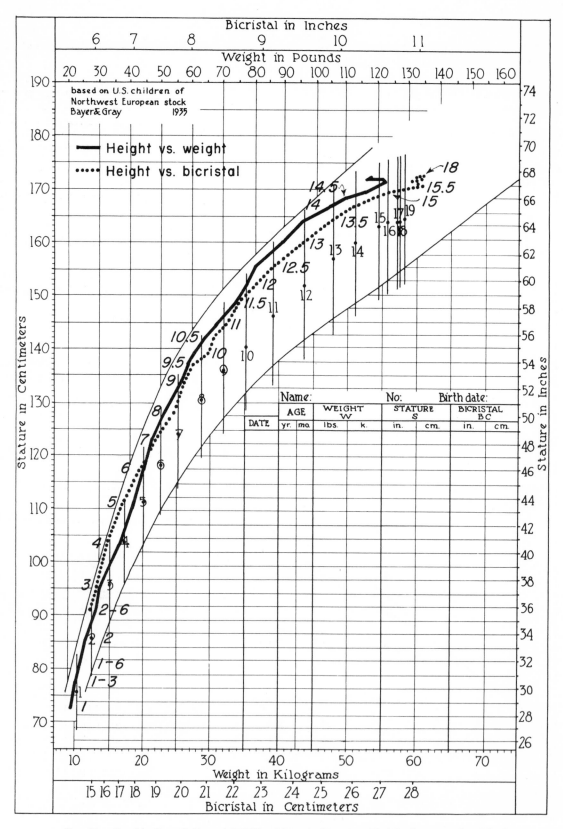

FIG. 81.—Graphic Growth Record, N-VII, with normal ranges of height for age and weight for height for girls, ages 1–19. Height vs. weight and height vs. bi-cristal plotted for N-VII.

Skeletal Development

In skeletal age (Fig. 82) she is consistently retarded about one year on the Greulich-Pyle standards. The Todd knee standards, used for the ratings during the first four years, show her to be average at ages 1 and 2, with a slowing-down soon after 2 years (Table 14).

Prediction of Adult Stature

Early assessments considerably underestimate this girl's eventual stature (Table 14; also see Fig. 79). After the puberal phase of growth starts, prediction becomes accurate within normal limits of error. The

TABLE 14

GROWTH DATA
CASE N-VII (Late-Maturing Girl)

| AGE (YR.– MO.) | WEIGHT | | STATURE | | BI- CRIS- TAL (CM.) | SA (YR.– MO.) | PRED. HT. (IN.) |
	Lb.	Kg.	In.	Cm.			
Birth	8.3						
1	10.1	4.6	22.0	55.8			
3	13.6	6.2	23.9	60.8			
6	17.3	7.8	25.8	65.5			
9	19.3	8.8	27.3	69.3			
1–0	21.3	9.6	28.5	72.5		1–0	
1–6	23.8	10.8	31.8	80.7			
2–0	26.0	11.8	33.5	85.1		2–0	
2–6	28.5	12.9	35.8	90.8	14.8		
3–0	30.3	13.7	37.6	94.6	15.4	2–6	
4–0	35.5	16.1	40.6	103.0	16.1	3–9	
5–0	41.0	18.6	43.7	111.0	17.2		
6–0	44.0	20.0	46.2	117.2	18.2		
7–0	46.9	21.3	48.4	123.0	18.9		
8–0	50.9	23.1	50.4	128.1	19.7	7–6	65.3
9–0	56.0	25.4	52.7	133.7	20.1	8–0	65.6
10–0	60.4	27.4	54.7	138.9	21.0	9–6	64.8
11–0	67.5	30.6	56.9	144.4	21.7	10–0	65.1
12–0	77.6	35.2	59.9	152.2	22.8	11–0	65.3
13–0	89.7	40.7	63.0	160.0	24.3	12–0	67.6
14–0	104.7	47.5	65.6	166.4	26.0	13–3	67.6
15–0	116.4	52.8	66.7	169.5	27.3	13–9	68.0
16–0	121.7	55.2	67.5	171.4	27.9	14–6	68.2
16–6	121.0	54.9	67.7	172.0	28.2	15–0	68.1
17–0	116.4	52.8	67.7	172.1	28.1	15–6	68.0
17–7	117.7	53.4	67.7	172.1	28.1	16–0	67.8
18–0	116.4	52.8	68.0	172.3	28.3	17–0	68.0
21–0	110.2	50.0	68.3	173.4	28.3		

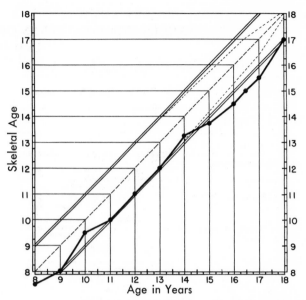

FIG. 82.—N-VII, skeletal age plotted against chronological age.

implication is that in this girl the effect of steroid stimulation is manifested in more vigorous linear growth as well as in maturation.

Androgyny Profile

This girl's picture was used as the standard for the hypofeminine build in Figure 22 (chap. 8). She is typical of many girls who would be rated similarly on the androgynic chart (Fig. 83), being relatively undifferentiated from childhood proportions. Her exceptional leg length probably reflects an additional factor related to her slow rate of maturing.

Comment

N-VII is a healthy, very slender child whose slow physical maturing appears to follow a genetic pattern. Her record provides an instance wherein a slow *tempo* is coupled with a slight inhibition of *degree of differentiation.*

ANDROGYNIC PATTERNS OF BODY FORM: RATING PROFILE
Bayley-Bayer Standards
17–18 Year Norms

FIG. 83.—Androgyny profile of N-VII at 18 years

CASE N-VIII (GIRL WITH TRANSIENT OBESITY)

Characterization

N-VIII is a normal, healthy girl (Fig. 84), with a transient prepubescent obesity. Her history shows her to be relatively free from disease. At 4 months the pediatrician noted "beginning rosary," but there were no later references to rachitic symptoms. She had very few colds; at 4 years infected tonsils were reported.

Anthropometric Values and Deviation Chart

At 12 years, during the atypical period of her growth, this girl is almost 2 S.D.'s above average in weight, 1 S.D. above average in stature, average in sit-

ting height, and moderately large in shoulder and pelvic diameters. Relative to her stature, she is very heavy and also definitely long-legged. In proportion to her shoulder width, her hips are broad (Fig. 85). With the exception of her weight, these deviations are characteristic of her at most ages, both before and after the period of obesity.

Secondary Sex Characters

Menarche was at age 12 years 8 months, close to the group average.

Breast development and pubic-hair development were slightly advanced.

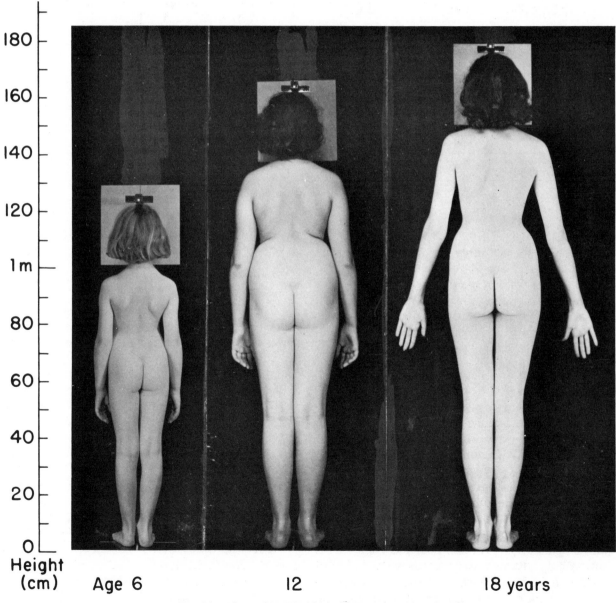

FIG. 84.—Views of N-VIII (Girl with Transient Obesity)

117

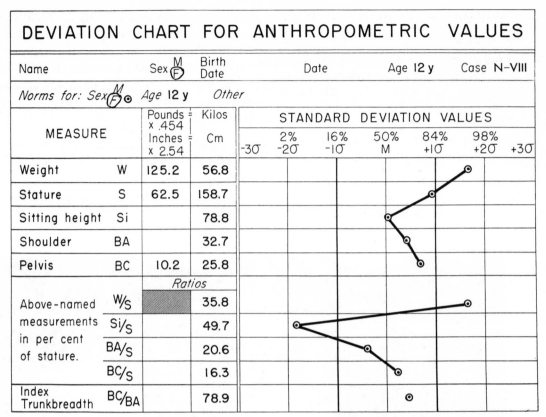

FIG. 85.—Deviation chart for N-VIII at 12 years; measures compared with norms for 12-year-old girls.

Growth Curves of Height by Age

Consistently tall for her age, N-VIII's curve (Fig. 86) follows that of girls who are accelerated until about 10 years, after which it more nearly parallels that for average-maturing girls, though higher on the scale. The curve of annual increments is similar to the average curve, with possibly greater than average increments during the first five years and with rapid pubescent growth lasting longer than is usual for girls.

Growth Curves of Weight by Age

Weight is near average until 8 years, after which the curve follows near that of accelerated girls, with a high point at 13 years (Fig. 87). N-VIII was sensitive about her weight and refused photographs at 13 years; however, her 12-year-old view in Figure 84 may be compared with her 6-year and 18-year pictures to note the characteristic trend toward this type of early-adolescent obesity. The annual increment curve illustrates the tendency toward rapid weight gains after 8 years, with the greatest gain between 11 and 12 years. This is only slightly advanced over the average age of most rapid gain for girls. Efforts to control her weight resulted in marked reduction, much of which was temporary, followed later by a reduction which remained stable.

Graphic Growth Record for Height, Weight, and Bi-Cristal

The obese period is shown clearly here (Fig. 88) with the weight curve moving far to the right of the bi-cristal curve between 11 and 14 years. Before 11 the two curves are closely approximated.

It is sometimes helpful to plot the same information on a variety of evaluation charts for comparative and defining purposes. If we were to plot N-VIII's data (Table 15) on the well-known Wetzel Grid, we would find that the child, somewhat slender in build for the first eight years, becomes progressively heavy for her height thereafter, moving from the "slender" channel on the Grid to the "heavy" channel, where she stays between ages 11.5 and 14.5. After this she rapidly moves back to central channels, becoming slender again by the age of 18.

Thus the Wetzel Grid, considering the entire growth history, presents this girl as being on the slender side of average, a diagnosis which agrees with our Graphic Growth Record, where it is verified by the

118

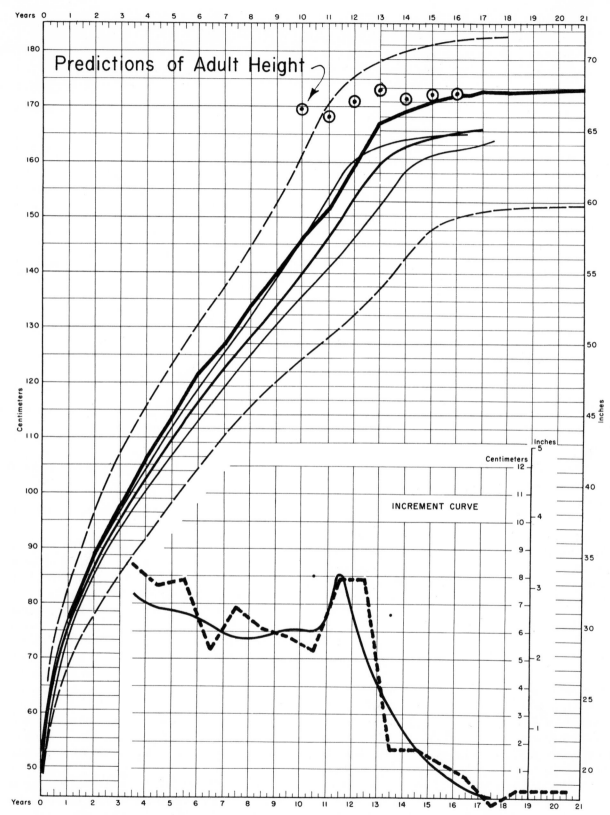

FIG. 86.—Curves of height by age for N-VIII: absolute measures, increments, and predictions of adult height.

Girl with Transient Obesity

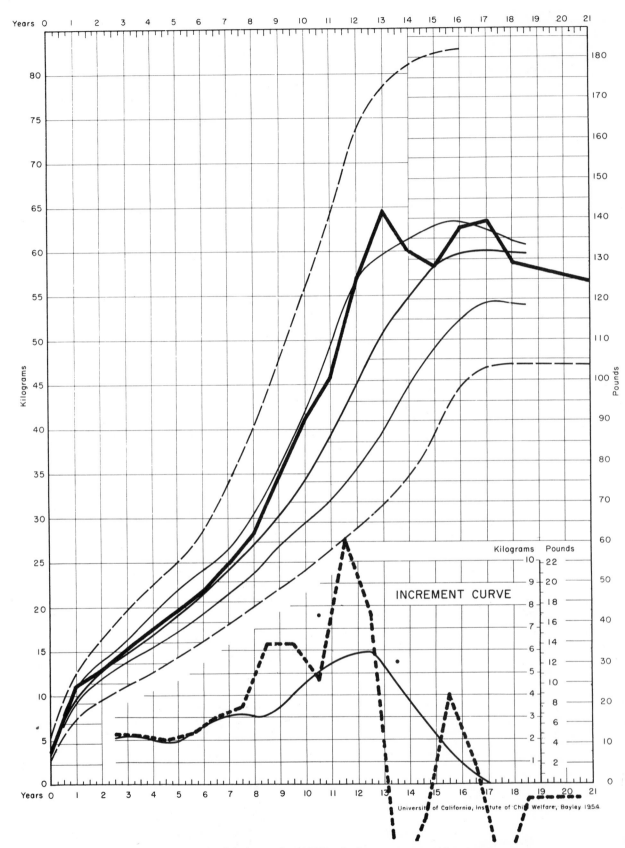

University of California, Institute of Child Welfare, Bayley 1954

FIG. 87.—Curves of weight by age for N-VIII: absolute measures and increments

120

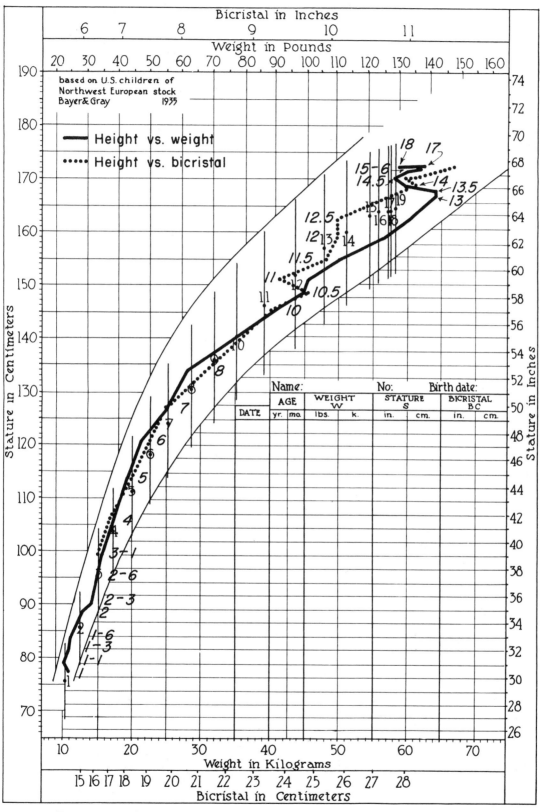

FIG. 88.—Graphic Growth Record, N-VIII, with normal ranges of height for age and weight for height for girls, ages 1–19. Height vs. weight and height vs. bi-cristal plotted for N-VIII.

Girl with Transient Obesity

TABLE 15

GROWTH DATA
CASE N-VIII (Girl with Transient Obesity)

AGE (YR.–MO.)	WEIGHT		STATURE		BI-CRISTAL (CM.)	SA (YR.–MO.)	PRED. HT. (IN.)
	Lb.	Kg.	In.	Cm.			
Birth	7.8						
1	10.8	4.9	22.3	56.7			
3	13.7	6.2	24.8	63.1			
6	18.0	8.2	27.3	69.3			
9	20.3	9.2	28.8	73.1			
1–0	24.2	10.8	30.4	77.3		1–3	
1–6	24.8	12.4	32.9	83.5			
2–0	28.5	12.9	35.0	89.0		2–3	
2–6	32.5	14.7	37.1	94.3			
3–0	33.5	15.2	39.0	99.1	16.4	3–10	
4–0	38.3	17.4	41.7	106.0	17.1	4–9	
5–0	42.8	19.1	44.7	113.6	18.4		
6–0	47.8	21.7	47.5	120.6	19.1		
7–0	54.5	24.7	49.9	126.8	19.9		
8–0	62.2	28.2	52.6	133.5	21.3		
9–0	76.2	34.6	55.0	139.7	22.6		
10–0	90.3	41.0	57.3	145.5	23.6	10–0	66.5
11–0	100.8	45.7	59.4	151.0	23.8	10–10	66.0
12–0	125.2	56.8	62.5	158.7	25.8	12–3	67.0
13–0	142.0	64.4	65.6	166.5	27.6	13–3	67.9
14–0	131.8	59.8	66.4	168.6	28.3	14–6	67.2
15–0	128.3	58.2	67.0	170.3	28.3	15–6	67.5
16–0	137.3	62.3	67.5	171.4	28.9	17–0	67.6
16–6	134.9	61.2	67.6	171.6	28.9		
17–0	139.1	63.1	67.8	172.3	29.2		
17–6	136.5	61.9	67.7	172.0	29.1		
18–0	129.4	58.7	67.7	172.1	28.9		
21–0	124.6	56.5	67.9	172.5	28.9		

height bi-cristal curve. However, if measures on the grid had been noted for the first time at 12 years, she would have been classified as a broad-built, heavy-set child, while her appearance and the Growth Record both show her to be moderately obese at this period rather than broad-built.

The curve on the Wetzel auxodrome would show this girl to be developmentally accelerated from an early age, and exceptionally so after 9 years. Our other information does not agree with this. As we have seen, her skeletal age is approximately average. Instead of being accelerated, her above-average height and weight result from (1) her being relatively long-legged and tall for her age and (2) a prepubescent fat period. This information cannot be deduced from the auxodrome.

It might be pointed out, furthermore, that basal

metabolic rates in normal adolescents have been found by D. H. Eichorn (1955) to be very different from the values presented on the Wetzel Grid.

Skeletal Development

The Todd knee readings for the first four years show N-VIII slightly accelerated in skeletal maturing (Table 15). The Greulich-Pyle assessments, starting at 10 years, continue approximately at age (Table 15, Fig. 89).

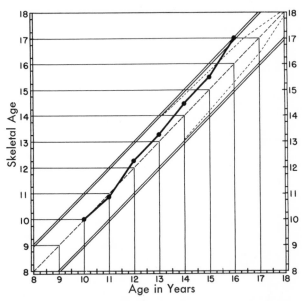

FIG. 89.—N-VIII, skeletal age plotted against chronological age.

Prediction of Adult Stature

Prediction is a little low until about 12 years, when it begins to approximate her 18-year stature.

Androgyny Profile

This girl's picture has been used as one of the hyperfeminine standards in Figure 22 (chap. 8). Except for her relatively long legs, she strongly expresses the feminine build (Fig. 90).

Comment

N-VIII is a healthy, tall, average-maturing girl with a hyperfeminine build, who was obese during early adolescence.

ANDROGYNIC PATTERNS OF BODY FORM: RATING PROFILE

Bayley-Bayer Standards
17–18 Year Norms

Name ___ Sex M/F ___ Date ___ Age 18.0 ___ Skeletal Age Mat. ___ Case Number N-VIII

ITEM	RATING				
("A" through "H" from rear-view photographs)	Hyper-masculine 1	Masculine 2	Intermediate, A-sexual, or Bi-sexual 3, 3a, 3b	Feminine 4	Hyper-feminine 5
I. A. **Surface modeling**	Exaggerated hardness of relief. O	Strong muscle molding. Bone, vein and tendon prominences. O	b. Muscular and fat. O / a. Little muscle or fat. O	Smooth and soft, with little muscle. ●	Very soft, fat, no muscle. O
II. **Trunk Contours** B. Shoulder girdle	Massive. O	Appears wide, heavy and muscular. O	b. Muscular and fat. O / a. Narrow, "bony."	Slight, soft and narrow ●	Frail, softly fat. O
C. Waist line	Marked torso narrowing to low waist: may have minimal indentation. O	Slight indentation due to narrowing of torso. O	b. Broad hip and shoulder; little O indentation. / a. Slight O symmetrical high concavity.	Definite line accentuated by hip widening. ●	Marked indentation. O
D. Hip flare	No widening. O	Slight widening of hips from waist. O	Intermediate. O	Flares into wide hips laterally and posteriorly. ●	Marked flare. O
E. Buttocks	Very flat. O	Flat and angular. O	Intermediate. O	Rounded and full ●	Very broad and rounded. O
III. **Leg Patterns** F. Thigh Form	Cylinder and/or bulging muscles. O	Approaches cylinder. Lateral outline convex. O	Intermediate. O	Funnel, fat and rounded. Lateral outline concave. ●	Fat, wide-top funnel. O
G. Interspace (whole leg)	Very open. O	Open center above and below knees. O	Intermediate. O	Closed center except small space below knees. ●	Thighs and knees together, feet apart. O
H. Muscle bulge (lower leg)	Strong bulge, no fat. O	Prominent inner bulge of gastrocnemius. O	b. Moderate muscle bulge. O / a. No muscle bulge; spindly.	Slight inner bulge; shapely, smooth, outer curve. O	Very little muscle, but smoothly rounded and outer curve. ●
J. Penis size	1 Very O 1.5 Large O	2 Average O	2.5 Small O 3 Very O		
K. Breast size			3 Very O 3.5 Small O	4 Average ●	4.5 Large O 5 Very O
L. Body hair density	1 O Heavy on thighs, etc.	2 O Easily discernible	2.5 O Sparse (3) O♂	♀ Absent ●	
M. Pubic pattern	Disperse O	Acuminate. O	Sagittal O O♂	Horizontal ●♀	
N. Bicristal / Biacromial Index **79.4**	− ←68 69 O	73 74 O	76 77 O	● O	82 83 → + O
P. Strength (Kg) Grip (R+L)+Thrust +Pull **118**	+ ←244 243 O	186 185 O	148 147 O	110 ●	109 → − O
Grip (R+L) **66**	O + ←126 125	O 95 94	O 80 79	O 59 ●	58 → − O
Androgyny Score (Sum of "A"–"H")	8 O	12 13 O	19 20 B O A 25 26	O 34 35 ● **35.5**	40 O
Characteristic Description (Circle one)	**Hypermasculine**	**Masculine**	**Intermediate Bisexual Asexual Disharmonious**	**Feminine**	(**Hyperfeminine**)

FIG. 90.—Androgyny profile of N-VIII at 18 years

Chapter 15

Giantism

Whether an adolescent is considered merely "very tall" or "a giant" depends on many factors. The patient, his relatives, and his friends are influenced especially by family and peer ideals. The physician is more influenced by whether or not he suspects and finds pathology. Height which gives token of topping 70 in. for girls or 76 in. for boys is usually cause for uneasiness and inquiry.

The two cases which follow illustrate the problem of excessive height in a girl and a boy who came, respectively, from a tall family and a family of average height. Each child suffered considerable personal distress as a result of robust growth, but in each case tallness was shown to be without pathological import.

CASE C-I (VERY TALL GIRL)

Presenting Problem at 14 Years 7 Months
Too tall and too thin (Fig. 91)
Recent rapid growth
Family data: mother, 71.3 in. tall; elder sister, 74.2 in.

Anthropometric Values and Deviation Chart
Compared with her age peers, this girl's absolute measurements are close to the mean, except for the very tall stature (Fig. 92). Relative to this stature, the trunk is notably small: the sitting height is too short; the breadth measures, too narrow. Her long-legged, slender, linear build is suggestive of slow maturation.

Secondary Sex Characters
The suggestion of slow maturation is confirmed by breast development and pubic-hair development, which are each at stage II (see Fig. 18) whereas the more common ages for reaching these points of sexual maturity are 10.6 and 11.6 years, respectively. Menarche has not occurred.

Growth Diagnosis
Very tall; rapid growth; slow maturation
Potential giant

Clinical Diagnosis
Menarche delayed, consonant with skeletal and physiological status
No evidence of pathological gonadal deficiency or pituitary activity
Tallness, constitutional

For nine months after the original workup, from 14 years 7 months to 15 years 4 months, this girl was treated with estrogens in an effort to speed maturation and discourage further growth.

124

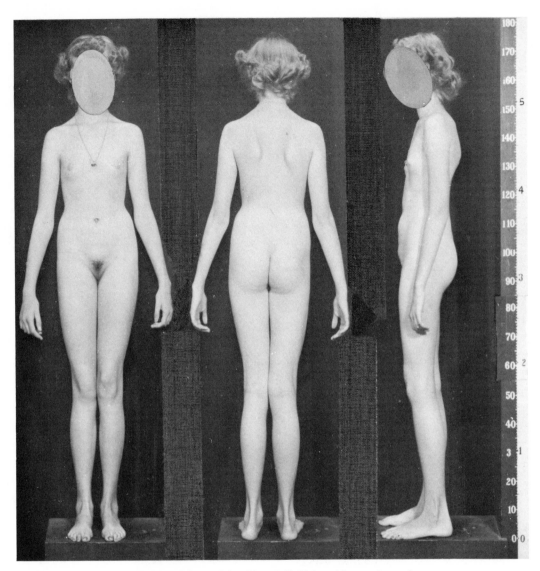

FIG. 91.—Views of C-I (Very Tall Girl) at 14 years 9 months

TABLE 16

GROWTH DATA
CASE C-I (Very Tall Girl)

AGE (YR.–MO.)	WEIGHT (LB.)	STATURE		BI-CRIS-TAL (CM.)	SA (YR.–MO.)	PRED. HT. (IN.)
		In.	Cm.			
12–8	105.0	67.0				
13–2	105.0	67.5				
14–9	117.0	70.9	180.0	26.0	13–0	73.5
15–2	130.0	71.1	180.5	26.7	13–6	72.8
15–7	134.0	71.9	182.5	27.5	13–11	73.1
16–4	123.0	72.3	183.5		15–0	72.6
17–0	127.0	72.9	185.0	27.5	15–6	73.2

Growth Curves of Height by Age

According to school data, C-I's height in the preceding two years had been increasing on a steep slope, without the tapering-off customary after age 13 (Fig. 93). This suggests that retarded maturation in this girl is coupled with a vigorous preadolescent growth spurt, corresponding to her physiological rather than to her chronological age. Even during the subsequent periods of treatment and observation, height and height increment curves continue at high levels, and stature predictions remain the same (Table 16).

Very Tall Girl

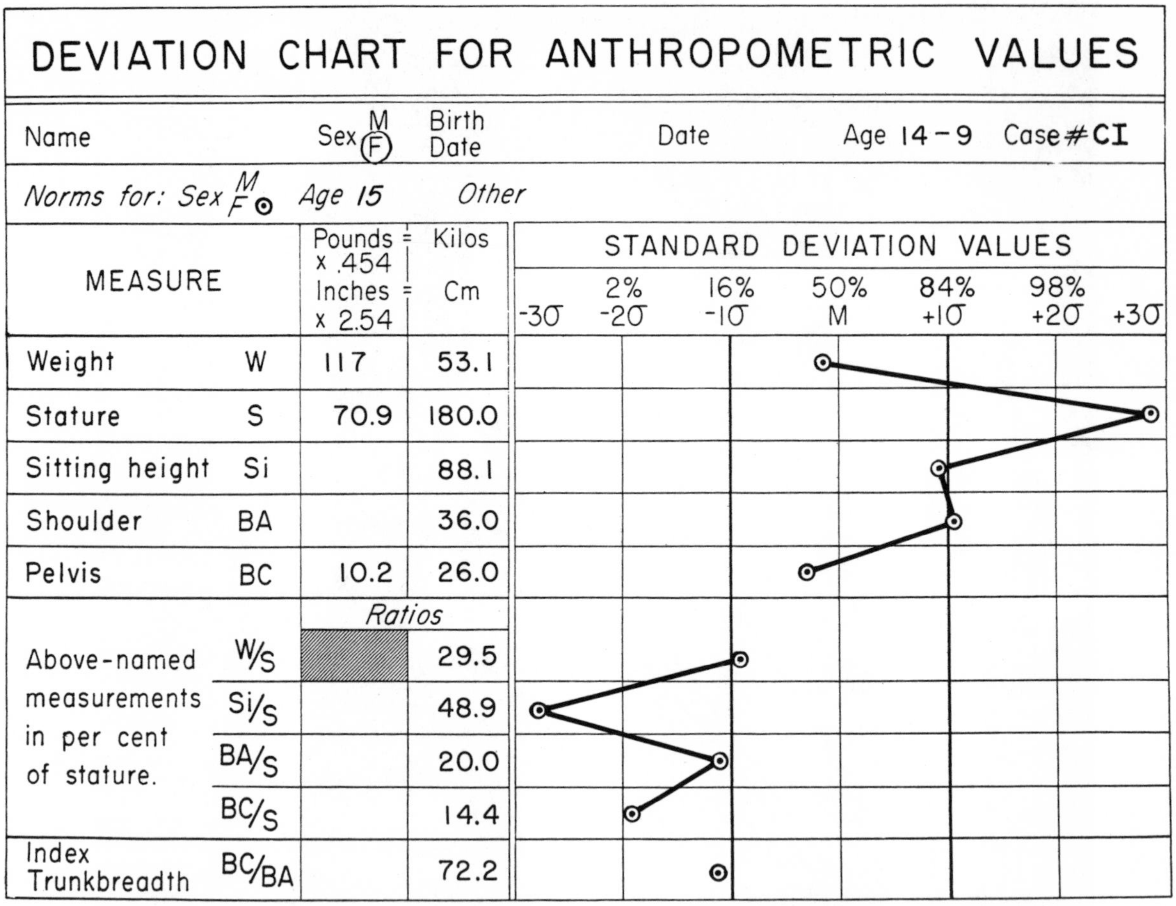

DEVIATION CHART FOR ANTHROPOMETRIC VALUES

Name		Sex M Ⓕ	Birth Date	Date		Age 14 − 9	Case # **CI**

Norms for: Sex M F⊙ Age 15 Other

MEASURE		Pounds ÷ x .454 Inches ÷ x 2.54	Kilos Cm	STANDARD DEVIATION VALUES						
				-3σ	2% -2σ	16% -1σ	50% M	84% +1σ	98% +2σ	+3σ
Weight	W	117	53.1				⊙			
Stature	S	70.9	180.0							⊙
Sitting height	Si		88.1					⊙		
Shoulder	BA		36.0					⊙		
Pelvis	BC	10.2	26.0				⊙			
Above-named measurements in per cent of stature.	W/S	*Ratios*	29.5				⊙			
	Si/S		48.9	⊙						
	BA/S		20.0			⊙				
	BC/S		14.4	⊙						
Index Trunkbreadth	BC/BA		72.2		⊙					

Fig. 92.—Deviation chart for C-I at 14 years 9 months; measures compared with norms for 15-year-old girls.

Graphic Growth Record of Height, Weight, and Bi-Cristal

Relative to her height, her weight in the years preceding treatment decreased (Fig. 94) during a period when a significant relative weight increase is the rule. However, weight increased significantly under treatment.

Follow-up

A period of withdrawal bleeding followed the withdrawal of estrogen. While this could not be called a true menarche, the appearance of menstrual blood did confirm the impression of a normal but delayed sexual development. Regular menstrual cycles began six months later (at 15 years 9 months) and continued. At 17 years, skeletal age was still retarded, and the girl had approached very close to the original confirmed prediction.

Comment

Altogether, these observations indicate that vigorous growth in this healthy girl was not readily suppressed.

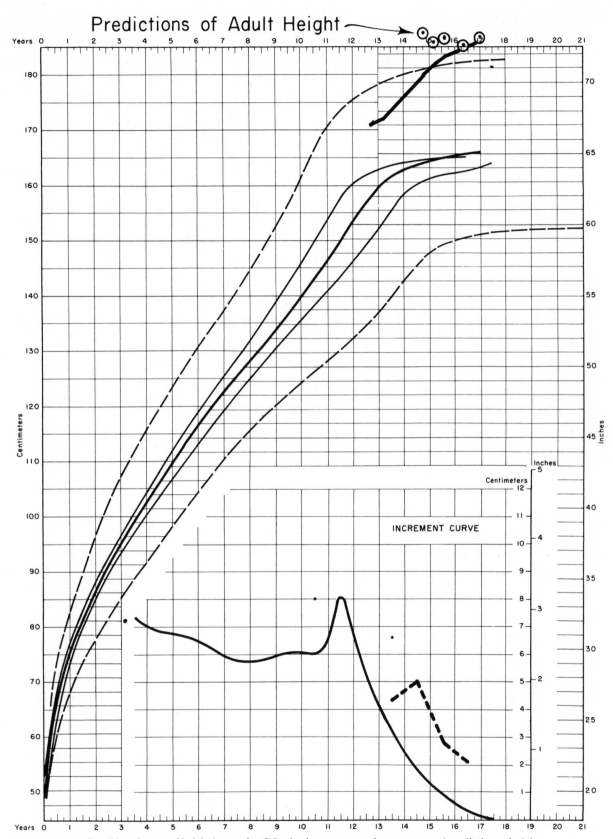

FIG. 93.—Curves of height by age for C-I: absolute measures, increments, and predictions of adult height.

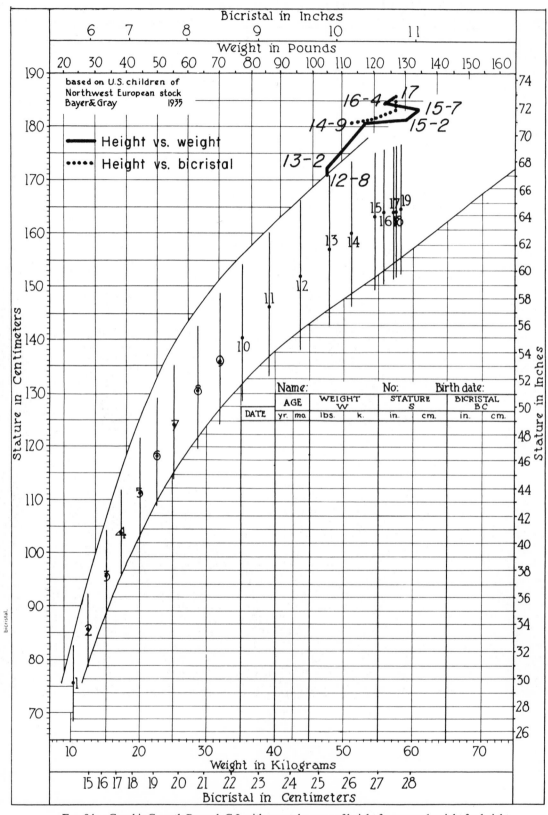

FIG. 94.—Graphic Growth Record, C-I, with normal ranges of height for age and weight for height, girls, ages 1–19. Height vs. weight; height vs. bi-cristal plotted.

CASE C-II (VERY TALL BOY)

Presenting Problem at 15 Years 10 Months
    Too tall (76 in.)
    Recent rapid growth, undocumented
    Family data: all known relatives of average
        height

Anthropometric Values and Deviation Chart

Absolute parameters are all too large except for an average shoulder breadth. Ratios are scattered, the most important deviations being the small Si/S, with its indication of long-leggedness and possible hypogonadism; the large BC/BA, implying some femininity of trunk form. In this case, the anthropometric values validate and qualify the impression gained from direct inspection and from photographs—that this is a very big boy with a disharmonious build (Figs. 95, 96).

Secondary Sex Characters

Development has reached sex stage V, which is average for his age.

Skeletal Age: 14 years 6 months

Stature Prediction: 80 in.

Growth Diagnosis: Giantism

Clinical Diagnosis: Giantism, constitutional

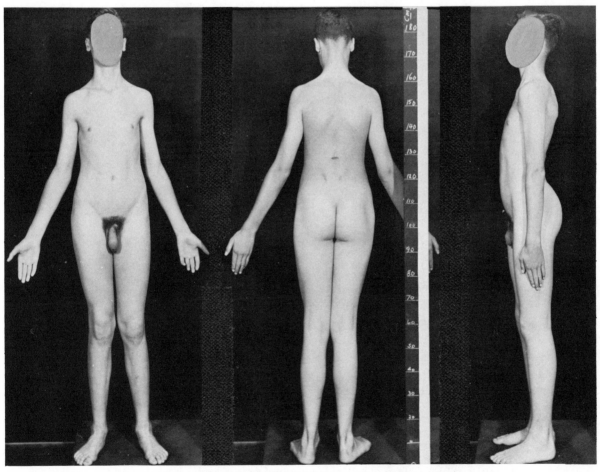

FIG. 95.—Views of C-II (Very Tall Boy) at 15 years 10 months

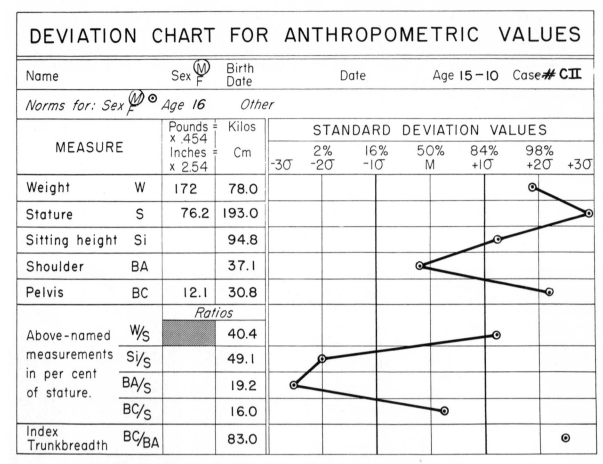

FIG. 96.—Deviation chart for C-II at 15 years 10 months; measures compared with norms for 16-year-old boys.

Various factors in this growth picture spurred a detailed search for causal pathology. The most disturbing observations were the boy's towering height, which was the presenting complaint and which stood in such marked contrast to the height of his relatives; the disharmonious build; the skeletal retardation. Complete studies, however, yielded evidence neither of pituitary hyperactivity nor of gonadal deficiency.

Longitudinal Growth Data

Despite continued vigorous growth, reassessment of height and skeletal age 8 months later yielded a slightly lower stature prediction. By 19 years 6 months the boy had actually reached 79.2 in. (Table 17).

TABLE 17

GROWTH DATA
CASE C-II (Very Tall Boy)

AGE (YR.–MO.)	WEIGHT		STATURE		BI-CRISTAL (CM.)	SA (YR.–MO.)	PRED. HT. (IN.)
	Lb.	Kg.	In.	Cm.			
15–10	172.0	78.0	76.2	193.4	37.1	14–6	80.2
16–6	184.0		77.8	197.4		15–4	79.8
16–11	183.0		78.5	199.2			
19–6	195.0		79.2	201.2			

Comment

This drop in predicted height was reassuring to the physicians, because it confirmed the benign nature of the excess growth. It was even more reassuring to the patient and his parents who had been fearful that his growth would continue without end.

Chapter 16

Dwarfism

As in the case of excessive height, the diagnosis of deficient height, or dwarfism, rests partly on the extent of the deviation, partly on the relevant pathology.

The three boys whose cases form this subgroup presented shortness in varying degrees. The associated diseases dictated the treatment procedures and largely determined the results. Evaluation methods emphasize the necessity for scrutinizing separately the vectors of linear growth and skeletal maturation.

CASE C-III (SHORT BOY WITH MILD HYPOTHYROIDISM)

Presenting Problem at 6 Years 10 Months

Lack of growth
Family data: a taller, younger brother

Anthropometric Values and Deviation Charts

When first seen, this boy (Fig. 97) was so much smaller than the brother three years his junior that it seemed useful to evaluate him against our regular American standards, despite his descent from a short Mediterranean family. Such an evaluation could at least provide a basis for judging body proportions and for noting future progress, even though its limitations were obvious.

The deviation chart (Fig. 98) shows that whereas all the absolute measures are small, the three trunk measures relative to stature are large; the main growth failure is in the legs. In a child of this age who is so

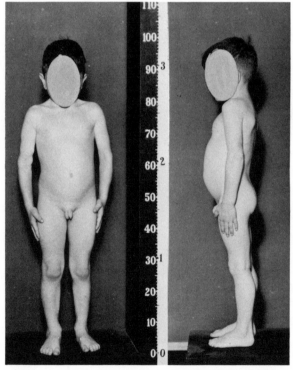

FIG. 97.—C-III (Short Boy with Mild Hypothyroidism) at 6 years 10 months.

small, this finding, especially of a large Si/S, suggests slow maturation and the persistence of an infantile body build.

The impression of immaturity is confirmed by plotting C-III's values against the norms for three-

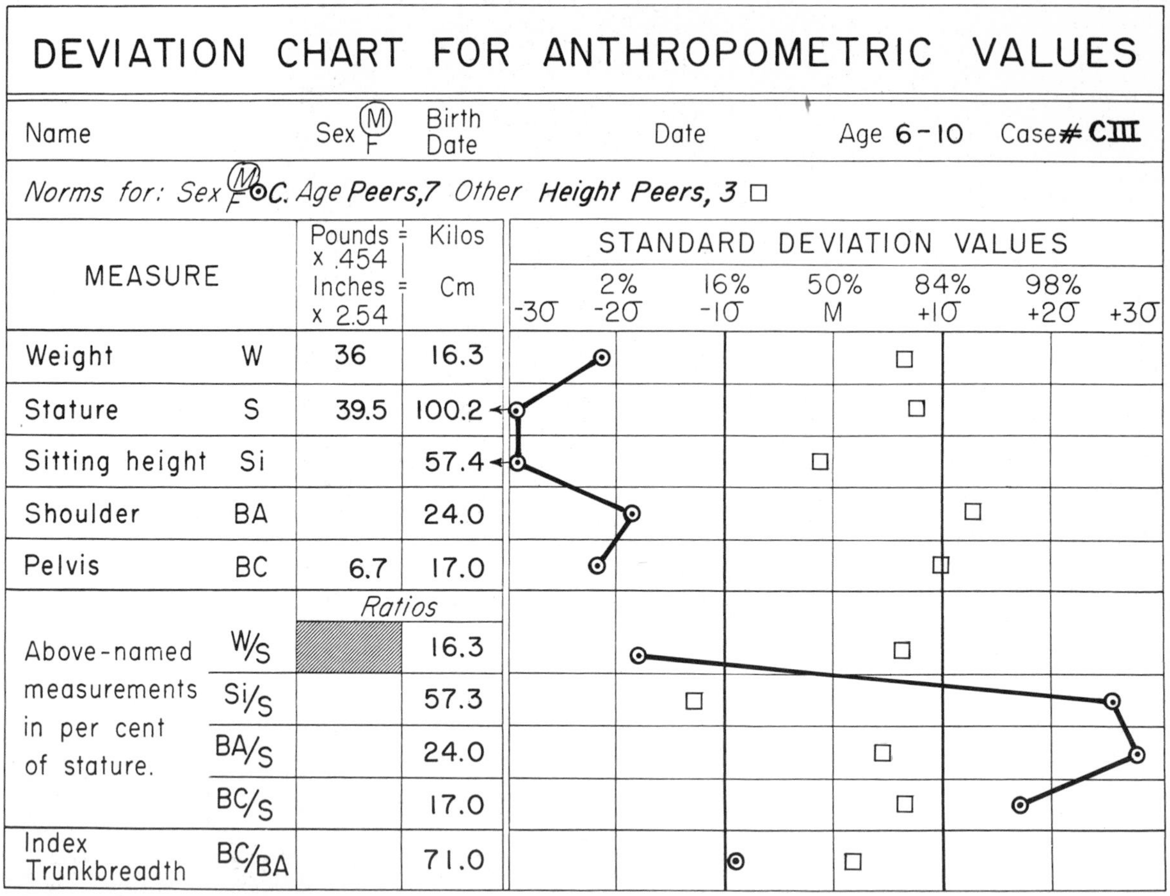

FIG. 98.—Deviation chart for C-III at 6 years 10 months; measures compared with norms for age peers (7-year-old boys) and norms for height peers (3-year-old boys).

year-olds, who are his height peers. Now the absolute measures come close to the mean, and so do most of the ratios. This time, however, the Si/S is comparatively small, showing that, while this boy's body build is much like that of children four years younger, he is slightly longer-legged.

Skeletal Age: 5 years 9 months (Todd, 1937).

Stature Prediction: By extrapolation, 56.9 in. (Bayley, 1946).

Growth Diagnosis
Retarded growth and development
Dwarfism

Clinical Diagnosis
Dwarfism, constitutional
Mild hypothyroidism

Follow-up

Data on this boy are available throughout his subsequent growth period (Table 18) and provide various insights into the contrasting behavior of growth versus maturation; of growth rate versus stature prediction.

Secondary Sex Characters

Evidence from the photo series (Figs. 99, 100), plus reference to clinical notes, place the approximate ages at which the various phases of maturity were reached as follows: stage II, 12 years; stage III, 13 years; stage IV, 14 years; and stage V, 15 years. In other words, sexual maturation proceeded at the normal time and rate.

132

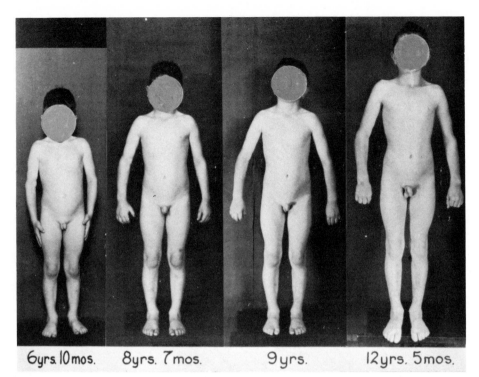

6yrs.10mos. 8yrs. 7mos. 9yrs. 12yrs. 5mos.

FIG. 99.—Views of C-III at various ages up to stage II of sexual maturity. This series of photos and those of the following figure from Bayer and Bayley, "Stature Prediction in Stature Control," *Stanford Medical Bulletin*, Vol. 7 (1949).

FIG. 100.—Views of C-III at various ages after reaching sexual maturity. From Bayer and Bayley, 1949.

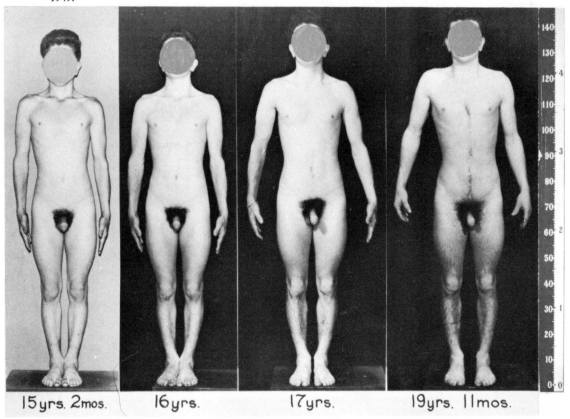

15yrs. 2mos. 16yrs. 17yrs. 19yrs. 11mos.

Case C-III: Short Boy

Mild Hypothyroidism

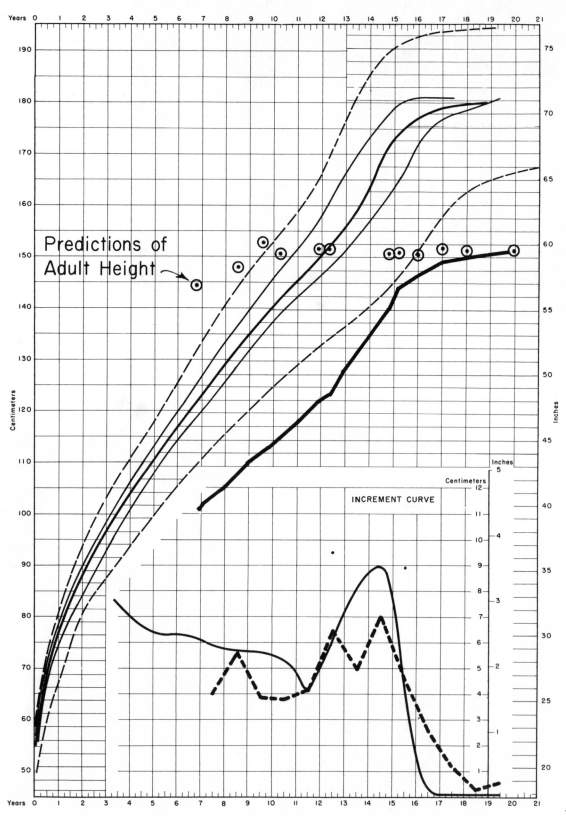

Predictions of Adult Height

INCREMENT CURVE

FIG. 101.—Curves of height by age for C-III: absolute measures, increments, and height predictions

134

Growth Curves of Height by Age

Stature remains short throughout, following a path below the lower limits of normal (Fig. 101). Curiously, the shape of the curve is more like that of the normal pattern than that of the small, skeletally retarded boy. This reflects the fact that the increment pattern, while flat and low through his fifteenth year, still has its peak at the normal time.

Growth Rate

This material permits three helpful inferences: (1) Whereas the growth rate prior to the original examination must have been low (since the boy had only achieved the size expected of a child half his age) the rate thereafter remains at normal levels. (2) The initial improved level coincides with a period when thyroid was the only treatment. (3) Several later isolated rate peaks coincide with periods of administration of other hormones (Table 19, Fig. 102).

Stature-Prediction Chart

This chart (Fig. 103), also drawn from the longitudinal data, highlights three main points: (1) There is an early rise in prediction. (2) Prediction stabilizes after age 9. (3) The skeletal lag is compensated by age 15.

TABLE 18

GROWTH DATA
CASE C-III (Short Boy with Mild Hypothyroidism)

AGE (YR.)	WEIGHT		STATURE		BI-CRIS-TAL (CM.)	SA (YR.-MO.)	PRED. HT. (IN.)
	Lb.	Kg.	In.	Cm.			
6.871	36.0	16.3	39.5	100.2	17.0	5–9	56.9
6.915				100.6			
7.057				101.6			
7.172				102.2			
7.824				105.0			
8.035				105.5			
8.468				107.2			
8.539	43.0	19.5	42.7	108.3	17.5	7–3	58.2
8.717				108.5			
9.032	44.0	20.0		110.1	17.9		
9.274				110.8			
9.523	46.0	20.9	44.3	112.5	18.1	7–9	60.1
9.830	46.0	20.9		113.3	18.4		
10.328	47.0	21.3	45.3	115.0	18.4	8–5	59.2
10.597				115.5			
10.867	51.0	23.1		117.2	18.5		
11.026				117.8			
11.314				119.3			
11.917			48.0	121.8		9–9	59.7
12.330	54.0	24.5	48.1	123.0	19.3	10–5	59.7
12.704				126.6			
12.857				128.0			
Yr.–Mo.							
14–9	80.0		55.4	140.5	22.4	14–5	59.2
15–2	86.0	39.0	56.7	143.8	22.9	15–0	59.3
15–7			57.1			15–6	58.9
16–0	91.0	41.3	57.7	146.5	23.6	16–0	59.1
17–0			58.7			16–7	59.7
18–0	105.0		59.2	150.2	24.5	17–9	59.5
19–11			59.5			adult	59.5

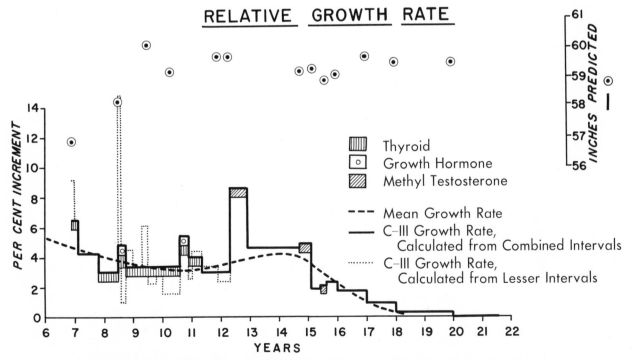

FIG. 102.—Growth Rate Graph, C-III. See text for discussion of treatment. See chap. 13 for description of this growth-diagnosis chart in general.

135

TABLE 19

GROWTH RATE: CALCULATION SHEET

Name: —— Case No.: C-III Key: Numbers 1–10 identify columns M = mean
Birthdate: June 9, 1929 Sex: M A = age dS = difference in stature
(.436.–.564) S = stature MS = average stature
d = difference dA = elapsed time

	OBSERVED DATA				CALCULATIONS				
1	2	3	4	5	6	7	8 (5/7)	9 (8/6)	10 (9×100)
Treatment	Date	Stature (m.)	Age	dS	MS	dA	dS/dA	dS/dA / MS	Growth Rate (Per Cent per Year)
Thyroid...................	1936 Apr. 23	1.002	6.871						
				.004	1.004	.044	.091	.091	9.1
	May 9	1.006	6.915						
				.009	1.010	.142	.063	.062	6.2
	June 30	1.015	7.057						
				.007	1.018	.115	.061	.060	6.0
DC Thyroid...............	Aug. 11	1.022	7.172						
				.028	1.036	.652	.043	.042	4.2
Thyroid...................	1937 Apr. 6	1.050	7.824						
				.005	1.052	.211	.024	.023	2.3
	June 22	1.055	8.035						
				.017	1.064	.433	.039	.037	3.7
Growth Hormone..........	Nov. 27	1.072	8.468						
				.011	1.078	.071	.155	.144	14.4
	Dec. 23	1.083	8.539						
				.002	1.084	.178	.011	.010	1.0
DC Growth Hormone........	1938 Feb. 26	1.085	8.717						
				.016	1.093	.315	.051	.047	4.7
	June 21	1.101	9.032						
				.007	1.104	.242	.029	.026	2.6
	Sept. 17	1.108	9.274						
				.017	1.116	.249	.068	.061	6.1
	Dec. 17	1.125	9.523						
				.008	1.129	.307	.026	.023	2.3
	1939 Apr. 8	1.133	9.830						
				.017	1.142	.498	.034	.030	3.0
	Oct. 7	1.150	10.328						
				.005	1.152	.269	.019	.016	1.6
Growth Hormone..........	1940 Jan. 13	1.155	10.597						
				.017	1.164	.268	.063	.054	5.4
DC Growth Hormone.......	Apr. 21	1.172	10.865						
				.006	1.175	.161	.037	.031	3.1
	June 15	1.178	11.026						
				.015	1.186	.288	.052	.044	4.4
DC Thyroid...............	Sept. 28	1.193	11.314						
				.025	1.206	.603	.041	.034	3.4
	1941 May 10	1.218	11.917						
				.012	1.224	.413	.029	.024	2.4
Testosterone...............	Oct. 4	1.230	12.330						
				.065	1.262	.604	.108	.086	8.6
DC......................	1942 May 16	1.295	12.934						
				.015	1.302	.249	.060	.046	4.6
	Aug. 15	1.310	13.183						
				.095	1.358	1.504	.063	.046	4.6
Testosterone...............	1944 Feb. 15	1.405	14.687						
				.033	1.422	.477	.069	.049	4.9
DC......................	Aug. 8	1.438	15.164						
				.006	1.441	.222	.027	.019	1.9
Testosterone...............	Oct. 28	1.444	15.386						
				.006	1.447	.192	.031	.021	2.1
DC......................	1945 Jan. 6	1.450	15.578						
				.015	1.458	.441	.034	.023	2.3
	June 16	1.465	16.019						
				.025	1.478	.997	.025	.017	1.7
	1946 June 15	1.490	17.016						
				.012	1.496	.948	.013	.009	0.9
	1947 May 27	1.502	17.964						
				.003	1.504	.690	.004	.003	0.3
	1948 Feb. 3	1.505	18.654						
				.006	1.508	1.266	.005	.003	0.3
	1949 May 11	1.511	19.920						
				.000	1.508	1.570	.000	.000	0.0
	1950 Dec. 5	1.511	21.490						

The column 10 rows are bracketed into groups labeled: a (first three rows), b (next two rows), c (next two rows), d (next five rows), e (next three rows), f (next two rows).

Stature Prediction versus Growth Rate

When these two sets of observations are combined, it is possible to make some further deductions.

The early period of prediction rise came during thyroid medication which fortunately was so adjusted that the growth rate was boosted toward normal; but skeletal maturation continued to lag.

Once the thyroid deficit was made up, its continuing administration had no further catalytic effect on speed of growth.

Later peaks in growth rate under androgen, while dramatic in themselves, coincided with periods of faster maturation, so that no further improvement in prediction was achieved. Peaks coinciding with growth hormone administration were never reproduced in other patients and must be considered as fortuitous.

Comment

In this child, various phases of development, such as linear growth and growth rate, sexual maturation and skeletal maturation, can be seen to behave somewhat independently. Judicious evaluation of progress, with or without treatment, required separate analysis of each phase. This is often true in pathological cases, since normality and harmony of growth tend to go together. The more abnormal the total picture, the more disparate may be its several elements and their responses. (See also Cases C-IV and C-V, which follow.)

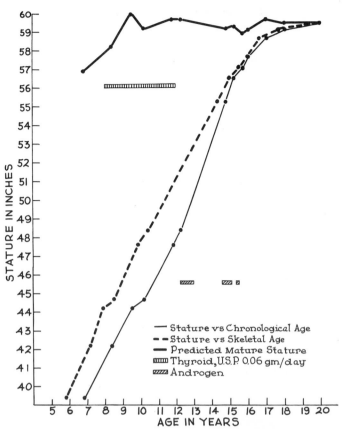

FIG. 103.—Growth of C-III expressed in stature by chronological age, stature by skeletal age, and predicted mature stature. From Bayer and Bayley, 1949.

TABLE 19—RECALCULATIONS

(Using Time Intervals Indicated in Braces Above)

1	2	3 Stature (m.)	4 Age	5 dS	6 MS	7 dA	8 (5/7) dS/dA	9 (8/6) ds/dA/MS	10 (9×100) Growth Rate (Per Cent per Year)
a		1.002	6.871	.020	1.012	.301	.066	.065	6.5
		1.022	7.172						
b		1.050	7.824	.022	1.061	.644	.034	.032	3.2
		1.072	8.468						
c				.013	1.078	.249	.052	.048	4.8
		1.085	8.717						
d				.070	1.120	1.880	.037	.033	3.3
		1.155	10.597						
e		1.172	10.865	.021	1.182	.449	.047	.040	4.0
		1.193	11.314						
f				.037	1.212	1.016	.036	.030	3.0
		1.230	12.330						

CASE C-IV (SHORT BOY WITH MULTIPLE CONGENITAL DEVIATIONS)

Presenting Problem at 6 Years 5 Months

Too small; hips too wide
Slow mental development
Undescended testicles; small penis
Imbalances of eye muscles
Family data: none available

Inspection of the boy and his photos (Figs. 104, 106) confirm the genital deficiency, the too-wide hips, the eye muscle deviations.

Anthropometric Values and Deviation Chart

Compared with his age peers (Fig. 105), this boy is too small in all measures but weight and bi-cristal breadth; his proportions, however, are within the normal range except for the two (*BC/S* and *BC/BA*) which reflect the broad hips.

Compared with his height peers, his absolute measures fall closer to the mean, but his indices scatter more widely.

These analyses imply that the small stature is not only the result of slow maturation but may reflect some general disharmony of growth.

Stature Prediction

Predictions from so young a skeletal age (4 years 6 months) have such limited validity that they are omitted here. The fact that his height is more than three standard deviations below the mean suggests that his short stature is pathological and not likely to correct itself spontaneously. At later ages, where predictions are possible and useful, they are presented (Table 20; see also Figs. 107, 111).

This boy was under observation for over nine years. Because he was retarded in both growth and skeletal maturation, and because of his migratory testicles, he was started on oral androgen. This was continued intermittently for five years; the testicles descended with each administration of steroids, receded with withdrawal of medication. The growth response looked promising (Table 21). Critical analysis of his growth curves, however, lead to a more cautious interpretation of the treatment response.

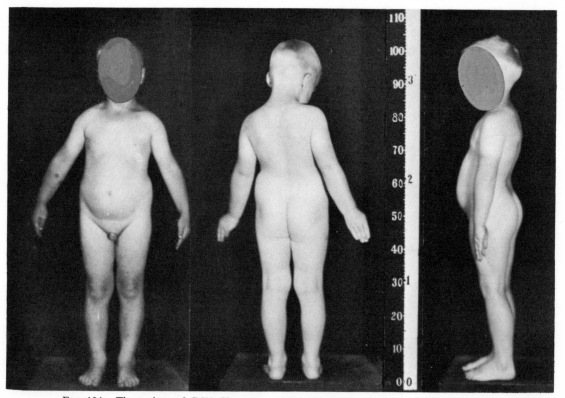

FIG. 104.—Three views of C-IV (Short Boy with Multiple Congenital Deviations) at 6 years 5 months.

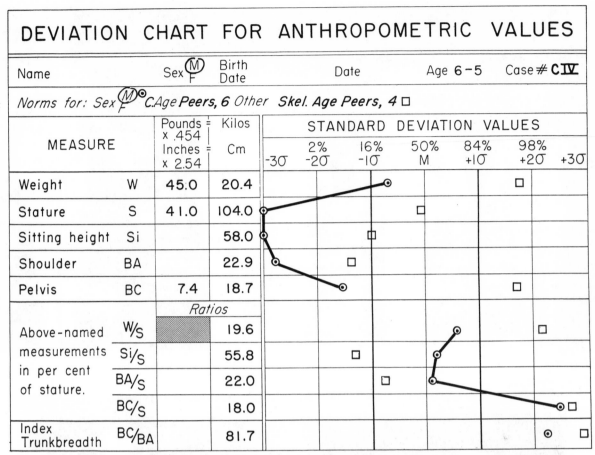

Fig. 105.—Deviation chart for C-IV at 6 years 5 months; measures compared with norms for age peers (6-year-old boys) and norms for skeletal-age peers (4-year-old boys).

TABLE 20

GROWTH DATA

CASE C-IV (Short Boy with Multiple Congenital Deviations)

AGE (YR.–MO.)	WEIGHT (LB.)	STATURE		BI-CRIS-TAL (CM.)	SA (YR.–MO.)	PRED. HT. (IN.)
		In.	Cm.			
6–5	45.0	41.0	104.0	18.7	4–6	
7–0	49.0	42.6	108.0	18.8	5–0	
7–5		44.0			6–0	
7–6	55.0	44.1	112.0	19.4		
8–2	58.0	45.7	116.0	19.4	8–0	63.0
8–8	60.0		118.5	20.7		
9–2	64.0	48.1	122.0		8–9	64.4
9–7	70.0		126.1			
9–10		50.0			11–3	64.4
10–1		51.2				
10–8		51.5			11–9	64.4
11–0	81.0	53.2	135.0	23.0	12–3	65.0
11–6	81.0	53.6	136.1	22.2	12–6	64.6
12–0		54.0	136.8	22.3	13–3	62.6
12–1	84.0	54.5	138.3	22.7		
12–7	85.0	54.8	139.0			
13–0	100.0	55.4	140.5	23.3	13–4	62.1
14–0	105.0	56.4	143.1	24.5	13–9	61.7
14–7			144.9			
15–0	112.0	58.5	148.5	25.1	13–10	63.7
15–3	116.0		150.1	25.7		

Growth Curves of Height by Age

Up to the age of 11, C-IV's height curve (Fig. 107) made an encouraging climb toward normal. Although it has again regressed, the boy is still relatively taller for his age than he was originally.

Annual height increments reached their peak between 9 and 10 years, receded for two years, and started to increase again between 11 and 12 years. Inspection suggests that the early peak is an artificial puberal response to androgen, the second peak a weak, late, true puberal rise.

Graphic Growth Record of Height, Weight, and Bi-Cristal

Figure 108 confirms the small stature, with the weight increasing disproportionately more than the height. The broad bi-cristal attests the maintenance of lateral build.

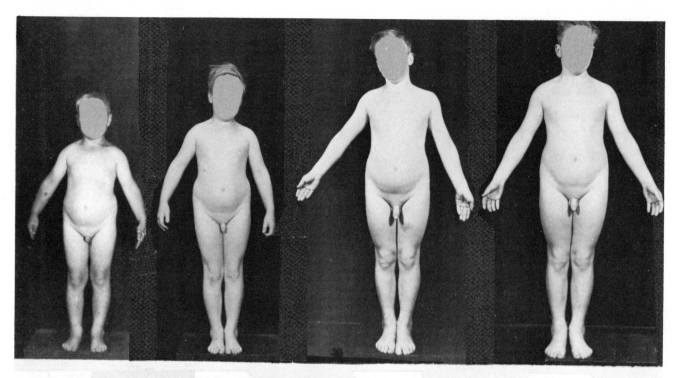

Age 6–5   8–2   10–8   11–11

FIG. 106.—Views of C-IV at various ages, from 6 years 5 months to 15 years

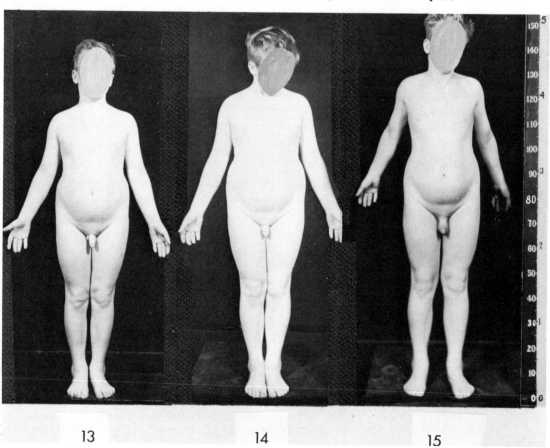

13   14   15

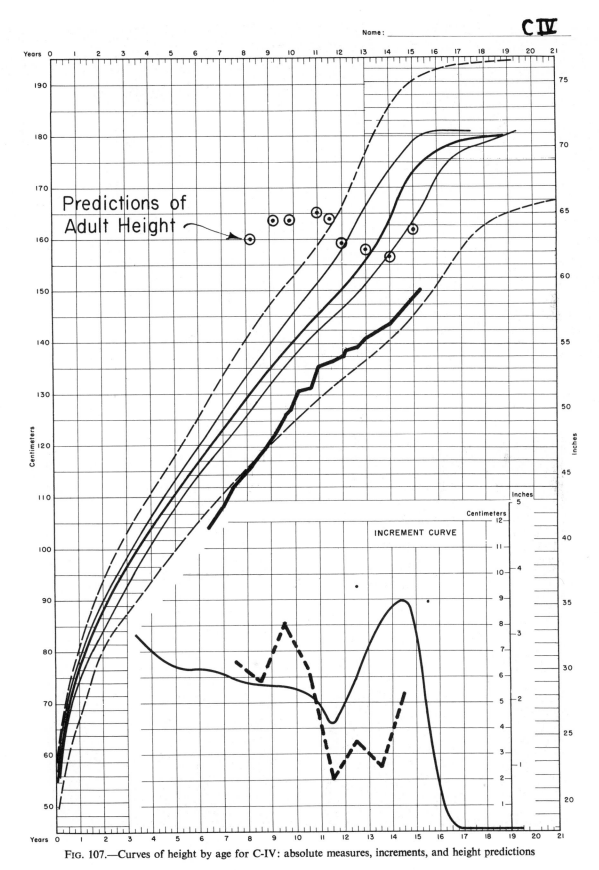

FIG. 107.—Curves of height by age for C-IV: absolute measures, increments, and height predictions

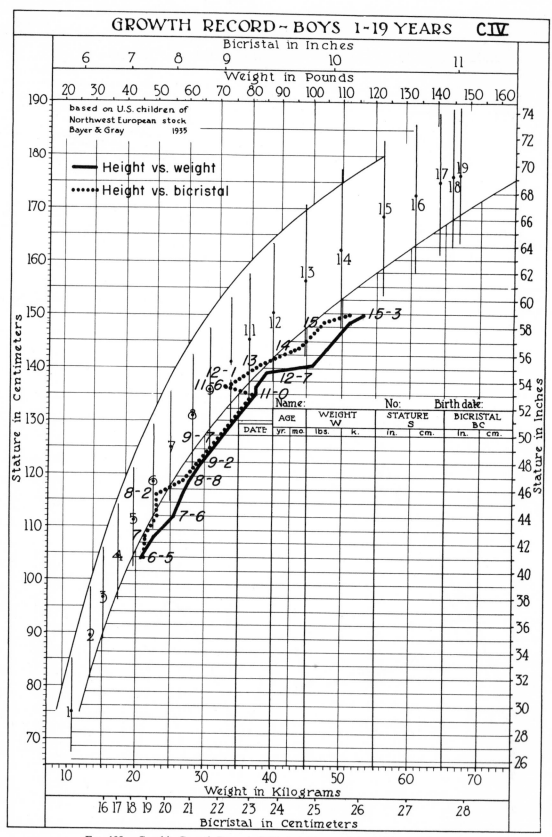

FIG. 108.—Graphic Growth Record, C-IV: height vs. weight; height vs. bi-cristal

TABLE 21

GROWTH RATE: CALCULATION SHEET

Name: ——— Case No.: C-IV Key: Numbers 1–10 identify columns M = mean
Birthdate: Feb. 26, 1940 Sex: M A = age dS = difference in stature
(.153–.847) S = stature MS = average stature
d = difference dA = elapsed time

OBSERVED DATA				CALCULATIONS					
1	2	3	4	5	5	7	8 (5/7)	9 (8/6)	10 (9×100)
Treatment	Date	Stature	Age	dS	MS	dA	dS/dA	dS/dA/ MS	Growth Rate (Per Cent per Year)
		In.	M.							

Treatment	Date	In.	M.	Age	dS	MS	dA	dS/dA	dS/dA/MS	Growth Rate
Thyroid	1946 July 18	41.0	1.040	6.352						
					.040	1.060	.665	.060	.057	5.7
DC Thyroid Rx Testosterone..	1947 Mar. 4	42.6	1.080	7.017						
					.040	1.100	.362	.110	.100	10.0
DC Testosterone No Rx.........	July 14	44.1	1.120	7.379						
					.042	1.141	.843	.050	.044	4.4
APL.............	1948 May 18	45.8	1.162	8.222						
					.008	1.166	.096	.083	.071	7.1
DC.............	June 22	46.1	1.170	8.318						
					.015	1.178	.348	.043	.037	3.7
APL.............	Oct. 27	46.7	1.185	8.666						
					.023	1.196	.091	.253	.212	21.2
DC.............	Nov. 29	47.6	1.208	8.757						
					.012	1.214	.350	.034	.028	2.8
Testosterone.......	1949 Apr. 6	48.1	1.220	9.107						
					.060	1.250	.672	.089	.071	7.1
DC.............	Dec. 7	50.4	1.280	9.779						
					.020	1.290	.364	.055	.043	4.3
Testosterone.......	1950 Apr. 19	51.2	1.300	10.143						
					.033	1.316	.499	.066	.050	5.0
DC.............	Oct. 18	52.5	1.333	10.642						
					.018	1.342	.421	.042	.031	3.1
	1951 Mar. 21	53.2	1.351	11.063						
					.008	1.355	.420	.019	.014	1.4
Stenediol	Aug. 21	53.5	1.359	11.483						
					.009	1.364	.482	.019	.014	1.4
DC.............	1952 Feb. 13	53.9	1.368	11.965						
					.020	1.378	.400	.050	.036	3.6
	July 9	54.7	1.388	12.365						
					.017	1.396	.611	.028	.020	2.0
	1953 Feb. 17	55.4	1.405	12.976						
					.008	1.409	.578	.014	.010	1.0
	Sept. 16	55.7	1.413	13.554						
					.018	1.422	.422	.042	.030	3.0
	1954 Feb. 17	56.4	1.431	13.976						
					.018	1.440	.594	.030	.021	2.1
	Sept. 22	57.1	1.449	14.570						
					.036	1.467	.422	.085	.058	5.8
	1955 Feb. 23	58.5	1.485	14.992						
					.016	1.493	.230	.070	.047	4.7
	May 18	59.1	1.501	15.222						
					.044	1.523	.441	.100	.066	6.6
	Oct. 26	60.9	1.545	15.663						

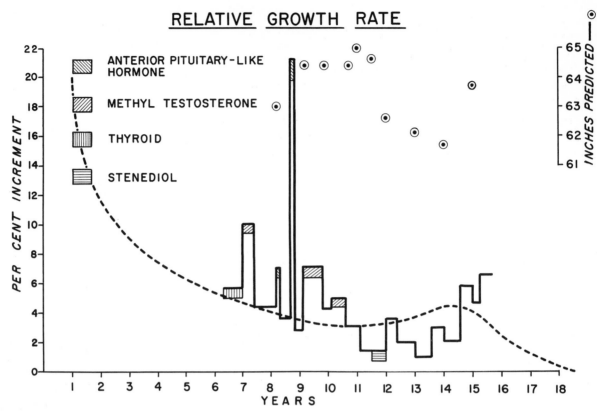

FIG. 109.—Growth Rate Graph, C-IV, showing dramatic results of treatment periods

Growth Rate

When plotted on the chart it is apparent that the growth rate rose dramatically during most treatment periods. Nevertheless, the over-all shape of the curve confirms the pattern of the simple increment chart of Figure 107, i.e., there is an artificial prepuberal spurt and a secondary puberal spurt, with the intervening rate falling below the normal level.

Skeletal Age and Stature Prediction

Figures 110 and 111 provide the explanation of the foregoing observations and tie them together. In Figure 110 skeletal age is plotted against chronological age; in Figure 111 stature is plotted against CA and against SA. Stature predictions are indicated for each chronological age where skeletal age readings permit this calculation.

From these charts it is possible to infer the limits often found in steroid treatment of growth deficiencies.

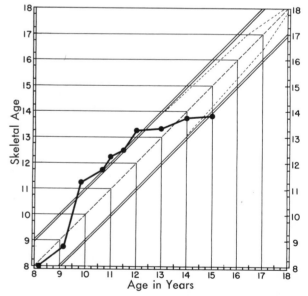

FIG. 110.—C-IV, skeletal age plotted against chronological age.

During the period of androgen treatment, skeletal age gradually overtakes chronological age. After steroid is withdrawn, the skeletal development again lags, remaining almost stationary in the last year.

During the artificial prepuberal spurt, rising height predictions coincide with exaggerated maturation rate until the skeletal age catches up with the chronological age; thereafter predictions begin to fall and androgen administration is discontinued. When maturation again lags and growth continues, the prediction again rises and may be expected to do so as long as the somatic growth impulse continues.

Comment

A counterpoint of falling predictions in spite of increased growth rate and because of disproportionately increased maturation rate is the main danger signal in the steroid treatment of dwarfism. Unless a truly effective growth hormone becomes available, there is no present indication in this case for treatment other than optimal nutritional support, which is always indicated in cases of deficient growth.

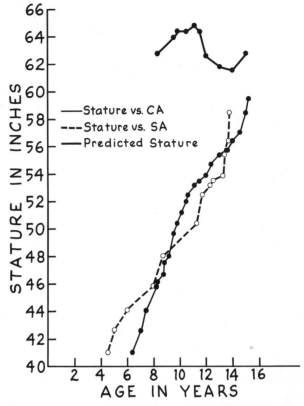

FIG. 111.—Growth in stature, C-IV: stature by chronological age; stature by skeletal age; predicted mature stature.

Marked Thyroid Deficiency

CASE C-V (SHORT BOY WITH MARKED THYROID DEFICIENCY)

Presenting Problem at 16 Years 9 Months
Small size
Slow development
Leg pains

Anthropometric Values and Deviation Chart

Plotted against the norms for his sex and chronological age, this patient's measures (Figs. 112, 113) are significantly small in every dimension. Proportions scatter irregularly around the chart, the noteworthy normal ratios being Si/S and BC/S, the most deviant one being W/S, which is small.

Plotted against the norms for his height peers (10 years), absolute measures come quite close to the mean, except for the shoulders, which are much broader than is expected in 10-year-olds. Now it is the two proportions which reflect the broad BA, i.e., a large BA/S and a small BC/BA, which deviate quite widely from the mean.

It is interesting that Si/S is close to average for either 17- or 10-year-old norms. This is because the mean values at these ages, several years before and after the main puberal spurt, are closely alike, whereas in between at age 14 the typical long-legged adolescent has an Si/S which is smaller. This illustrates the fact that the meaning of a particular proportion in a particular child—in this case the normal Si/S—contributes to the total understanding but must be interpreted in the light of the total picture. Here we see a Si/S which is normal for a boy's age-peers despite the fact that other evidence shows maturation to be greatly delayed. (As this boy responded to thyroid with more leg growth, his Si/S took the intermediate adolescent position when his chronological age was near 20. See chap. 5, "Changing Body Proportions.")

Secondary Sex Characters

At CA 16 years 9 months, he had reached stage II, typical of a preadolescent boy.

Skeletal Age: SA 14 years at CA 17 years

Stature Prediction: 62.7 in.

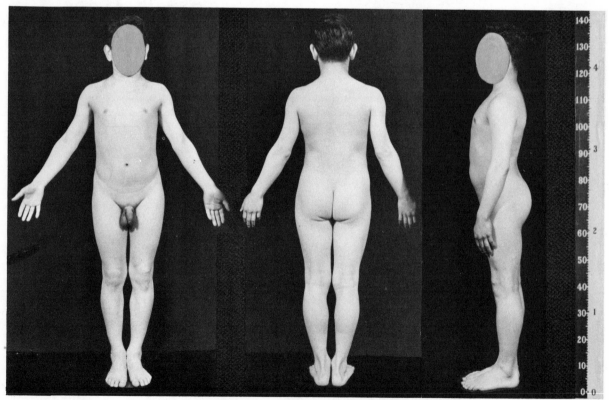

FIG. 112.—Three views of C-V (Short Boy with Marked Thyroid Deficiency) at 16 years 9 months

146

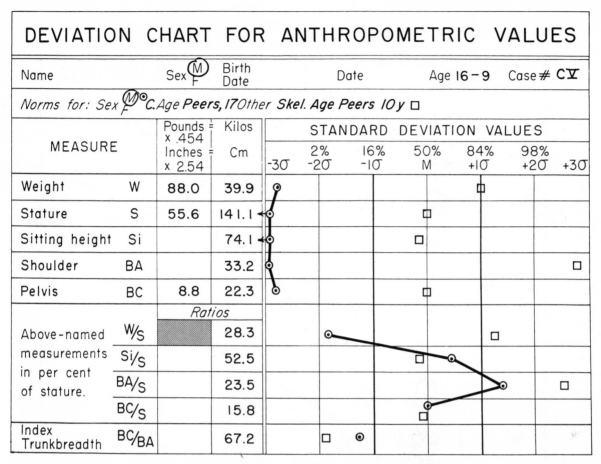

FIG. 113.—Deviation chart for C-V at 16 years 9 months; measures compared with norms for age peers (17-year-old boys) and norms for height peers (10-year-old boys).

Growth Diagnosis

Retarded growth and development
Potential dwarfism

Clinical Diagnosis

Hypothyroidism was established by classical laboratory findings. Timing the occurrence of the metabolic deficiency could only be somewhere between ages 7.6 years and 16.7 years, on the basis of the only past height records which were available.

Longitudinal Growth Data

As with several of our cases, sporadic observations reached back into the years before the nodal point of the first main growth workup. These contribute to a dynamic understanding of the problem (Table 22).

TABLE 22

GROWTH DATA
CASE C-V (Short Boy with Marked Thyroid Deficiency)

AGE (YR.)	WEIGHT (LB.)	STATURE		BI-CRISTAL (CM.)	SA (YR.–MO.)	PRED. HT. (IN.)
		In.	Cm.			
0.074	8.2	21.5	54.6			
1.093	20.0	28.8	73.0			
7.666	47.0	46.3	117.6			
16.713	88.0	55.6	141.1	22.3		
16.962	88.0	56.1	142.5	22.4	14–0	62.7
17.482	105.0		147.5	22.8		
17.995	102.0	59.3	150.4	24.3	14–6	62.5
18.474	105.0		152.0			
18.954	109.0	60.2	152.8	25.0	15–9	61.6
19.495	109.0	60.5	153.5		16–9	61.2
19.989	116.0	60.5	153.6	25.0	17–0	61.0
20.565	115.0	60.8	154.4	25.0		

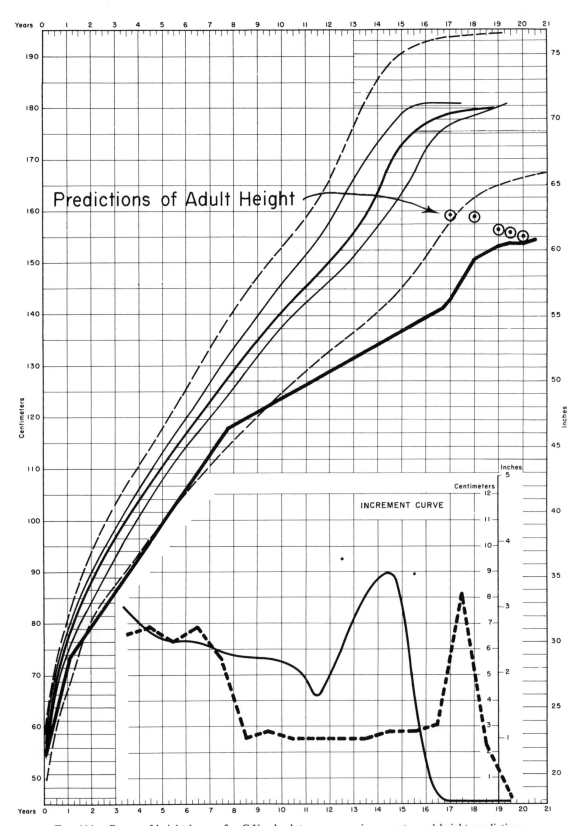

Fig. 114.—Curves of height by age for C-V: absolute measures, increments, and height predictions

Growth Curve of Height by Age

In stature this boy was normal at birth, only slightly below normal at 1 year, and between the seventh and eighth birthdays he was still only moderately small—a size actually compatible with his family height pattern. Nine years later, however, when he reappeared at the clinic, he had gained only about nine inches, when the minimum expected gain would have been closer to sixteen inches. His height at age 16 years 9 months was thus far below even wide limits of statistical deviation. After treatment was started, the growth curve reverted to a more normal shape.

Stature increment calculations emphasize the low level at which linear growth proceeded in the long interval preceding the time of diagnosis and the brisk rise

after thyroid was started. This rise has the general contour of a delayed adolescent spurt and is self-limited, despite the vigorous continuation of thyroid administration.

Stature-prediction points plotted on the same graph delineate a gradually falling growth potential despite four years of active growth.

Growth Rate Graph

Precise analysis of the growth response is best shown by the growth rate graph of Figure 115, based on the growth-rate calculations of Table 23. It is clear that growth response to thyroid reached its peak within nine months after treatment was started and was dissipated after twenty-seven months.

TABLE 23

GROWTH RATE: CALCULATION SHEET

Name: ———   Case No.: C-V   Key: Numbers 1–10 identify columns   M = mean

Birthdate: May 30, 1934   Sex: M   A = age   dS = difference in stature

(.408–.592)   S = stature   MS = average stature

                                d = difference   dA = elapsed time

OBSERVED DATA				CALCULATIONS					
1	2	3	4	5	6	7	8 (5/7)	9 (8/6)	10 (9×100)
Treatment	Date	Stature (In. / M.)	Age	dS	MS	dA	dS/dA	dS/dA/MS	Growth Rate (Per Cent per Year)
None............	1934 June 26	21.5 / .546	.074						
				.184	.638	1.019	.181	.284	28.4
	1935 July 3	28.75 / .730	1.093						
				.446	.953	.573	.068	.071	7.1
	1942 Jan. 28	46.3 / 1.176	7.666						
				.235	1.294	9.047	.026	.020	2.0
Thyroid..........	1951 Feb. 14	/ 1.411	16.713						
				.014	1.418	.249	.056	.039	3.9
	May 16	/ 1.425	16.962						
				.050	1.450	.520	.096	.066	6.6
	Nov. 22	/ 1.475	17.482						
				.029	1.490	.513	.057	.038	3.8
	1952 May 28	/ 1.504	17.995						
				.016	1.512	.479	.033	.022	2.2
	Nov. 19	/ 1.520	18.474						
				.008	1.524	.480	.017	.011	1.1
	1953 May 13	/ 1.528	18.954						
				.007	1.532	.537	.013	.008	0.8
	Nov. 25	/ 1.535	19.491						
				.001	1.536	.498	.002	.001	0.1
	1954 May 26	/ 1.536	19.989						
				.008	1.540	.576	.014	.009	0.9
	Dec. 22	/ 1.544	20.565						
				.002	1.545	.882	.002	.001	0.1
	1955 Nov. 9	/ 1.546	21.447						

Androgyny Profile

If these pictures at 18 years of age are compared with those taken fifteen months earlier, they show a striking metamorphosis from a childlike form to a form which is well on its way to normal masculine differentiation (Figs. 116 and 117).

Comment

These observations illustrate the fact that in the realm of growth stimulation, ultimate triumph cannot be assumed from temporary success (see also case C-IV). In most clinical growth problems, as in the case at hand, treatment methods are relatively more potent in stimulating maturation than in stimulating linear growth.

Taken together, these growth curves suggest that in the boy C-V thyroid served as a potentiator, or catalyst, of growth but not as its direct stimulant. The falling growth rate, coinciding with a later temporary period of inadvertent overtreatment, particularly highlights the limits of thyroid effectiveness, especially when treatment is delayed.

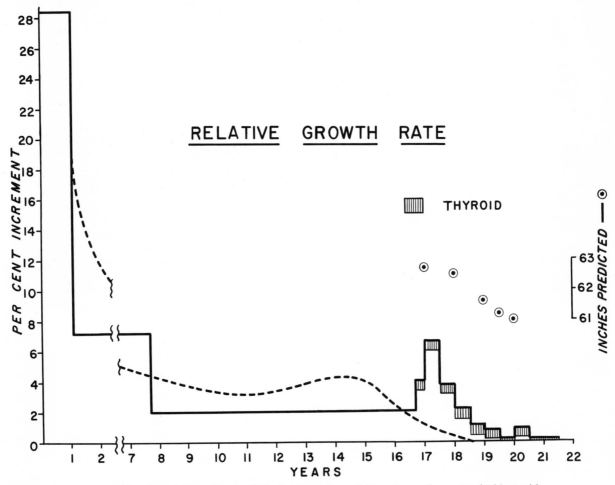

FIG. 115.—Growth Rate Graph, C-V, showing a late adolescent growth spurt coincident with thyroid administration.

150

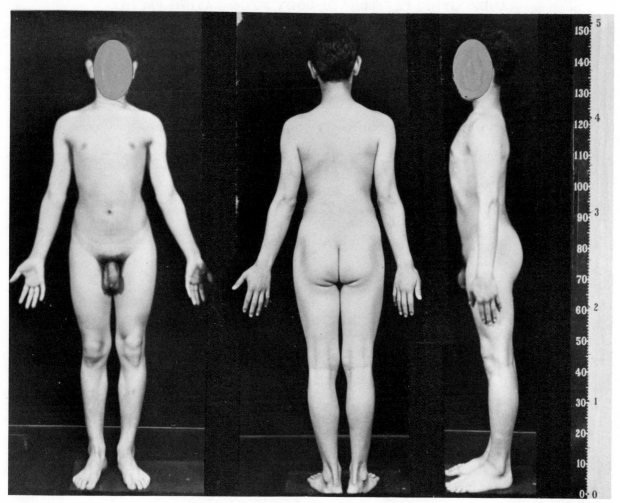

FIG. 116.—Three views of C-V at 18 years

Case C-V: Short Boy

Marked Thyroid Deficiency

ANDROGYNIC PATTERNS OF BODY FORM: RATING PROFILE

Bayley-Bayer Standards*

17–18 Year Norms

Name		Sex Ⓜ F Date		Age 18	Skeletal Age	Case Number CV
ITEM			R A T I N G			
("A" through "H" from rear-view photographs)	**Hyper-masculine** 1	**Masculine** 2	**Intermediate, A-sexual, or Bi-sexual** 3, 3a, 3b	**Feminine** 4	**Hyper-feminine** 5	
I. A. **Surface modeling**	Exaggerated hardness of relief. ○	Strong muscle molding. Bone, vein and tendon prominences.	b. Muscular and fat. ● a. Little muscle or fat. ○	Smooth and soft, with little muscle. ○	Very soft, fat, no muscle. ○	
II. **Trunk Contours** B. Shoulder girdle	Massive. ○	Appears wide, heavy and muscular. ●	b. Muscular and fat. ○ a. Narrow, "bony."	Slight, soft and narrow. ○	Frail, softly fat. ○	
C. Waist line	Marked torso narrowing to low waist: may have ○ minimal indentation.	Slight indentation due to narrowing of torso. ○	b. Broad hip and shoulder; little ○ indentation. ● a. Slight ○ symmetrical high concavity.	Definite line accentuated by hip widening. ○	Marked indentation. ○	
D. Hip flare	No widening. ○	Slight widening of hips from waist. ○	Intermediate. ● ○	Flares into wide hips laterally and posteriorly. ○	Marked flare. ○	
E. Buttocks	Very flat. ○	Flat and angular. ○	Intermediate. ● ●	Rounded and full. ○	Very broad and rounded. ○	
III. **Leg Patterns** F. Thigh Form	Cylinder and/or bulging muscles. ○	Approaches cylinder. Lateral outline convex. ●	Intermediate. ○	Funnel, fat and rounded. Lateral outline concave. ○	Fat, wide-top funnel. ○	
G. Interspace (whole leg)	Very open. ○	Open center above and below knees. ○	Intermediate. ● ○	Closed center except small space below knees. ○	Thighs and knees together, feet apart. ○	
H. Muscle bulge (lower leg)	Strong bulge, no fat. ○	Prominent inner bulge of gastrocnemius. ●	b. Moderate muscle bulge. ○ a. No muscle bulge; spindly.	Slight inner bulge; shapely, smooth, outer curve. ○	Very little muscle, but smoothly rounded and ○ outer curve.	
J. Penis size	1 Very ○	1.5 Large ●	2 Average ○	2.5 Small ○	3 Very ○		
K. Breast size				3 Very ○	3.5 Small ○	4 Average ○	4.5 Large ○	5 Very ○
L. Body hair density	1 ○ Heavy on thighs, etc.	2 ○ Easily discernible	2.5 ● Sparse.	(3) ○ ♂	○ ♀ Absent	
M. Pubic pattern	Disperse ○	Acuminate. ○	Sagittal ●	○ ♂	Horizontal ○ ♀	
N. Bicristal ——— Index Biacromial **70**	– ←68│69 ○	73│74 ●	76│77 ○	82│83 → + ○	○	
P. **Strength (Kg)** Grip (R+L)+Thrust +Pull	+ ←244│243 ○	186│185 ○	148│147 ○	110│109 → – ○	○	
Grip (R+L)	+ ←126│125 ○	95│94 ○	80│79 ○	59│58 → – ○	○	
Androgyny Score (Sum of "A"–"H") **19.5**	8 ○ 12│13	○ 19│20 ●	B ○ 25│26 A	34│35 ○	40	
Characteristic Description (Circle one)	**Hypermasculine**	(**Masculine**)	**Intermediate Bisexual → Asexual Disharmonious**	**Feminine**	**Hyperfeminine**	

FIG. 117.—Androgyny profile of C-V at 18 years

152

Chapter 17

Growth and Maturation of Girls with Idiopathic Precocious Menarche

While these two records both illustrate the syndrome of idiopathic precocious puberty, they point up differences as well as similarities between cases. The patients are alike in demonstrating the characteristic discrepancy between progress in maturation and in growth. But they differ so much in the intensity of the underlying disturbance that they present very different clinical problems. Thus, the first case emphasizes the benign nature of a mild deviation, whereas the second illustrates the bizarre results of a severe upset in the maturation timetable. The latter case has been more completely reported elsewhere (Bayer and Bayley, 1953).

CASE C-VI (GIRL WITH MODERATELY PRECOCIOUS MENARCHE)

Presenting Problem at 9 Years 1 Month

Too big in dimensions; overdeveloped in appearance (Fig. 118)

Behavioral difficulties; babyish at home

Prefers girls 14–15 years old; not well adjusted in school

Anthropometric Values and Deviation Chart

Compared with her age peers, this girl is too big in every dimension (Fig. 119). Ratios scatter irregularly around the mean, confirming the visual impression that this girl's build does not resemble that of a normal 9-year-old.

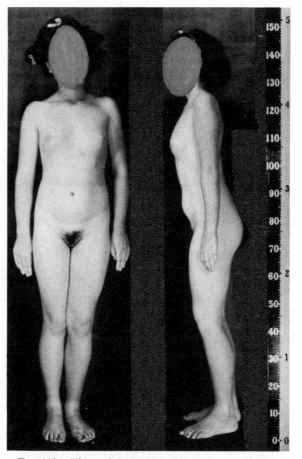

FIG. 118.—Views of C-VI (Girl with Moderately Precocious Menarche) at 9 years 1 month.

153

DEVIATION CHART FOR ANTHROPOMETRIC VALUES

Name	Sex M Ⓕ	Birth Date	Date	Age 9 – 1	Case # CⅥ

Norms for: Sex Ⓜ●C. Age *Peers, 9 Other Skel. Age Peers, 12* □

MEASURE		Pounds = x .454 Inches = x 2.54	Kilos Cm	STANDARD DEVIATION VALUES						
				-3σ	2% -2σ	16% -1σ	50% M	84% +1σ	98% +2σ	+3σ
Weight	W	100	45.4				□			
Stature	S	59.9	152.1				□			
Sitting height	Si		79.5				□			
Shoulder	BA		34.1					□		
Pelvis	BC	9.5	24.1			□				
Above-named measurements in per cent of stature.	*Ratios*									
	W/S		29.8				□			
	Si/S		52.3				□			
	BA/S		22.4					□		
	BC/S		15.9			□				
Index Trunkbreadth	BC/BA		70.7		□					

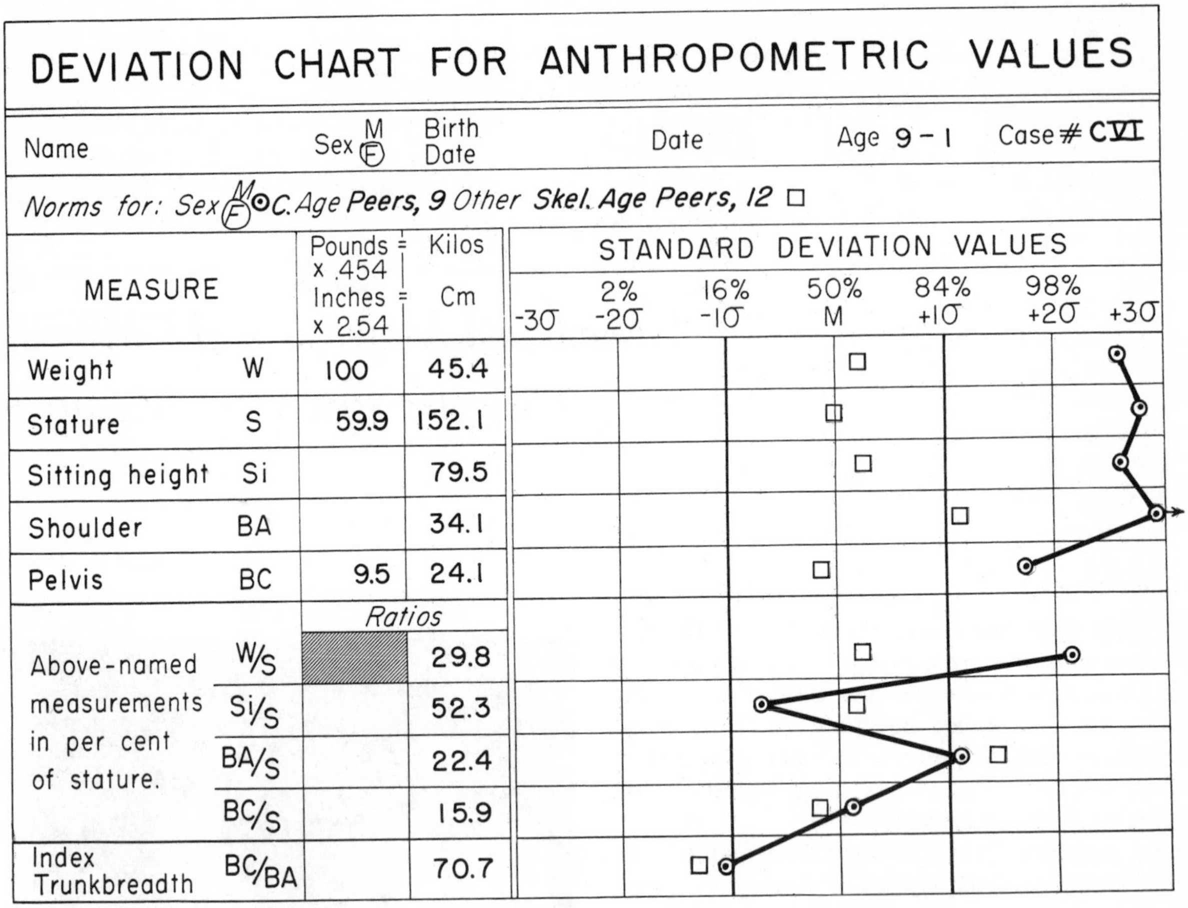

FIG. 119.—Deviation chart for C-VI at 9 years 1 month; measures compared with norms for 9-year-old girls and norms for C-VI's skeletal-age peers (12-year-old girls).

When her measurements are replotted against her skeletal-age peers (12-year norms), a very different picture results. Now both absolute and relative measures fall close to the mean. The only scatter beyond one standard deviation of the mean are those that reflect the relatively broad shoulders, giving a large *BA/S* and small *BC/BA.*

Secondary Sex Characters
  Breasts at stage III of development
  Pubic hair at stage III
This is a level of development reached by the average girl between 11 years of age and 12 years 6 months.

Skeletal Age: 12 years 5 months

Stature Prediction: 65.9 in.

Growth Diagnosis: Accelerated growth and maturation

TABLE 24

GROWTH DATA
CASE C-VI (Girl with Moderately Precocious Menarche)

AGE (YR.– MO.)	WEIGHT (LB.)	STATURE		BI- CRIS- TAL (CM.)	SA (YR.– MO.)	PRED. HT. (IN.)
		In.	Cm.			
7–11	99.0		140.6			
8–0	92.0		141.6			
8–5	91.0		144.2	22.3		
8–9	102.0	58.5	148.6		12–1	64.9
9–1	100.0	59.9	152.1	24.1	12–5	65.9
9–3 Me- narche						
9–4	104.0		155.2	24.7		
9–8	106.0		156.8			
10–0	116.0	63.2	160.4	26.0	13–9	65.0
10–6	126.0		161.0			
11–6	138.0		164.9			
11–9	142.0		165.0	27.6		
16–7	142.0	65.3	165.8	27.6	ma- ture	65.3

Clinical Diagnosis: Idiopathic precocious maturation

Longitudinal Growth Data

The early menarche, which occurred at 9 years 3 months, quickly confirmed the diagnosis of precocious maturation. Data preceding and following the first complete examination are listed in Table 24 and are illustrated in several graphs whose patterns are characteristic of the growth of early-maturing children.

Growth Curves of Height by Age

Stature climbs rapidly to age 10 and then tapers off rapidly. Indeed, the stature increments (Fig. 120) show that in the total period under observation the largest advance was in the year following the eighth birthday, and that deceleration already started after age 9.

Stature predictions are quite stable and are confirmed.

Growth Curves of Weight by Age

Weight increase also comes very early, with the mature level attained before the twelfth birthday, and the peak increment coming between ages 10 and 11, or two years later than the peak height increment (Fig. 121).

Graphic Growth Record of Height, Weight, and Bi-Cristal

When height, weight, and bi-cristal measures are combined in Figure 122, it appears that whereas weight is appropriate for build at 9 years, it later increases somewhat beyond build expectations. This relative overweight (Fig. 123) is frequently found in children whose adult height is reached early, as though the somatic impulse to grow continues after linear growth is no longer possible.

Comment

This record provides an instance in which growth and maturation data alone gave the clue to a benign and favorable diagnosis. Although maturation rate was more than three years accelerated, growth had kept adequate pace with development so that a normal height prediction could be made with considerable assurance.

Case C-VI

Moderately Precocious Menarche

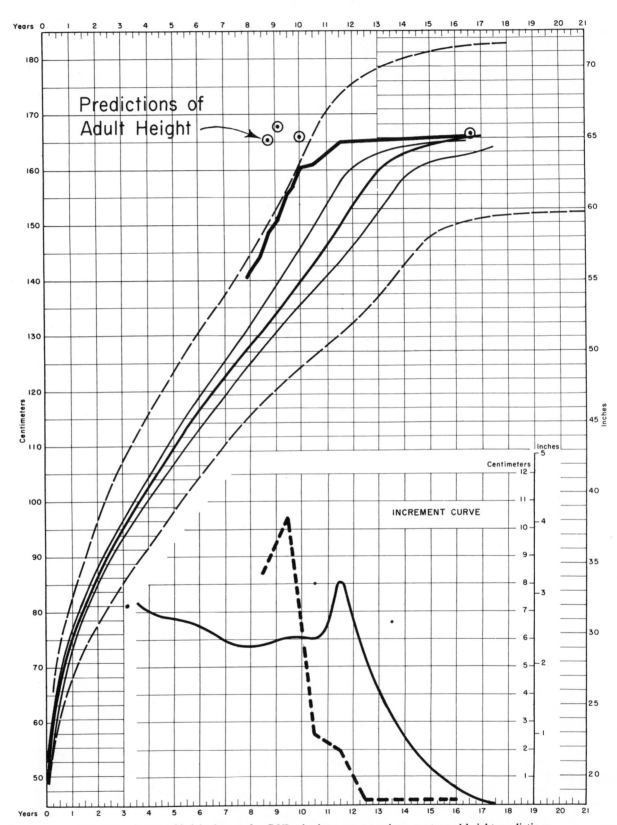

Fig. 120.—Curves of height by age for C-VI: absolute measures, increments, and height predictions

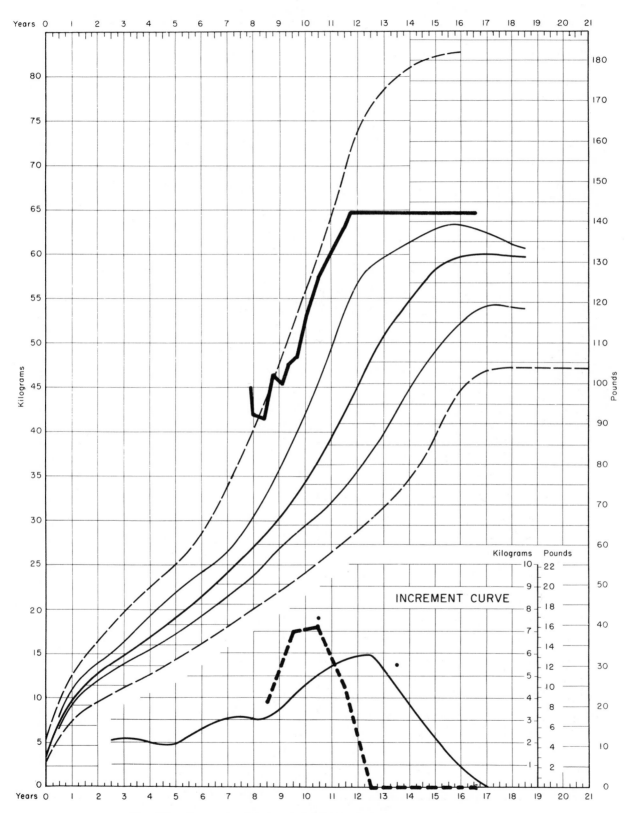

INCREMENT CURVE

FIG. 121.—Curves of weight by age for C-VI: absolute measures and increments

Case C-VI

Moderately Precocious Menarche

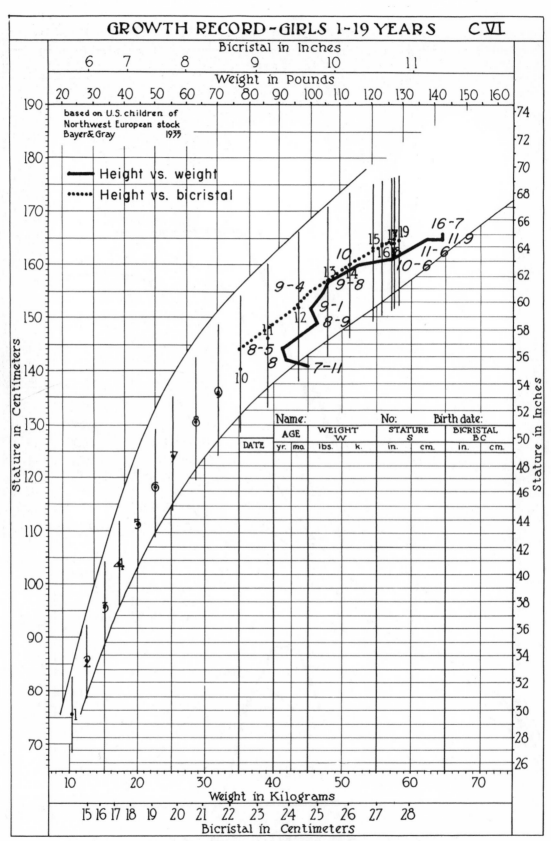

FIG. 122.—Graphic Growth Record, C-VI; height vs. weight; height vs. bi-cristal

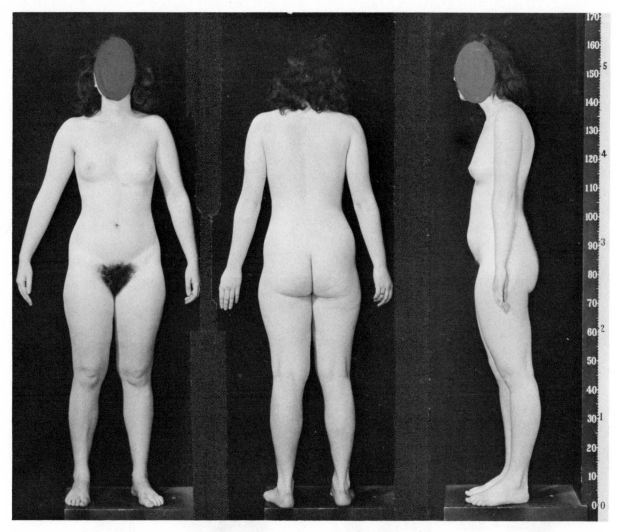

Fig. 123.—Three views of C-VI at 16 years 7 months

Excessively Precocious Menarche

CASE C-VII (GIRL WITH EXCESSIVELY PRECOCIOUS MENARCHE)

Presenting Problem at 3 Years 6 Months
  Regular menses since the age of 7 months
  Rapid growth
  Behavioral disorders

Anthropometric Values and Deviation Chart
Compared with her age peers, this little girl (Fig. 124) is too big in every dimension except shoulder breadth; relative to her height, the measures show an irregular scatter.

Compared with her skeletal-age peers, the picture is reversed. She is much smaller than the children of 9 who have normally reached her stage of skeletal differentiation; and her body proportions are different (Fig. 125).

Her body build thus falls between the normal for her chronological age and for her skeletal maturation.

Secondary Sex Characters
Pubic hair has reached stage II; breasts are at stage III; she is already almost three years past the menarche. This places the secondary sex characters at a level between ages 11 and 12; the precocious menarche is twelve years earlier than the mean, nine years earlier than early normal expectations.

Skeletal Age: 9 years 6 months

Stature Prediction: 54 in.

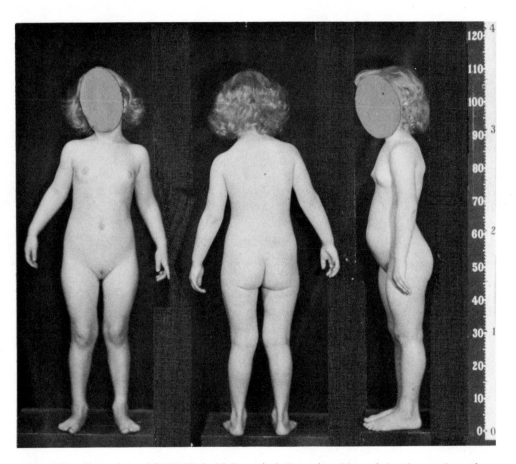

FIG. 124.—Three views of C-VII (Girl with Excessively Precocious Menarche) at 3 years 6 months

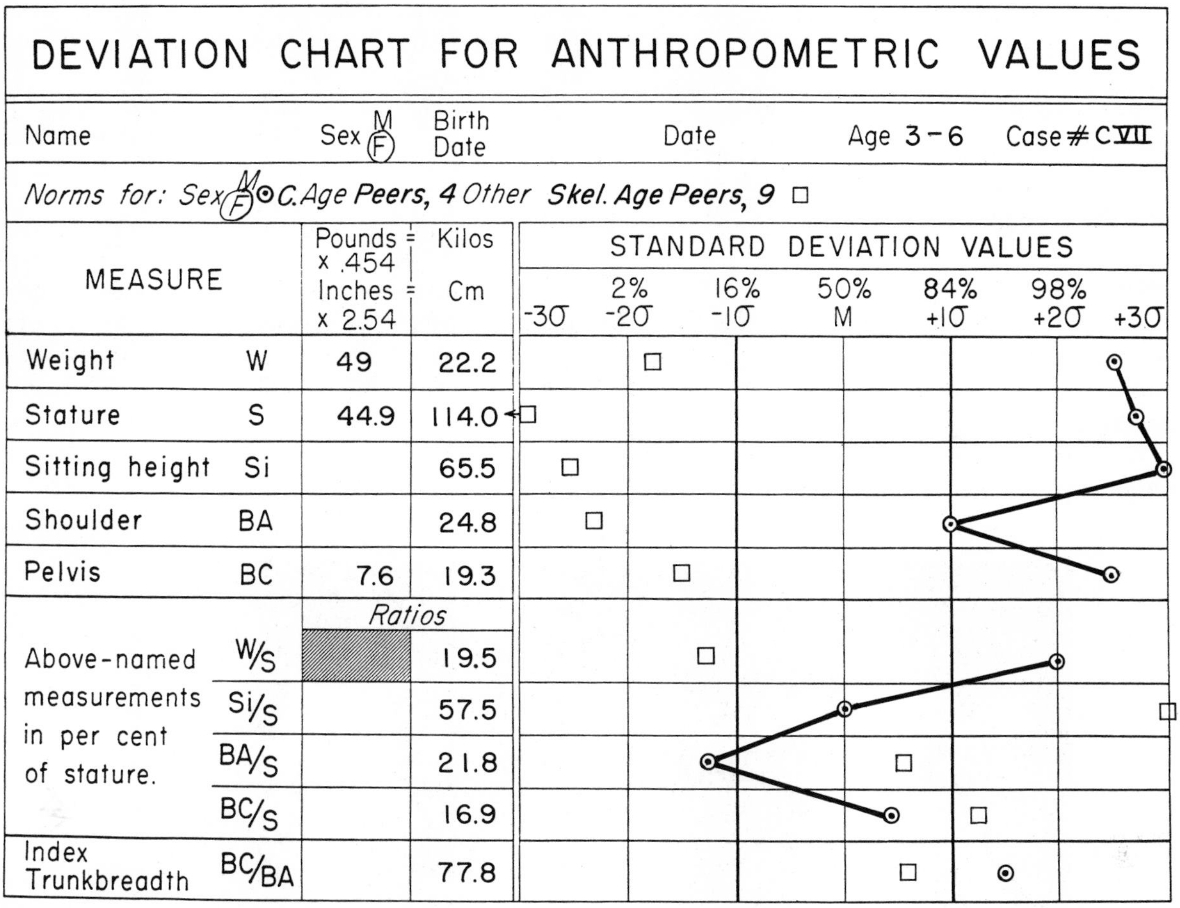

FIG. 125.—Deviation chart for C-VII at 3 years 6 months; measures compared with 4-year-old girls' norms and norms for C-VII's skeletal-age peers (9-year-old girls).

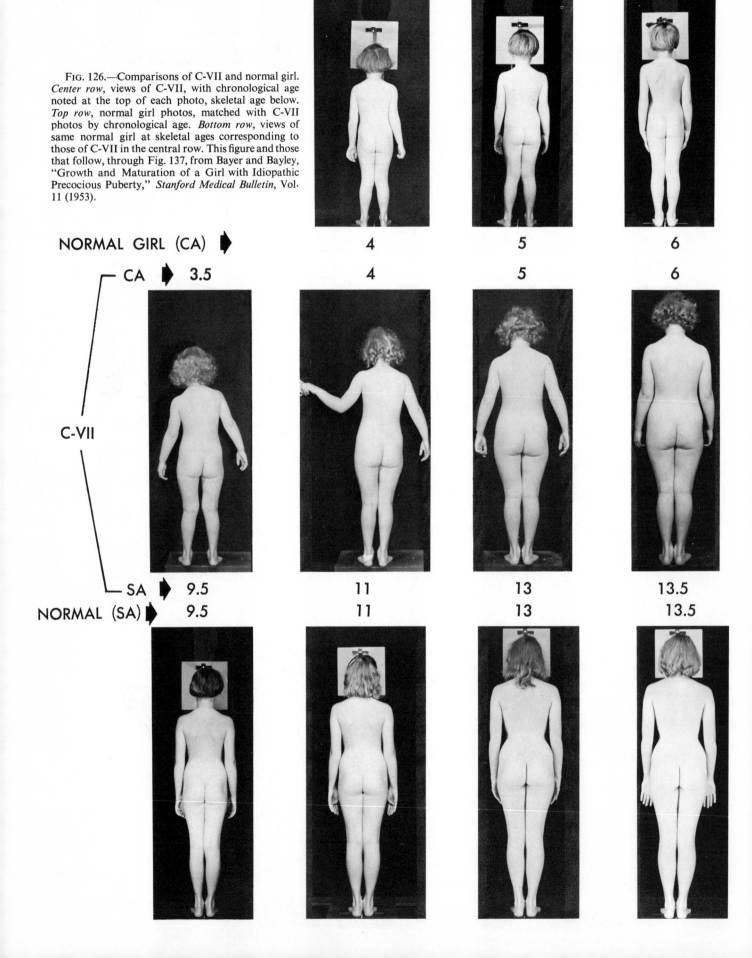

FIG. 126.—Comparisons of C-VII and normal girl. *Center row*, views of C-VII, with chronological age noted at the top of each photo, skeletal age below. *Top row*, normal girl photos, matched with C-VII photos by chronological age. *Bottom row*, views of same normal girl at skeletal ages corresponding to those of C-VII in the central row. This figure and those that follow, through Fig. 137, from Bayer and Bayley, "Growth and Maturation of a Girl with Idiopathic Precocious Puberty," *Stanford Medical Bulletin*, Vol. 11 (1953).

NORMAL GIRL (CA) ▶   4   5   6

CA ▶   3.5   4   5   6

C-VII

SA ▶   9.5   11   13   13.5

NORMAL (SA) ▶   9.5   11   13   13.5

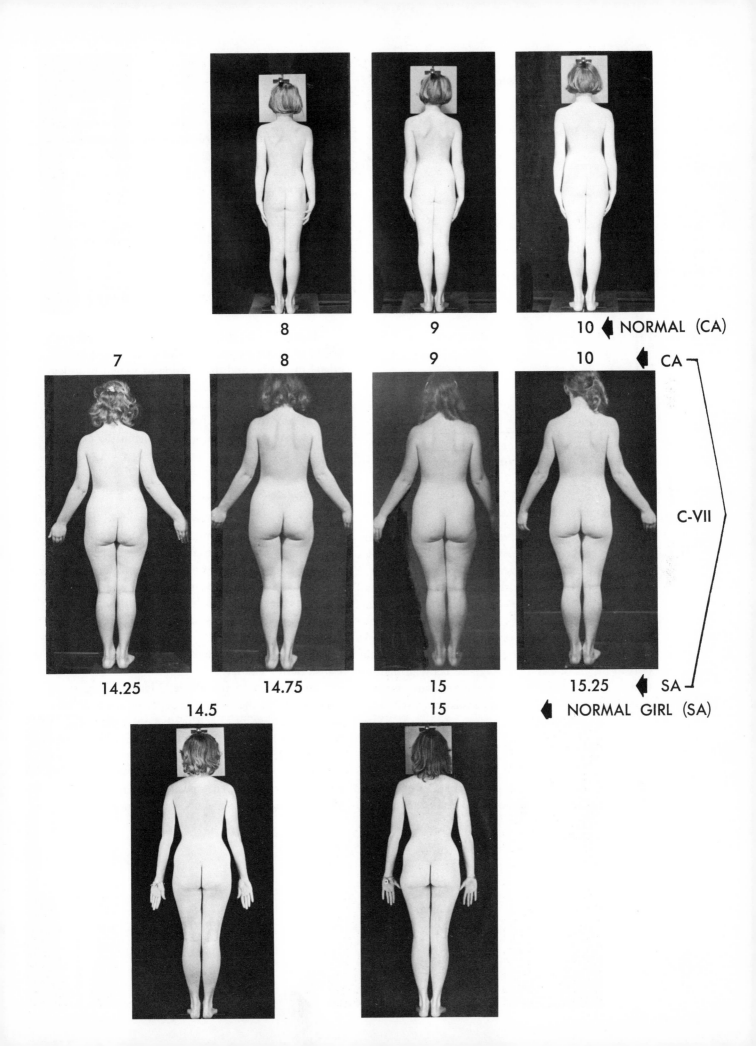

8   9   10 ◀ NORMAL (CA)

7   8   9   10 ◀ CA

C-VII

14.25   14.75   15   15.25 ◀ SA

14.5   15   ◀ NORMAL GIRL (SA)

Excessively Precocious Menarche

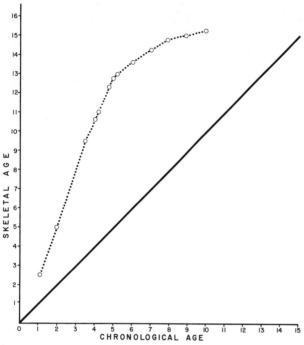

FIG. 127.—C-VII, skeletal age plotted against chronological age.

Longitudinal Growth Data

This case has been represented elsewhere as a clinical study (Bayer and Bayley, 1953). For the purposes at hand, the growth data are abstracted and presented as a longitudinal study which documents in some detail the processes by which the original tallness and accelerated maturation associated with precocious menarche led to the expected end result of relative dwarfism in maturity. Since the data are so unusual, and since the crux of the picture is the divergence between maturation and chronology, the material is presented in charts designed especially to emphasize this contrast.

Skeletal Age versus Chronological Age

Figure 127 shows the crux of the case: the rapid advance of skeletal maturation over chronological age. The curve is very steep up to SA 13 years 6 months (at CA 6 years), after which it flattens out. The maximum skeletal precocity is recorded at 4 years 2 months when the skeletal age is 11 years. If this relation were expressed as a developmental quotient similar to that used in expressing intelligence, the degree of acceleration at this point would be 132/50, or 264 per cent.

All X-ray readings were made by Dr. Bayley; copies of the eleven hand films have recently been published in the 1959 Greulich-Pyle Atlas.

Graphic Growth Record of Height, Weight, and Bi-Cristal

Figure 128 provides comparisons of the patient's height to height norms, the relation of weight and bicristal to height, and the relation of weight to weight predictions. According to this graph, the patient is at first very tall, but at 10 years her height is just about at the 10-year mean. She is both heavy and broad for her height, so that weight is never far from the expected value for her build.

Absolute Measures

Figures 129–133 show five standard measurements compared to normal curves when plotted first against chronological age and then against skeletal age. In every instance these standard parameters are too large for the former, too small for the latter. It is also clear that the patient's early growth advantage is gradually lost as her peers overtake her; they will later surpass her.

The normals are drawn from the data comprising our deviation charts.

In addition to the above, Figure 130 carries a curve showing the stature predictions made at each skeletal-age reading. Each prediction is derived from considerations of simultaneous values for chronological age, skeletal age, and stature. In spite of the deviant maturation, predictions are remarkably stable, ranging from 53.9 to 56.4 in. The upward trend happens to begin at the moment of the androgen treatment.

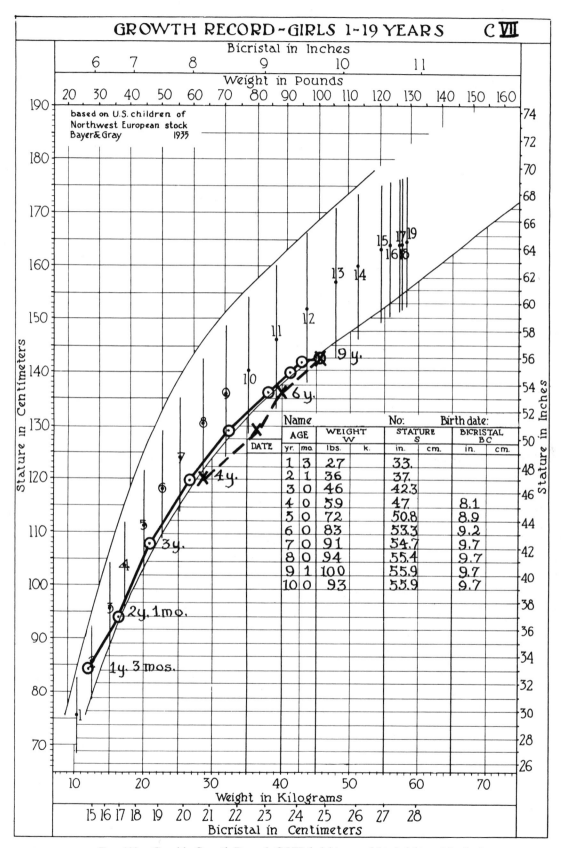

FIG. 128.—Graphic Growth Record, C-VII: height vs. weight; height vs. bi-cristal

Excessively Precocious Menarche

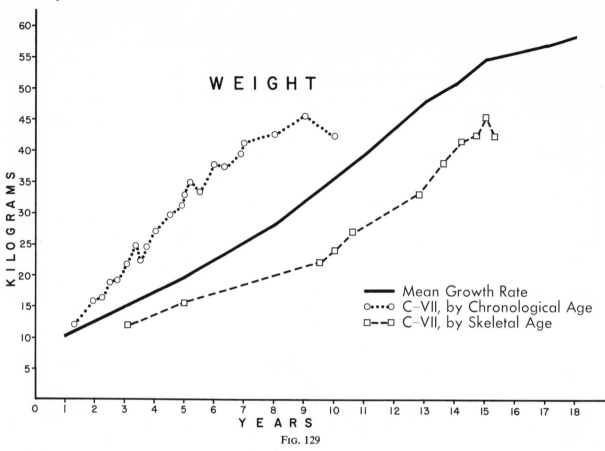

WEIGHT

FIG. 129

- Mean Growth Rate
- C-VII, by Chronological Age
- C-VII, by Skeletal Age

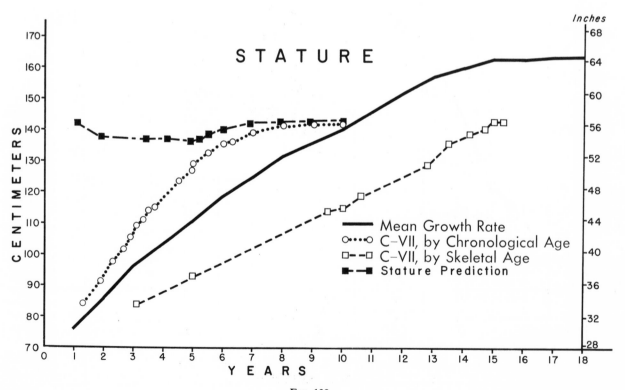

STATURE

FIG. 130

- Mean Growth Rate
- C-VII, by Chronological Age
- C-VII, by Skeletal Age
- Stature Prediction

166

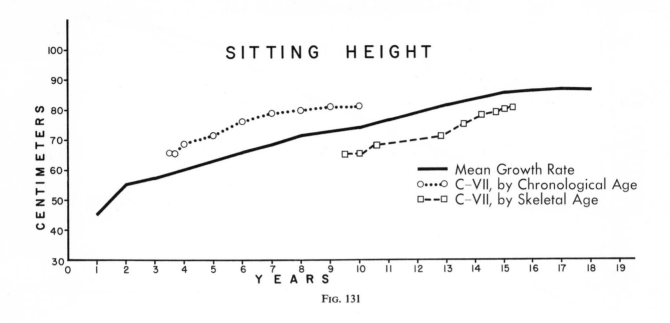

SITTING HEIGHT

Mean Growth Rate
C–VII, by Chronological Age
C–VII, by Skeletal Age

FIG. 131

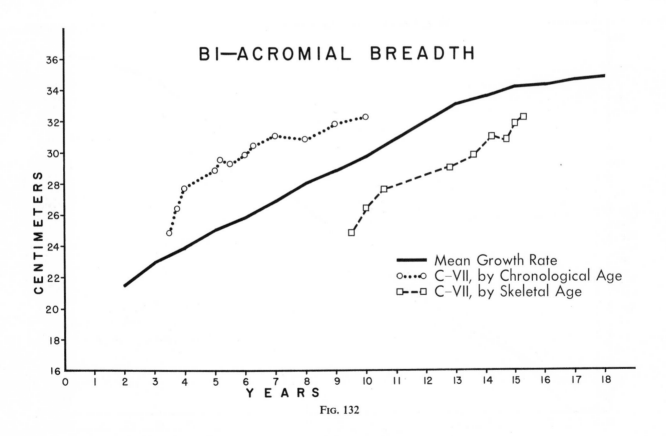

BI—ACROMIAL BREADTH

Mean Growth Rate
C–VII, by Chronological Age
C–VII, by Skeletal Age

FIG. 132

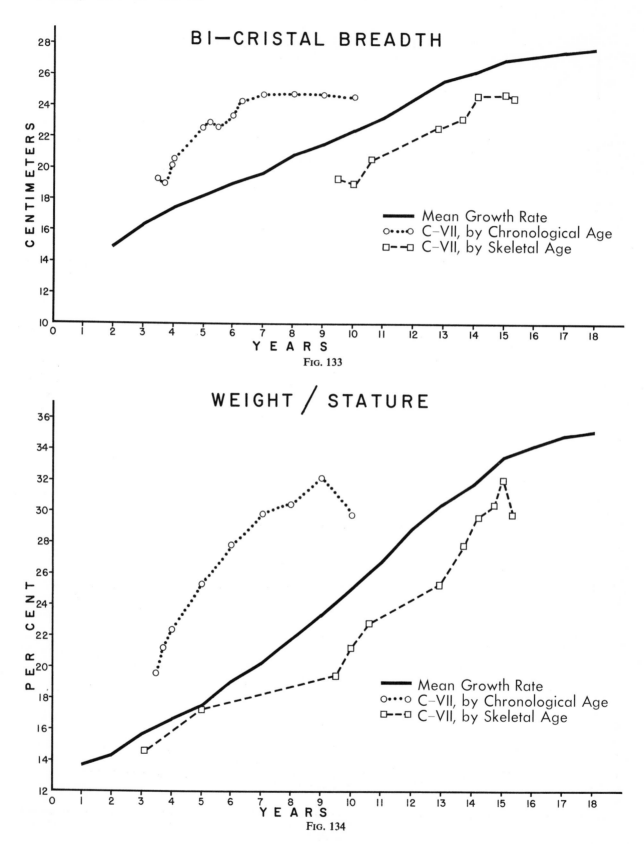

BI-CRISTAL BREADTH

—— Mean Growth Rate
o···o C-VII, by Chronological Age
□--□ C-VII, by Skeletal Age

Fig. 133

WEIGHT / STATURE

—— Mean Growth Rate
o···o C-VII, by Chronological Age
□--□ C-VII, by Skeletal Age

Fig. 134

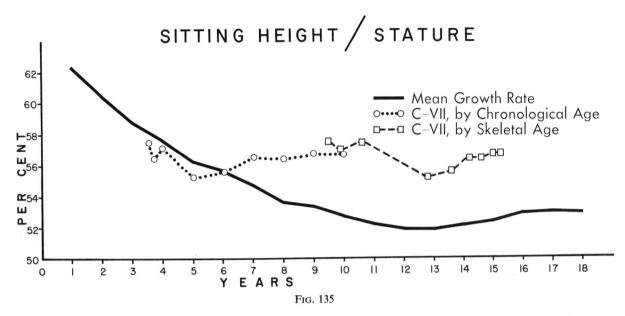

SITTING HEIGHT / STATURE

FIG. 135

Measures Relative to Stature

Figures 134 through 136 show the same measurements in percentage of stature, again plotted for both chronological and skeletal ages. Of this group, by far the most interesting graph is that for sitting height/ stature, i.e., the one which shows relative long-leggedness or short-leggedness. From this graph one may note that relative leg growth begins to decline as early as the fifth chronological year, just before the thirteenth skeletal year. This latter is close to the same point at which the "dip" comes in the normal pattern.

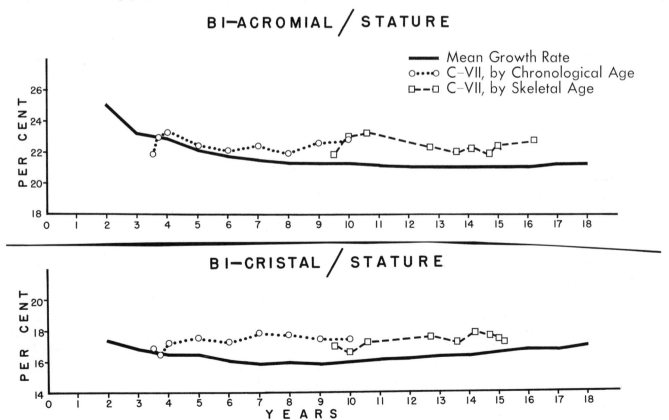

BI-ACROMIAL / STATURE

BI-CRISTAL / STATURE

FIG. 136

Excessively Precocious Menarche

TABLE 25

GROWTH RATE: CALCULATION SHEET

Name: _____	Case No.: C-VII	Key: Numbers 1–10 identify columns	M = mean
Birthdate: _____	Sex: F	A = age	dS = difference in stature
		S = stature	MS = average stature
		d = difference	dA = elapsed time

OBSERVED DATA				CALCULATIONS					
1	2	3	4	5	6	7	8 (5/7)	9 (8/6)	10 (9×100)
Treatment	Date	Stature (m.)	Age	dS	MS	dA	dS/dA	dS/dA / MS	Growth Rate (Per Cent per Year)
		.838	1.296	.102	.889	.759	.134	.151	15.1
		.940	2.055	.063	.972	.444	.142	.146	14.6
		1.003	2.499	.071	1.038	.498	.143	.138	13.8
		1.074	2.997	.066	1.107	.480	.138	.125	12.5
		1.140	3.477	.055	1.168	.506	.109	.093	9.3
		1.195	3.983	.043	1.216	.499	.086	.071	7.1
		1.238	4.482	.035	1.256	.458	.076	.061	6.1
Testosterone........		1.273	4.940	.027	1.286	.249	.108	.084	8.4
DC..............		1.300	5.189	.025	1.312	.290	.086	.066	6.6
		1.325	5.479	.029	1.340	.537	.054	.040	4.0
		1.354	6.016	.005	1.356	.269	.019	.014	1.4
		1.359	6.285	.031	1.374	.652	.048	.035	3.5
		1.390	6.937	.010	1.395	.499	.020	.014	1.4
		1.400	7.436	.007	1.404	.565	.012	.009	0.9
		1.407	8.001	.013	1.414	1.059	.012	.008	0.8
		1.420	9.060	.000	1.420	.866	.000	.000	0.0
		1.420	9.926						

Growth Rate

Figure 137, based on the calculations of Table 25, now considers stature in terms of annual-increment rates. As already noted, this method is useful in evaluating short-term treatment effects as well as in giving another insight into the total growth picture. The increment pattern differs sharply from the normal whether plotted according to chronological age or skeletal age. This is not surprising since the normal pattern reflects an orderly sequence in which a puberal growth spurt appears just when what might be called the primary somatic growth impetus is waning. In this case, the two growth impulses are telescoped and superimposed.

The brief period associated with androgen administration shows a peak of accelerated growth whichever way it is plotted. The peak does not appear to be an aberrant adolescent spurt since it rises above a general and persistent fall which more nearly parallels the final normal adolescent growth decline.

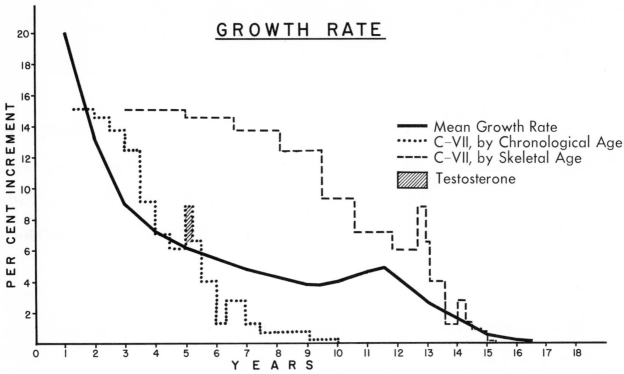

FIG. 137.—Growth rate of C-VII, plotted by chronological age and by skeletal age, with the mean growth rate for normal girls added for comparison.

Growth Diagnosis

Precocious growth
Precocious maturation
Eventual dwarfism

Clinical Diagnosis

Idiopathic precocious puberty
"Epileptic spells of psychomotor type, also related to emotional tension"; "acute brain syndrome associated with convulsive disorders"

Since both the developmental and behavioral deviations can be traced back to early infancy, it seems reasonable to assume that both aspects of pathology originated in some primary cerebral disorder.

Comment

Such a longitudinal record which documents the effect of accelerated maturation on the total growth pattern leads to the following deductions:

1. When the puberal spurt is superimposed on normal childhood growth, the resultant development falls somewhere between the expected curves as these would be related to either chronological or skeletal age.

2. The phases of growth which depend most specifically on the epiphyseal status of the long bones are very closely related to skeletal age. Among these are the periods in which relative leg growth begins to lag and in which growth in stature stops.

Chapter 18

Obesity in Boys, Associated with Excessive Growth and Bisexual Characteristics

Because the two boys described here are not typical overweight boys, their records underscore the necessity of analyzing many phases of the total picture before the essential dynamics of a given case can be understood.

"Fröhlich's Syndrome" is often a diagnostic label which suggests itself when an obese boy is first examined, although, in fact, very few "fat boys" fit this specification. Fröhlich (1901) described a classical pathological entity associated with a pituitary tumor (translated by Bruch, 1939). Shortness of stature and genital retardation were among the manifestations accompanying the obesity.

Although the genitals of fat boys frequently appear to be small, short stature is the exception rather than the rule. Obesity in boys does, however, have some common developmental associations. Among these is a suggestion of femininity: soft contours, wide hips, knock-knees; there is a slight skeletal delay. This is in contrast to the characteristic situation in girls, where obesity is commonly associated with an exaggeration of both degree and tempo of feminine differentiation.

The captions introducing each of these two big boys register their presenting complaints. The cases are offered as instances of obesity associated with an excess rather than a deficit of hormonal stimulation, as evidenced by the accompanying tall stature and skeletal acceleration. Most likely their gynecomastia is also a response to excess or faulty stimulation or to a superabundant tissue response rather than to any steroid lack. This deduction from growth observations is supported by the clinical observation that administration of androgen in one boy led to further breast growth, a not infrequent sequence.

CASE C-VIII (BOY WITH OBESITY AND POOR HEALTH)

Presenting Problem at 13 Years 2 Months

Too heavy and too tall (Fig. 138)
Recurrent infections
Weakness; invalidism

Anthropometric Values and Deviation Chart

Although the length measures (S and Si) and their ratio (Si/S) are within the broad range of normal, all weight and width measures and indices are exceedingly high (Fig. 139).

Secondary Sex Characters

Maturation of secondary sex characters is minimal; there is a slight amount of pigmented pubic hair, testicles are small (approx. $3 \times 2 \times 2$ cm. each), and the penis is very small; i.e., the boy is between stages I and II, a level which is not remarkably retarded but is most often reached two years earlier.

Androgyny

Although this patient is too young to be rated against the androgyny standards, certain significantly feminine features are notable: soft, fat surface-modeling, gynecomastia, and knock-knees.

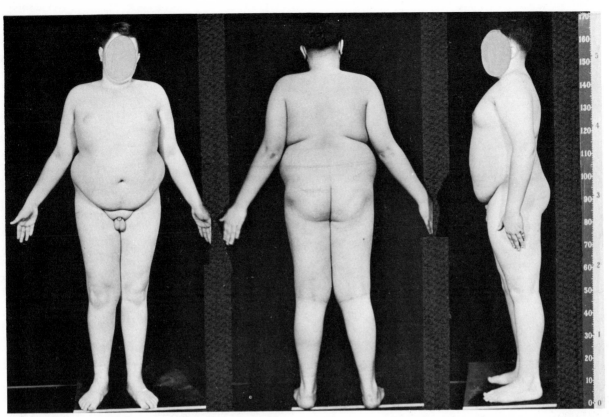

FIG. 138.—Three views of C-VIII (Boy with Obesity and Poor Health) at 13 years 2 months

Name		Sex Ⓜ F	Birth Date		Date		Age 13-2	Case # C VIII

Norms for: Sex Ⓜ ○ F *Age 13* *Other*

MEASURE		Pounds = x .454 Inches = x 2.54	Kilos Cm	STANDARD DEVIATION VALUES						
				-3σ	2% -2σ	16% -1σ	50% M	84% +1σ	98% +2σ	+3σ
Weight	W	225	102.2							
Stature	S	67.3	170.7							
Sitting height	Si		86.6							
Shoulder	BA		40.0							
Pelvis	BC	⟨13.1	⟨33.3							
Above-named measurements in per cent of stature.		*Ratios*								
	W/S	▨	59.9							
	Si/S		50.7							
	BA/S		23.4							
	BC/S		19.5							
Index Trunkbreadth	BC/BA		83.2							

FIG. 139.—Deviation chart for C-VIII at 13 years 2 months; measures compared with norms for 13-year-old boys.

Obese Boy in Poor Health

TABLE 26

GROWTH DATA

CASE C-VIII (Boy with Obesity and Poor Health)

AGE (YR.– MO.)	WEIGHT (LB.)	STATURE		BI-CRISTAL		SA (YR.– MO.)	PRED. HT. (IN.)
		In.	Cm.	In.	Cm.		
5–0	56.0	46.8					
5–7	63.0	47.5					
8–5	112.0	58.0					
9–6	123.0	61.8					
13–2	226.0	67.2	170.7	<13.0	<33.3	14–0	72.5
13–6	206.0	68.0					
13–10	205.0	68.4					

Skeletal Age: 14 years.

Stature Prediction: 72.5 in.

Longitudinal Growth Data

Previous records of height and weight permitted an analysis of the growth pattern which led to the present status (Table 26).

Growth Curves of Height by Age

Stature has been very large for as long a period as the record covers; the greatest advance in height comes between ages 9 and 10; in the last year there is a return toward the mean (Fig. 140).

Stature increments reflect the shape of the growth curve by maintaining a high level to age 10, falling thereafter.

Growth Curves of Weight by Age

Weight excess has been relatively greater than height acceleration throughout most of the record.

Weight increments show a pattern (Fig. 141) which is almost the inverse of that for stature increments, with a second weight increment peak coming during the decline of height increment. The late decline of the weight curve is a response to treatment.

Graphic Growth Record of Height, Weight, and Bi-Cristal

By combining the data on height and weight, this graph shows in another way that the great height spurt preceded the great weight gain: at age 9 years 6 months, the boy is already at a 13-year stature level, but his build is at the upper level of normal lateral dimensions. After that, excess weight gains take him completely away from normal width and weight standards (Fig. 142).

Growth Diagnosis

The outstanding impression is that there has been exaggerated growth in both height and weight with successive peaks for their increments; that physiologic maturation is disharmonious, with skeletal age somewhat advanced and secondary sex characters somewhat retarded; that the direction of development is bisexual, since there are definite feminine features.

Clinical Diagnosis

Obesity: constitutional, endocrine, exogenous
Adrenocortical hyperactivity: functional
Increased susceptibility to infection
Psychological disturbances, largely secondary to the long history of deviant growth and repeated illness

Although there was clear laboratory evidence of increased adrenocortical activity and response to stimulation, there was no evidence of focal pathology. Whatever imbalance had initiated the unusual growth pattern seemed no longer to be operative. Laboratory and clinical findings returned to normal under treatment geared especially to meet the patient's nutritional and emotional problems.

Comment

The over-all pattern suggests that whatever hormonal deviation existed in this case was in the nature of an excess or imbalance rather than a deficit. The small genitalia and the existence of feminine characteristics reflect constitutional variations which could be either hormonally or genetically conditioned.

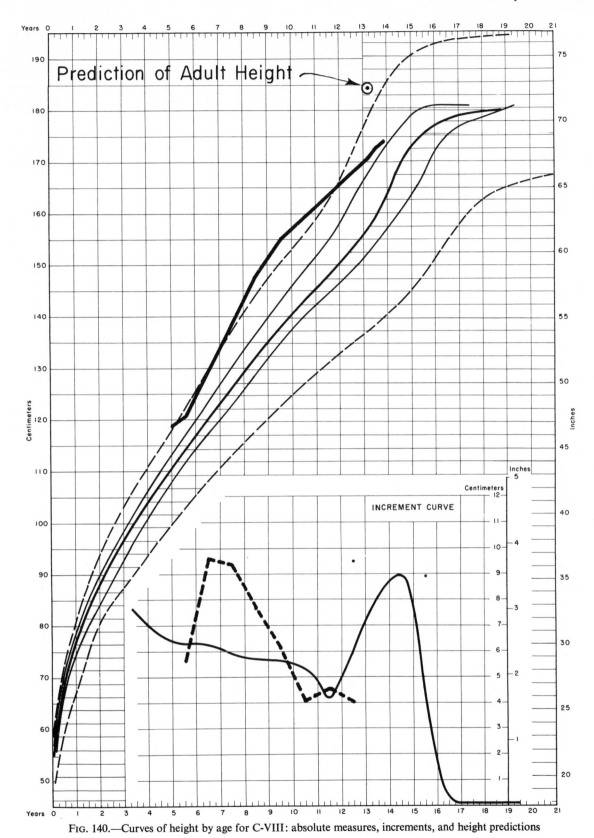

Prediction of Adult Height

INCREMENT CURVE

FIG. 140.—Curves of height by age for C-VIII: absolute measures, increments, and height predictions

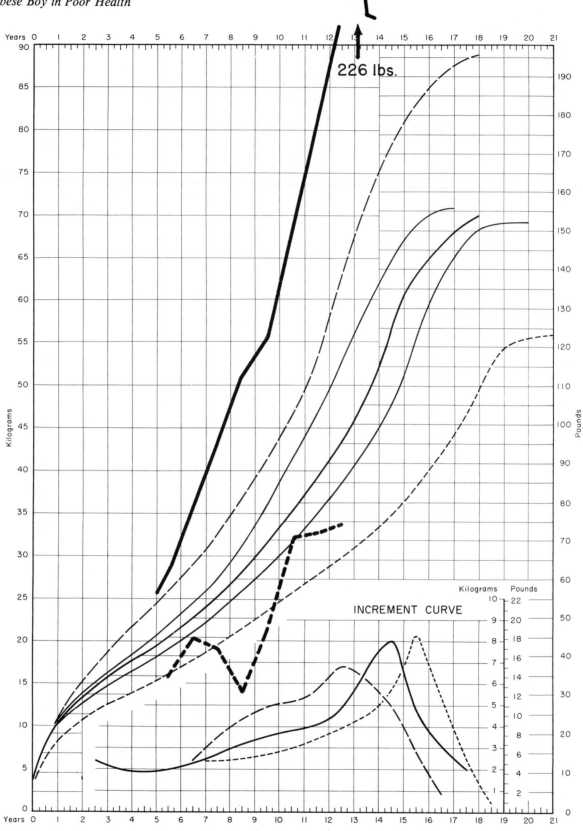

226 lbs.

INCREMENT CURVE

FIG. 141.—Curves of weight by age for C-VIII: absolute measures and increments

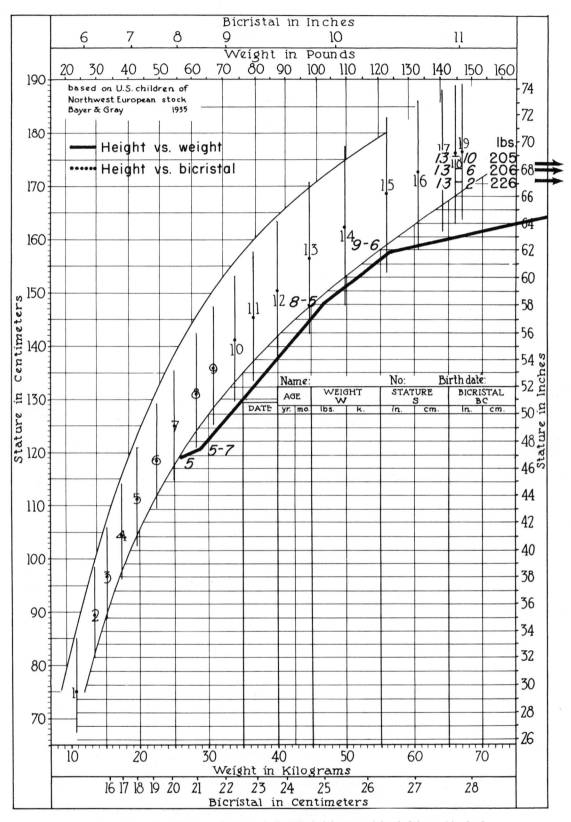

Fig. 142.—Graphic Growth Record, C-VIII: height vs. weight; height vs. bi-cristal

CASE C-IX (BOY WITH OBESITY AND GYNECOMASTIA)

Presenting Problem at 10 Years 7 Months
Too heavy and too tall (Fig. 143)
Gynecomastia, for which androgen had previously been given
Aggressive behavior

Anthropometric Values and Deviation Chart

Compared with boys his own age, this boy is too large in every dimension, the greatest excess being in weight and pelvic breadth (Fig. 144). When the measures are expressed in per cent of stature, the ratios involving sitting height and shoulder breadth are normal, although the others remain too large.

Compared with boys two years older—his skeletal-age peers—stature becomes normal, although the general deviation profile is about as deviant as with chronological-age norms. The wide pelvis is reflected in the very large trunk breadth, *BC/BA*, which shows up as too big against either 11- or 13-year standards, i.e.,

this boy is too broad-hipped for either his chronological or his skeletal age.

Secondary Sex Characters

This boy is still in sex stage I, which is appropriate for his chronological age but behind his skeletal level.

Gynecomastia is rather marked and would correspond to breast stage II in a girl. Palpation suggests that this is real mammary tissue rather than a simple fat deposit.

Androgyny

Feminine characteristics, inappropriate for even a young adolescent boy, are the heavy fat padding, broad hips, breast prominences, and knock-knees.

Skeletal Age: 13 years.

Stature Prediction: 73 in.

Longitudinal Growth Data

Previous height and weight records, included in Table 27, while suggesting some probable inaccuracies at the 2- and 3-year levels, permit some analysis of the

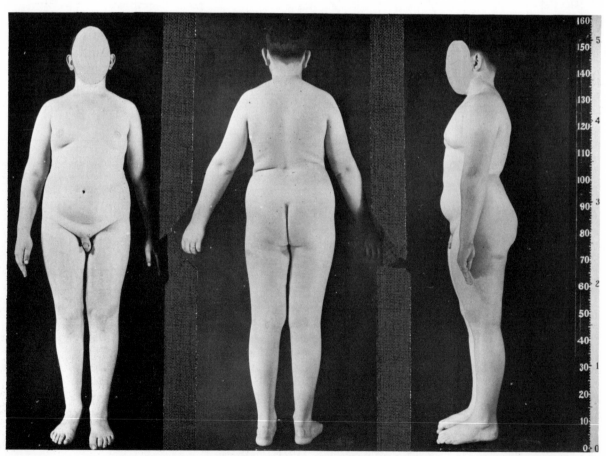

FIG. 143.—Three views of C-IX (Boy with Obesity and Gynecomastia) at 10 years 7 months

178

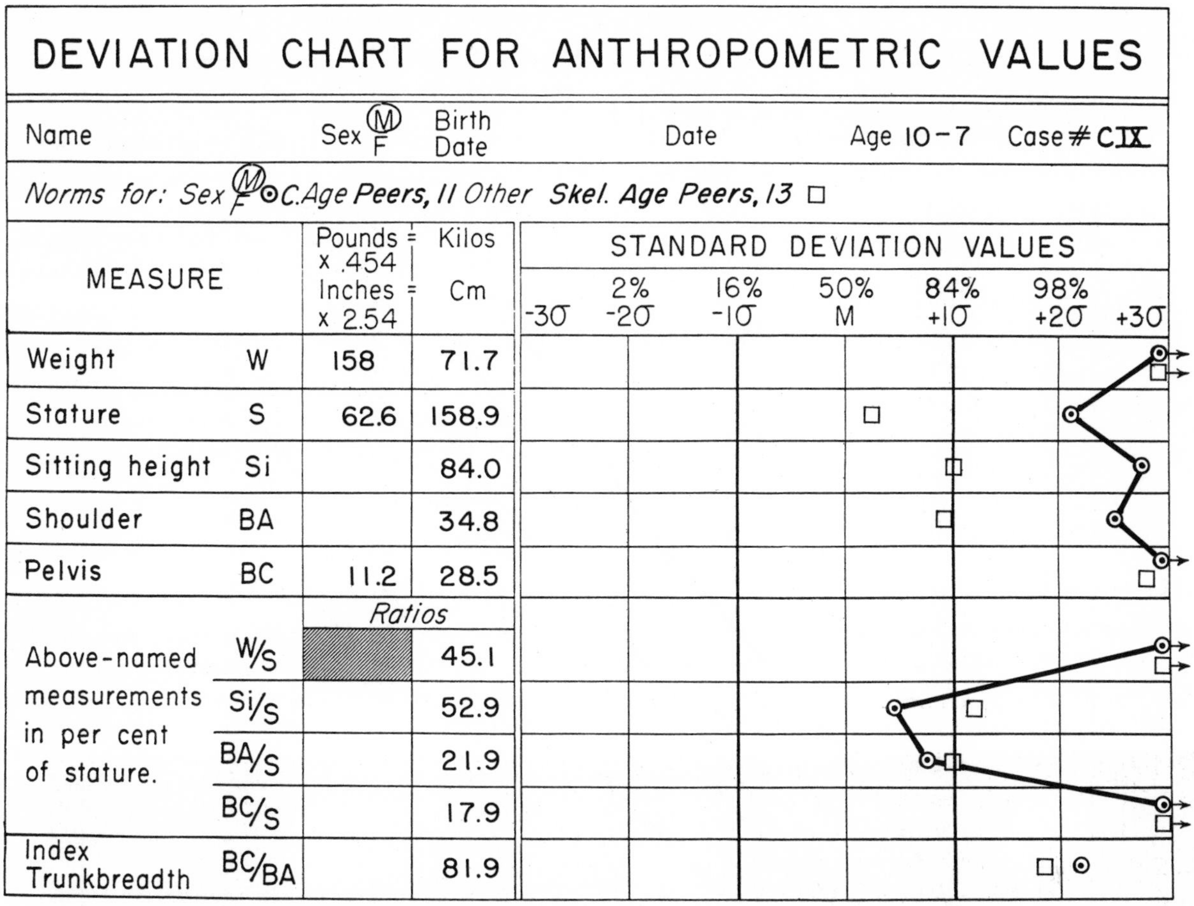

FIG. 144.—Deviation chart for C-IX at 10 years 7 months; measures plotted against norms for 11-year-old boys and norms for C-IX's skeletal-age peers (13-year-old boys).

growth pattern prior and subsequent to the above complete examination.

TABLE 27

GROWTH DATA
CASE C-IX (Boy with Obesity and Gynecomastia)

AGE (YR.-MO.)	WEIGHT (LB.)	STATURE		BI-CRIS-TAL (CM.)	SA (YR.-MO.)	PRED. HT. (IN.)
		In.	Cm.			
Birth	8.0	20.0	50.8			
0–4	17.0	27.0	68.6			
1–0	30.0	32.5	82.6			
2–0	34.0	36.0	91.4			
3–0	45.0	45.0	114.3			
4–0	55.0	47.5	120.6			
5–0	72.0	50.0	127.0			
9–4	134.0	59.0	149.8			
10–4	146.0	62.0	157.5			
10–8	158.0	62.6	158.9	<28.5	13–0	73.0
11–4	133.0	64.3				
11–7	138.0	65.6	166.6	27.5		
12–2	158.0	67.9		28.1		
12–8	173.0	69.3		28.5		

Growth Curves of Height by Age

Starting from average stature at birth, a great spurt occurred in the early years, so that by age 3 this boy was already as tall as an average boy two and one-half years older; he has maintained this lead ever since (Fig. 145). During the period from 2 to 5 years, the curve seems beyond all normal observations. Later the curve fairly well matches that for boys with skeletal acceleration such as this patient actually shows.

The increment curve starts only after the first spurt is already finished. During the two years under our observation, a second spurt occurred, with its peak at 11.5 years, about three years earlier than average; this is closer to his skeletal than his chronological expectations.

Growth Curves of Weight by Age

Weight and weight increments are high throughout (Fig. 146), except for the brief period of weight loss under treatment. When a relapse to former eating habits occurred, weight climbed back to a point which falls

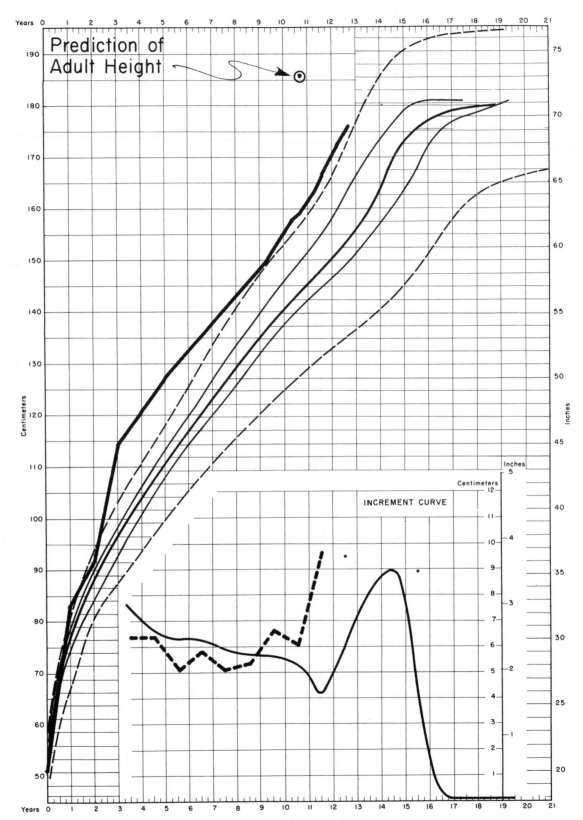

Fig. 145.—Curves of height by age for C-IX: absolute measures, increments, and height predictions

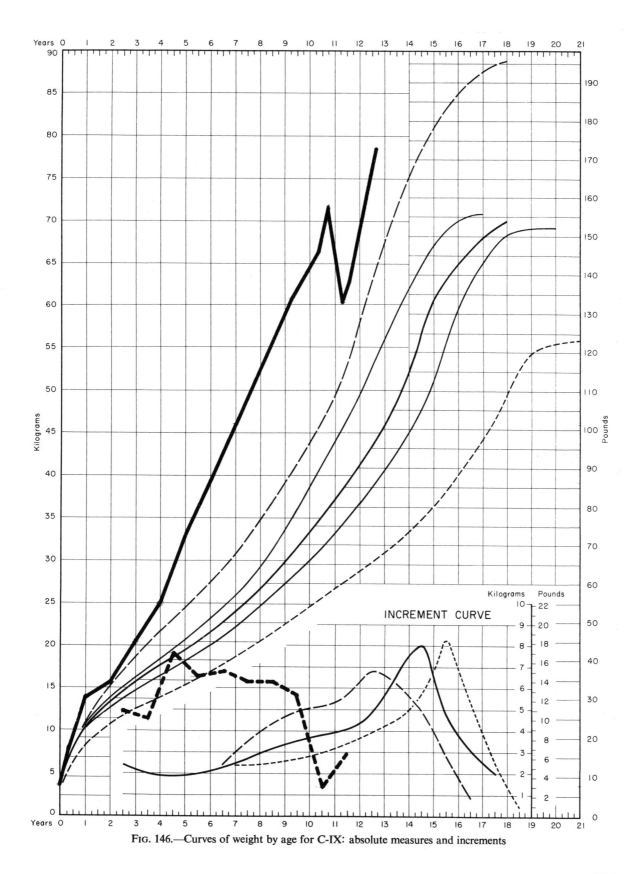

FIG. 146.—Curves of weight by age for C-IX: absolute measures and increments

INCREMENT CURVE

Obese Boy with Gynecomastia

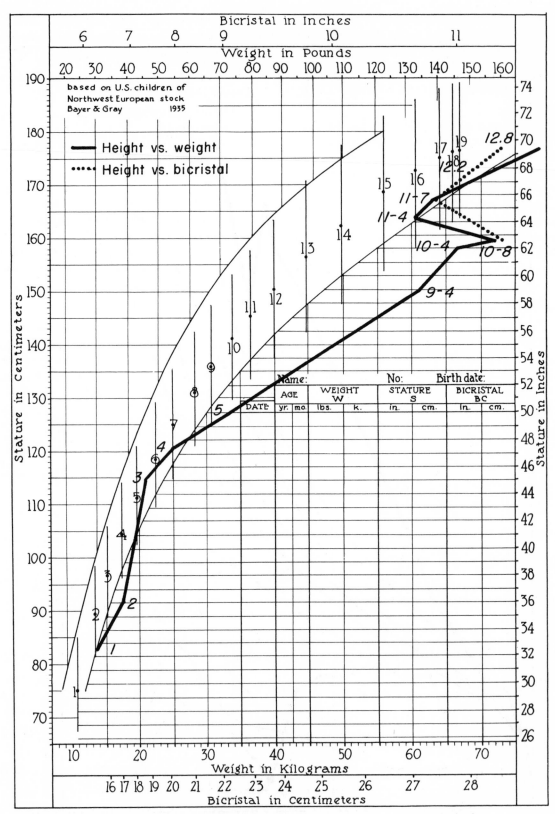

FIG. 147.—Graphic Growth Record, C-IX: height vs. weight; height vs. bi-cristal

almost on a continuum with the previous trend. Comparison of the weight with the height curve shows that gains in these two parameters were successive rather than synchronous.

Graphic Growth Record of Height, Weight, and Bi-Cristal

While this graph (Fig. 147) confirms the early height spurt followed by a dramatic weight gain, the main contribution of this graph is the demonstration that the weight loss in the year of treatment brought this boy's build into line with normal, and that the further weight gain was paced by his stature gain, so that build stayed at the upper limit of normal. The bi-cristal measure, though artificially broad because of fat over the pelvic crests, still indicates a lateral build, predicting a weight expectation at the upper extreme of the normal range.

Growth Diagnosis

Exaggerated growth in height and weight
Physiologic maturation, disharmonious; skeletal age definitely accelerated
Androgynic pattern: significant feminine features

Aggressive behavior, while not documented here, seems in this boy to be related to his own awareness, and that of his classmates, that he is "too big" and "does not fit."

Clinical Diagnosis

Obesity and overgrowth
Gynecomastia
No laboratory evidence of either primary or secondary gonadal deficiency

Follow-up

Build remained atypical, although the obesity lessened notably. Considerable mammary tissue remained and may later require surgical removal; one hopes that loss of enough subcutaneous fat may, however, decrease the total breast prominence to the point where it is no longer distressing.

Comment

The fact that mammary growth increased during his ninth year, when androgen was given, confirms the idea that the kind of bisexual development exhibited by this patient reflects either excessive growth stimulation or excessive somatic response.

Chapter 19

Growth Following Castration in Adolescent Girls

As dramatic an injury as castration in early adolescence is generally expected to have important effects on subsequent development. Fortunately, this is a trauma which is exceedingly rare; surprisingly, no known published records of serial measurements delineate the growth effects of this critical loss in girls.

Observations on two girls are presented which document their somatic progress from the time of their castration for grave pathology to maturity.

The similarities and contrasts between the cases make them an interesting pair. The cases are alike in that at the time of castration neither girl had menstruated; they were within one year of each other in age; at the first subsequent measurement they were within 1.1 in. of each other in height (at maturity, within 1 in.). They differ in that one had been castrated as a consequence of X-ray to the spine which only incidentally involved the ovaries, the other by direct surgery; one received no endocrine treatment, the other received cyclic stilbestrol.

These two longitudinal records thus offer some tentative answers to the questions about what happens to an adolescent girl who loses her ovaries. Does she become a giant? Does she mature somatically? What is the effect of replacement therapy?

We think they also demonstrate that repeated morphological observations on growing patients can contribute certain insights into the total understanding of the growth process which laboratory and clinical studies alone cannot provide.

Taken together, these two studies imply that estrogen deficiency, continuing beyond the age of expected menarche, has a direct effect on skeletal maturation, on body proportions, and on secondary sex characters. It appears to have a lesser effect on body contours and on eventual height. A further implication is that genetic determinants and complex hormonal patterns dominate basic somatic development.

Estrogen replacement seems to have had a normalizing effect on body proportions, body contours, and breast development. It appears to have had less effect on the growth of sexual hair and on total height.

Noteworthy in this connection is the observation that both girls grew only a little more than would normally have been expected, but where the deficiency was uncompensated, a disproportionate amount of the growth was in the legs.

Since the primary diagnoses were so grave in both girls, attention was not focused on their growth until confidence was established in their continued survival and health. The early growth observations are thus somewhat "spotty" in both instances and are supplemented by a judicious guess as to the probable skeletal status at the time of the first stature measurements.

These two cases have been reported somewhat more fully by Bayer (1956).

CASE C-X (CASTRATED GIRL: NO REPLACEMENT THERAPY)

Presenting Problem at 16 Years 4 Months

Failure to develop secondary sex characters

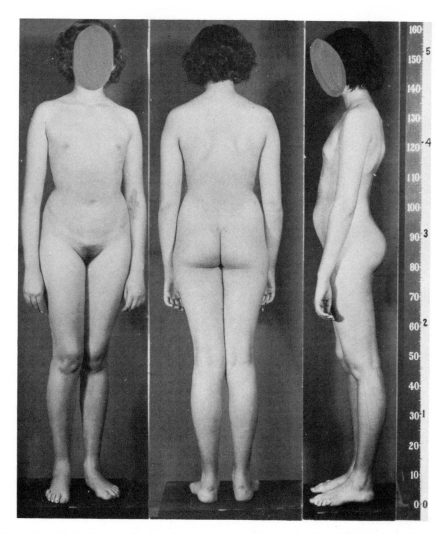

Fig. 148.—Three views of C-X (Castrated Girl: No Replacement Therapy) at 16 years 4 months. Figs. 148 through 156 from Bayer, "Growth Following Castration in Two Adolescent Girls," *J. Amer. Med. Women's Assoc.*, Vol. 11 (1956).

History
At 13 years 1 month presented problem of having been unable to walk for three and one-half months
Diagnosis: malignant neoplasm of the 4th lumbar vertebra; Ewing sarcoma
Treatment: deep X-ray therapy
Result: cure of tumor

Anthropometric Values and Deviation Chart
Measures are remarkable only in the short sitting height which shows up both absolutely and in the small *Si/S*, indicating a long-legged build (Figs. 148, 149).

Secondary Sex Characters
No menarche at 16 years 4 months
Breast development at stage I; pubic hair, at stage III

In her seventeenth year, this girl is thus essentially preadolescent with regard to secondary sexual development, except for the appearance of pubic hair.

Growth Diagnosis
Long-legged, hypogonadal build
Retarded sexual maturation

Clinical Diagnosis: X-ray castration

185

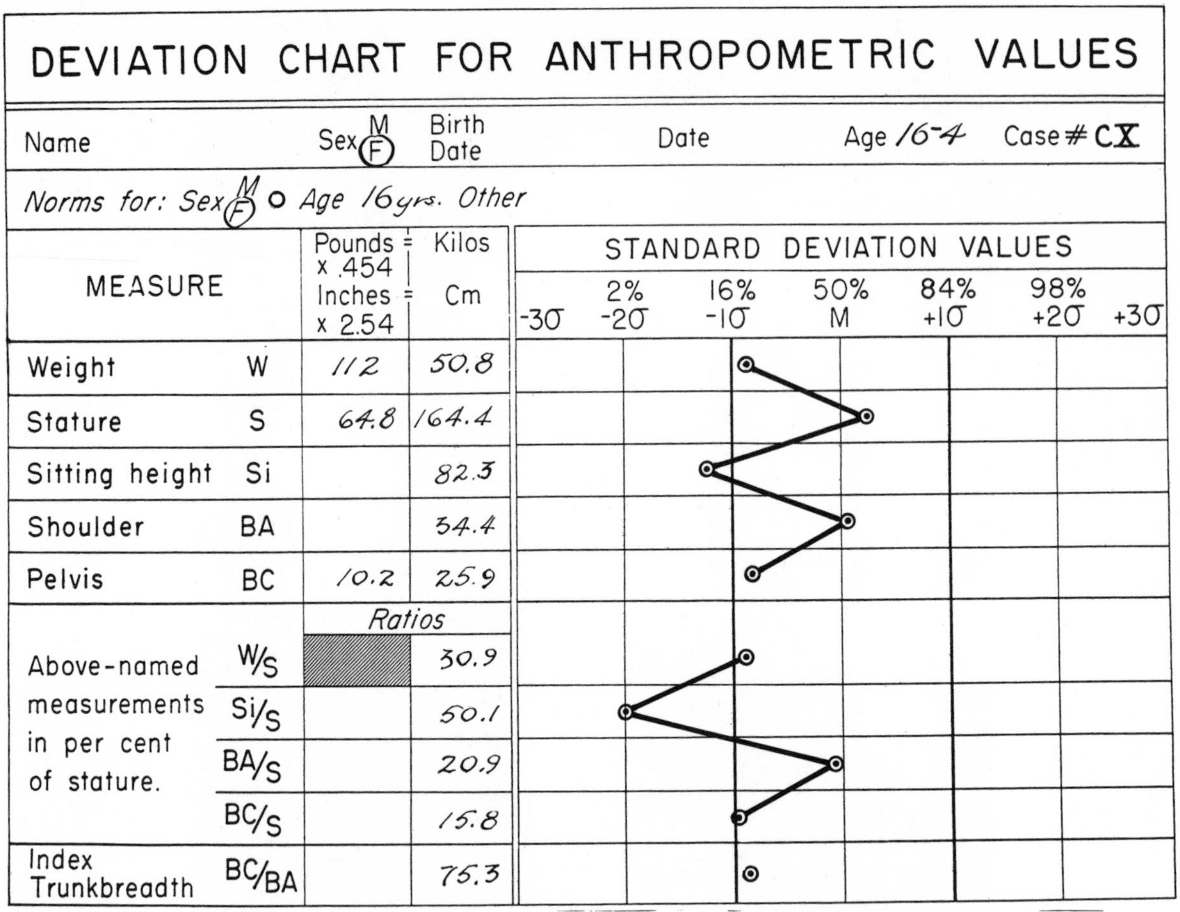

No Replacement Therapy

FIG. 149.—Deviation chart for C-X at 16 years 4 months; measures compared with norms for 16-year-old girls

Longitudinal Growth Data

Serial anthropometric measurements (Table 28) emphasize the relative failure in trunk growth, in that the *Si/S* and the *BC/S* tend to grow progressively smaller. These measures therefore confirm the sexually undifferentiated pattern.

Growth Curves of Height by Age

From the first height observation at 13 years 5 months to age 17, the stature curve follows, with surprising conformity, the curve for girls maturing at average rates (Fig. 150). From there on, it differs in that it continues to rise a little for at least three years longer.

The increment curve reflects this continued growth by the delayed return to zero.

Stature predictions are added to this graph. They are on solid ground only at ages 18, 19, and 20 when hand X-ray films are available. However, there is no reason to assume that there was any growth or maturation failure prior to castration at age 13 years 1 month.

TABLE 28

GROWTH DATA
CASE C-X (Castrated Girl with No Replacement Therapy)

AGE (YR.– MO.)	WEIGHT (LB.)	STATURE (IN.)	BI- CRISTAL (CM.)	SA (YR.– MO.)	PRED. HT. (IN.)
13–5	81.0	62.9		13–1	65.6
13–9	88.0	63.0		(assumed)	
13–10	91.0	63.1			
14–2	93.0	63.6			
14–3	93.0	63.7			
14–5	90.0	63.7			
14–6	96.0	63.8			
14–9	101.0	64.0			
15–4	104.0	64.4			
15–7	104.0	64.4			
16–3	111.0	64.8	25.9		
17–0	110.5	65.2			
18.0	109.0	65.5		13–6	67.4
18–4	113.0				
19–0	111.0	65.8	26.4	13–9	67.3
20–0		65.8		14–0	67.1
20–5	115.0	66.0			
20–10	110.0	66.2			
33–5		66.2			

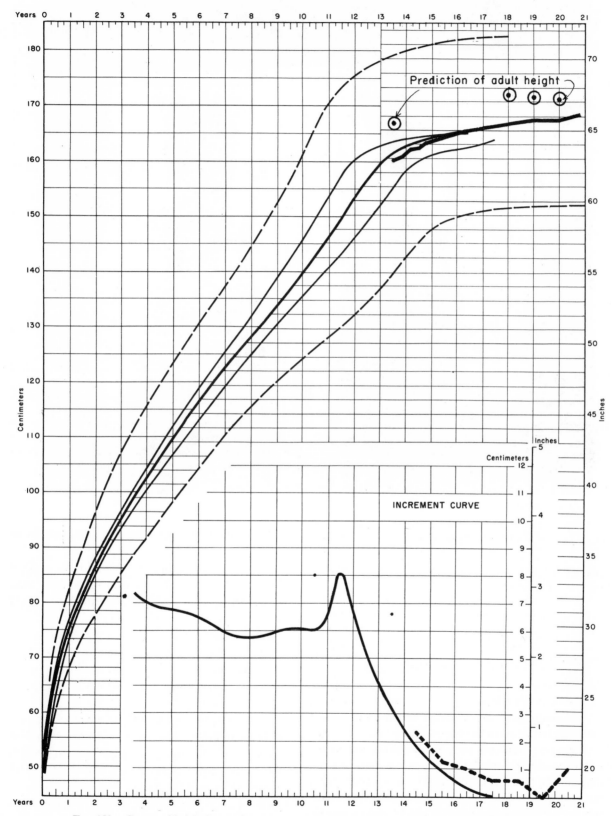

FIG. 150.—Curves of height by age for C-X: absolute measures, increments, and height predictions

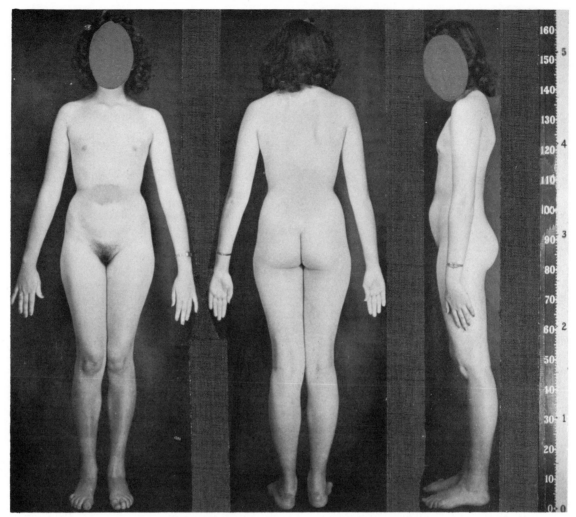

FIG. 151.—Three views of C-X at 18 years 11 months

It therefore seems reasonable to assume that the stature prediction for 13 years 5 months, the time of the first height observation, also applies to 13 years 1 month, when castration occurred. Assuming 65.6 in. to be a valid prediction, it appears that she grew only 1.5 in. more than would have been expected in a normal girl in her fourteenth year. Later data show that the growth falls an inch short of what would be expected from the almost stationary skeletal status at ages 18, 19, and 20.

Androgyny Profile

The androgynic rating at 18 years 11 months shows that, while secondary sexual differentiation has developed very little since the original photos, the body itself is essentially feminine, with a rating toward the hypofeminine (Figs. 151, 152).

Comment

Growth continued to 66.2 in., gaining only 1.5 in. more than anticipated on the basis of an assumed normal skeletal age at 13 years 1 month.

Maturation retardation is evidenced especially by the long lag in epiphyseal closure which in turn is associated with a relative excess of leg growth over trunk growth.

Body form at maturity reflects typical deviations in a hypogonadal direction, with relative long-leggedness and the persistence of straight childish contours, without breast development and with little axillary or pubic hair.

In this girl, irradiation of the gonads, although presumably removing the source of female sex hormone, resulted in only moderately increased linear growth, despite retarded epiphyseal closure and hypofeminine build; i.e., growth did not proceed to "giant" proportions, even though the epiphyses remained open so late.

188

ANDROGYNIC PATTERNS OF BODY FORM: RATING PROFILE
Bayley-Bayer Standards*
17–18 Year Norms

Name	Sex M/F	Date	Age 18-11	Skeletal Age	Case Number CX

ITEM	RATING				
("A" through "H" from rear-view photographs)	Hyper-masculine 1	Masculine 2	Intermediate, A-sexual, or Bi-sexual 3, 3a, 3b	Feminine 4	Hyper-feminine 5
I. A. **Surface modeling**	Exaggerated hardness of relief.	Strong muscle molding. Bone, vein and tendon prominences.	b. Muscular and fat. / a. Little muscle or fat.	Smooth and soft, with little muscle.	Very soft, fat, no muscle.
II. **Trunk Contours** B. Shoulder girdle	Massive.	Appears wide, heavy and muscular.	b. Muscular and fat. / a. Narrow, "bony."	Slight, soft and narrow.	Frail, softly fat.
C. Waist line	Marked torso narrowing to low waist: may have minimal indentation.	Slight indentation due to narrowing of torso.	b. Broad hip and shoulder; little indentation. / a. Slight symmetrical high concavity.	Definite line accentuated by hip widening.	Marked indentation.
D. Hip flare	No widening.	Slight widening of hips from waist.	Intermediate.	Flares into wide hips laterally and posteriorly.	Marked flare.
E. Buttocks	Very flat.	Flat and angular.	Intermediate.	Rounded and full.	Very broad and rounded.
III. **Leg Patterns** F. Thigh Form	Cylinder and/or bulging muscles.	Approaches cylinder. Lateral outline convex.	Intermediate.	Funnel, fat and rounded. Lateral outline concave.	Fat, wide-top funnel.
G. Interspace (whole leg)	Very open.	Open center above and below knees.	Intermediate.	Closed center except small space below knees.	Thighs and knees together, feet apart.
H. Muscle bulge (lower leg)	Strong bulge, no fat.	Prominent inner bulge of gastrocnemius.	b. Moderate muscle bulge. / a. No muscle bulge; spindly.	Slight inner bulge; shapely, smooth, outer curve.	Very little muscle, but smoothly rounded and outer curve.
J. Penis size	1 Very / 1.5 Large	2 Average	2.5 Small / 3 Very		
K. Breast size		**Absent**	3 Very / 3.5 Small	4 Average	4.5 Large / 5 Very
L. Body hair density	1 / Heavy on thighs, etc.	2 / Easily discernible	Sparse. / (3) ♂	♀ Absent	
M. Pubic pattern	Disperse / Acuminate.	Sagittal	♂	Horizontal ♀ **Scant**	
N. Bicristal/Biacromial Index	−←68 69	73 74	76 77	82 83→+	
P. Strength (Kg) Grip (R+L)+Thrust +Pull	+←244 243	186 185	148 147	110 109→−	
Grip (R+L)	+←126 125	95 94	80 79	59 58→−	
Androgyny Score (Sum of "A"–"H") **30.5**	8 / 12 13	19 20	B/A 25 26	● 34 35	40
Characteristic Description (Circle one)	**Hypermasculine**	**Masculine**	Intermediate Bisexual Asexual Disharmonious	(**Feminine**)	**Hyperfeminine**

Supplementary Criteria

FIG. 152.—Androgny profile of C-X at 18 years 11 months

Replacement Therapy

CASE C-XI (CASTRATED GIRL: REPLACEMENT THERAPY)

Presenting Problem at 15 Years 2 Months

Growth evaluation requested

History

At 12 years 3 months had suffered abdominal swelling, bloody ascites, and masses

Diagnosis: Theca-cell tumors of the ovaries

Treatment: panhysterectomy

Replacement therapy begun at 12 years 11 months: cyclic administration of stilbestrol over the years

Anthropometric Values and Deviation Chart

All measures and ratios are essentially normal (Figs. 153, 154), including the critical Si/S ratio which remained normal throughout the period of subsequent observations.

Secondary Sex Characters

No menarche at 15 years 2 months

Breast stage III

Hair stage I (no axillary or pubic hair)

Skeletal Age: 15 years

Stature Prediction: 67.2 in

Growth Diagnosis

Normal adolescent except for absence of sexual hair.

Clinical Diagnosis

Surgical castration adequately compensated with stilbestrol therapy.

Longitudinal Growth Data

Again, as in case C-X, the growth data (Table 29) are incomplete but still worthy of record.

Growth Curve of Height by Age

The first two stature observations (Fig. 155) lie close to the mean for girls maturing at an average rate; it is thus reasonable to assume that this was indeed the pattern prior to surgery. Thereafter, the curve con-

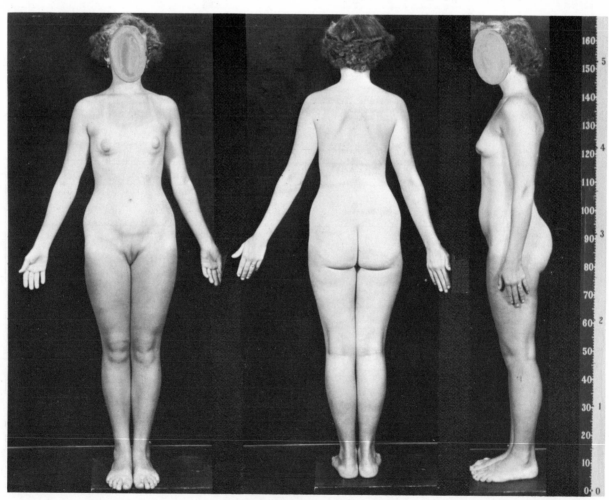

FIG. 153.—Three views of C-XI (Castrated Girl: Replacement Therapy) at 15 years 2 months. From Bayer, 1956.

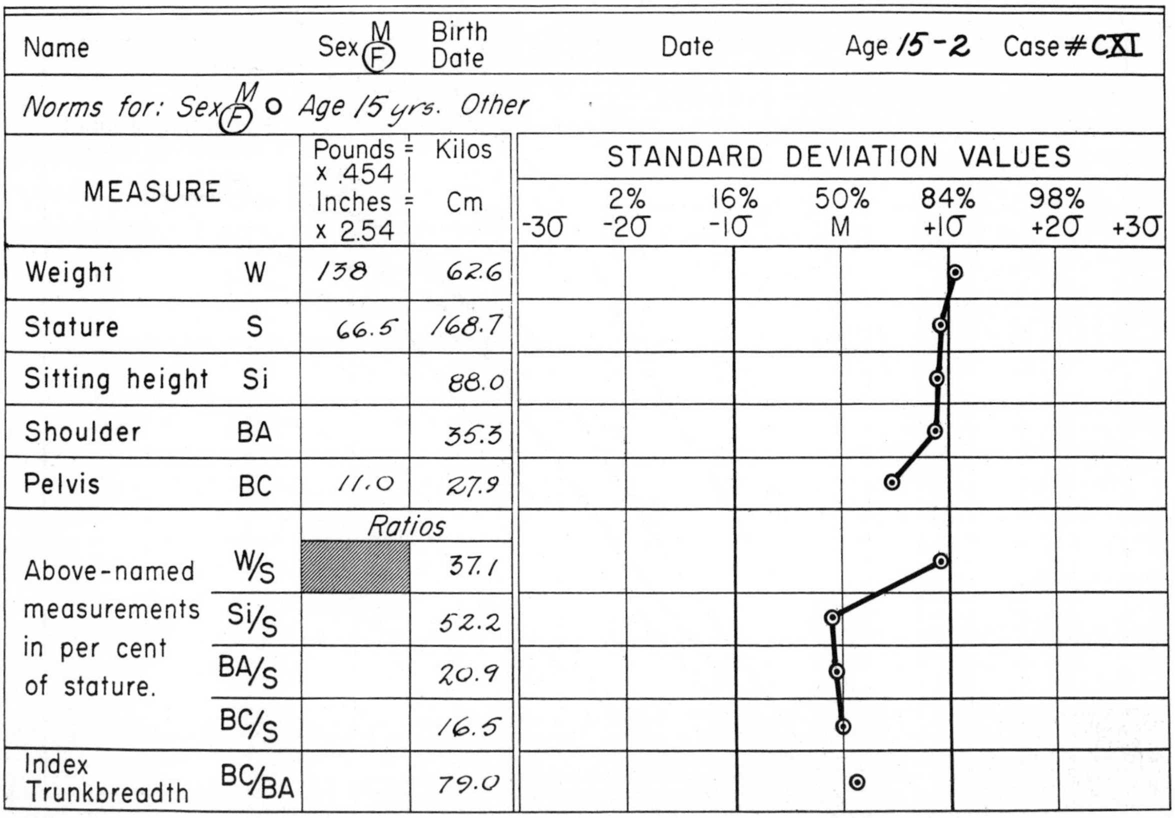

Fig. 154.—Deviation chart for C-XI at 15 years 2 months; measures compared with norms for 15-year-old girls.

tinues an upward trend which proceeds longer and higher than the mean.

As a corollary of the continued growth, increment calculations follow a path similar to that for slow-maturing girls.

Stature predictions, after the first hand X-ray at age 15 years 2 months, are notably stable and correct. Even a hypothetical prediction based on a hypotheti-

cally normal skeletal age at the first stature recording is only 1.1 in. below the adult stature attained.

Androgyny Profile

An androgyny rating at 19 years from direct observation of the patient shows a remarkably normal feminine build (Fig. 156). Only a slight deficiency of breast size and a minimal appearance of axillary and pubic hair agree with the known fact of castration.

Comment

Growth continued several years longer than would have been expected in a normal girl, but it did not exceed the documented expectation at age 15 and exceeded by only 1.1 in. the guessed expectation at time of surgery.

An inhibition of maturation is evidenced by the slightly deficient development of secondary sex characters, but there is no significant skeletal delay until the final lag after age 17.

Body form had a normal ratio of leg length to total height and was essentially feminine.

The record suggests, therefore, that in this girl the consistent oral replacement of estrogen encouraged the development of an essentially normal body form, although total growth may have proceeded slightly beyond genetic expectation.

TABLE 29

GROWTH DATA

CASE C-XI (Castrated Girl with Replacement Therapy)

AGE (YR.– MO.)	WEIGHT (LB.)	STATURE		BI- CRIS- TAL (CM.)	SA (YR.– MO.)	PRED. HT. (IN.)
		In.	Cm.			
12–4	92.0	61.8			12–4 (assumed)	66.1
12–6	104.0	62.0				
12–8	111.0	63.0				
13–0	113.0	63.5				
13–5	124.0	64.5				
13–11	132.0	65.5				
14–3	134.0	65.75				
14–9	134.0	66.25				
15–2	138.0	66.5	168.7	27.9	15–0	67.2
16–0	140.0	66.7	169.3	28.1	15–6	67.2
17–3	142.0	66.9	169.7	29.1	16–9	67.0
17–10	145.0	67.0	170.0	29.4		
18–6	151.0	67.0	170.0			
19–0	156.0	67.2	170.6	29.4	17–6	67.2

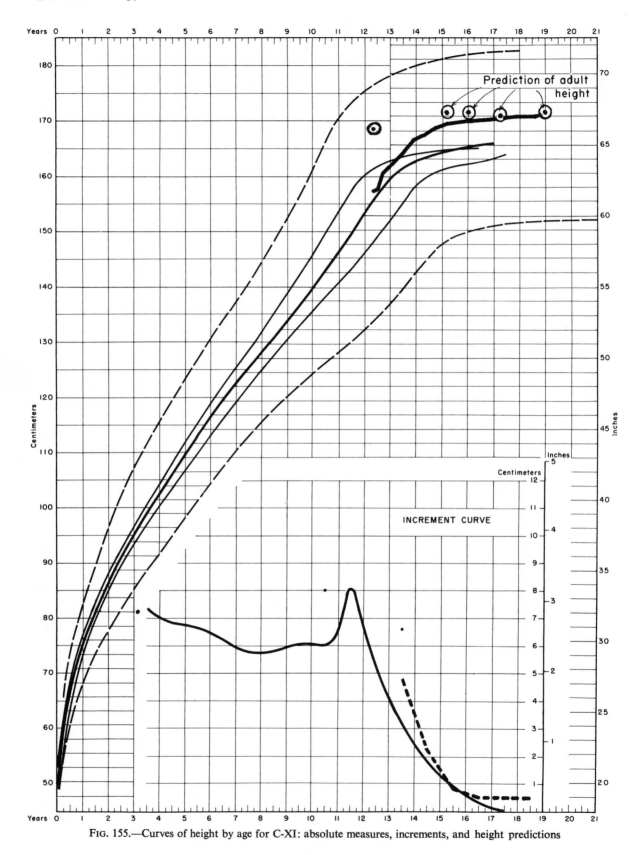

FIG. 155.—Curves of height by age for C-XI: absolute measures, increments, and height predictions

ANDROGYNIC PATTERNS OF BODY FORM: RATING PROFILE
Bayley-Bayer Standards*
17–18 Year Norms

Name		Sex M/F	Date		Age 19	Skeletal Age 17-6	Case Number CXI

ITEM	RATING				
("A" through "H" from rear-view photographs)	**Hyper-masculine** 1	**Masculine** 2	**Intermediate, A-sexual, or Bi-sexual** 3, 3a, 3b	**Feminine** 4	**Hyper-feminine** 5
I. A. **Surface modeling**	Exaggerated hardness of relief.	Strong muscle molding. Bone, vein and tendon prominences.	b. Muscular and fat. a. Little muscle or fat.	Smooth and soft, with little muscle.	Very soft, fat, no muscle.
II. **Trunk Contours** B. Shoulder girdle	Massive.	Appears wide, heavy and muscular.	b. Muscular and fat. a. Narrow, "bony."	Slight, soft and narrow.	Frail, softly fat.
C. Waist line	Marked torso narrowing to low waist: may have minimal indentation.	Slight indentation due to narrowing of torso.	b. Broad hip and shoulder; little indentation. a. Slight symmetrical high concavity.	Definite line accentuated by hip widening.	Marked indentation.
D. Hip flare	No widening.	Slight widening of hips from waist.	Intermediate.	Flares into wide hips laterally and posteriorly.	Marked flare.
E. Buttocks	Very flat.	Flat and angular.	Intermediate.	Rounded and full.	Very broad and rounded.
III. **Leg Patterns** F. Thigh Form	Cylinder and/or bulging muscles.	Approaches cylinder. Lateral outline convex.	Intermediate.	Funnel, fat and rounded. Lateral outline concave.	Fat, wide-top funnel.
G. Interspace (whole leg)	Very open.	Open center above and below knees.	Intermediate.	Closed center except small space below knees.	Thighs and knees together, feet apart.
H. Muscle bulge (lower leg)	Strong bulge, no fat.	Prominent inner bulge of gastrocnemius.	b. Moderate muscle bulge. a. No muscle bulge; spindly.	Slight inner bulge; shapely, smooth, outer curve.	Very little muscle, but smoothly rounded and outer curve.
J. Penis size	1 Very / 1.5 Large	2 Average	2.5 Small / 3 Very		
K. Breast size			3 Very / 3.5 Small	4 Average	4.5 Large / 5 Very
L. Body hair density	1 Heavy on thighs, etc.	2 Easily discernible	2.5 Sparse.	(3) Absent	
M. Pubic pattern	Disperse / Acuminate.	Sagittal		Horizontal	
N. Bicristal / Biacromial Index **80**	– ← 68 | 69	73 | 74	76	82 | 83 → +	
P. Strength (Kg) Grip (R+L) +Thrust +Pull	+ ← 244 | 243	186 | 185	148 | 147	110 | 109 → –	
Grip (R+L)	+ ← 126 | 125	95 | 94	80 | 79	59 | 58 → –	
Androgyny Score (Sum of "A"–"H") **31.5**	8 | 12 | 13	19 | 20	B / O / A | 25 | 26	34 | 35	40
Characteristic Description (Circle one)	**Hypermasculine**	**Masculine**	**Intermediate Bisexual Asexual Disharmonious**	**Feminine**	**Hyperfeminine**

FIG. 156.—Androgyny profile of C-XI at 19 years

Chapter 20

Growth in a Hypogonadal Boy

Just as the cases of the two castrated girls gained in value by comparisons between them, this case of a hypogonadal boy gains in value by comparison with the two girls. Noteworthy among the similarities is the fact that eventual height did not surpass the original prediction, even though epiphyses remained open past the twentieth birthday. Furthermore, as in the untreated girl, the body build demonstrates the long-leggedness and lack of sexual differentiation that is typical of hypogonadism.

Besides the more obvious genital inadequacy in the boy, there is another greater difference between this case and the cases of the girls: in the male the gonadal deficiency is constitutional, whereas in the girls it was traumatic. In this boy, as in many others, the central growth abnormality is associated with other evidence of imperfect evolution, whereas the girls were castrated as a result of isolated, though decisive, traumatic episodes.

CASE C-XII (HYPOGONADAL BOY WITH SKELETAL DEFORMITIES)

Presenting Problem at 16 Years 8 Months
 Short stature
 Delayed sexual development
 Skeletal deformities
 Weakness

Anthropometric Values and Deviation Chart
Compared with his age peers, this boy is definitely too small in every absolute dimension (Figs. 157, 158),

most strikingly so in sitting height and bi-acromial breadth. Even relative to his short stature, his other measures are low. The most significant deviation is the small Si/S, indicating that his growth failure is principally in the trunk. He thus has a typically long-legged, hypogonadal build.

Compared with his skeletal-age peers, chronologically four years his juniors, his absolute and relative measures are closer to the mean. However, even here, the Si/S is remarkably small.

Secondary Sex Characters
There are no advances of genital size or pubic-hair growth beyond the childhood state.

Besides sexual immaturity, inspection of the boy and his photos reveals great awkwardness of posture and gait; body contours are asymmetrical; voice is high-pitched.

Skeletal X-Ray Survey
The skeletal age is 12 years 9 months at CA 16 years 8 months.

Skeletal deformities include inequalities of the femurs, sclerosis of the sacroiliac joints, kyphosis, and tibial deformities. The skull is normal.

Stature Prediction: 71.7 in.

Growth Diagnosis
 Retardation of growth, with special lag in trunk growth
 Retardation of maturation

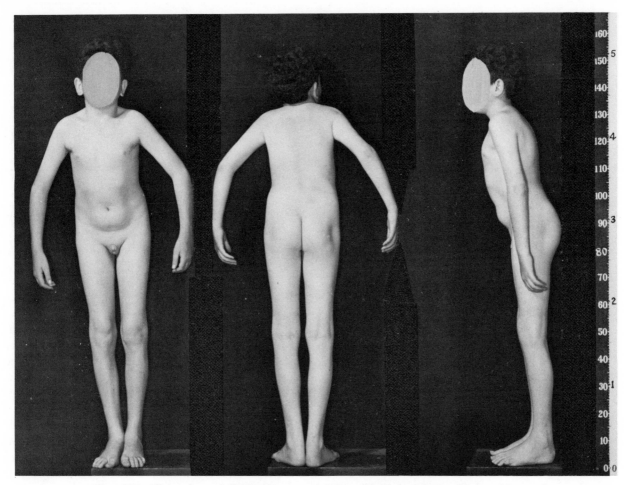

FIG. 157.—Three views of C-XII (Hypogonadal Boy with Skeletal Deformities) at 16 years 8 months.

Clinical Diagnosis

Pituitary deficiency, primary
Hypogonadism, secondary
Hypothyroidism, secondary

Longitudinal Growth Data

From the records of the child's pediatrician, it was possible to reconstruct the growth history of the first eight years (Table 30). The graphs show the data, plus data subsequent to the time of the above workup.

Growth Curves of Height by Age

There are two periods in the early record when efforts were made to stimulate growth by giving injections of anterior pituitary-like substances. A brief posi-tive response in both instances is indicated by a steeper slope of the growth curve (Fig. 159). There are insufficient data to allow more precise evaluation.

After age 16 years 8 months, thyroid and androgen were given almost continuously in small doses which were doubled at age 18 years 6 months. No clear effect can be demonstrated from the lesser dosages. The larger doses were followed by an increased pitch in the curve.

When the age-stature data are combined with the bone ages, four prediction points become available. From these it appears that the growth prediction first dropped, then rose again, but that even later, with epiphyses still open, growth had not exceeded the original prediction.

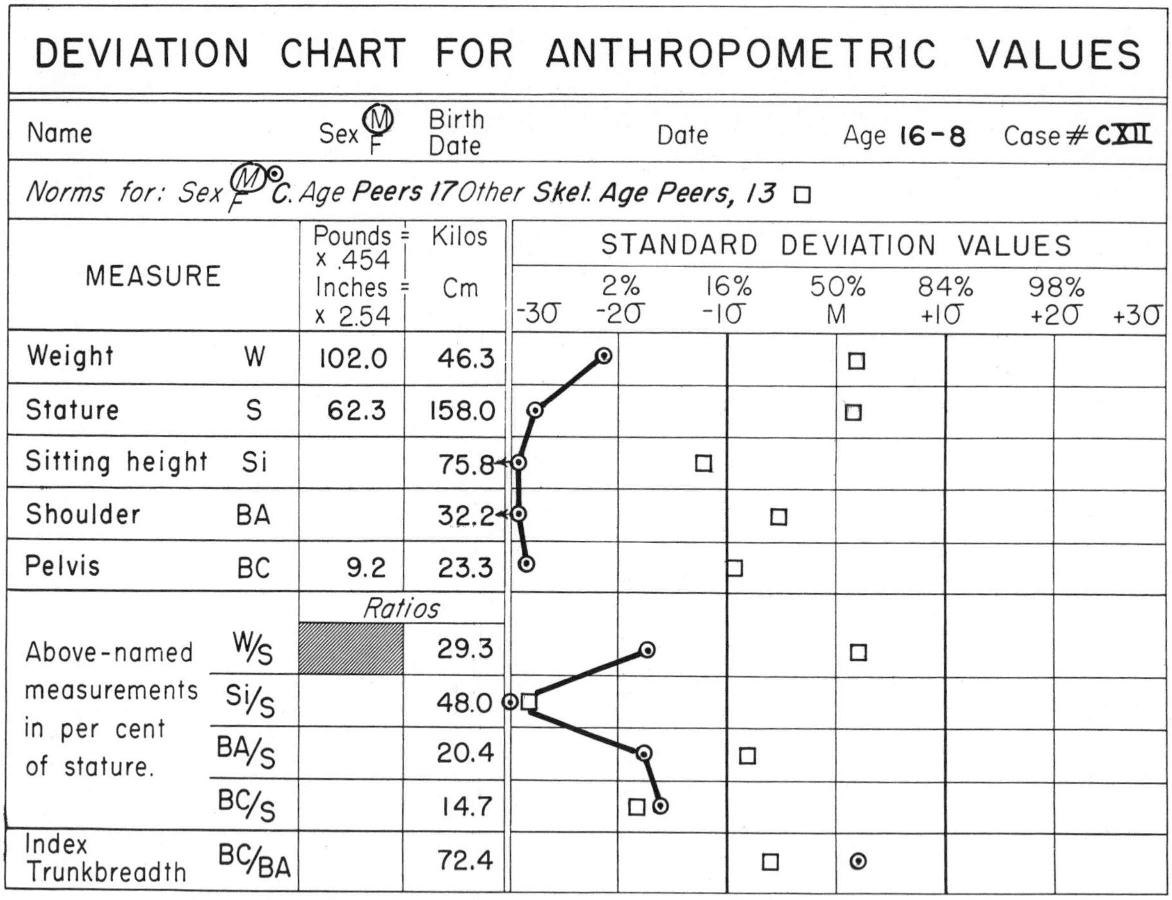

FIG. 158.—Deviation chart for C-XII at 16 years 8 months; measures compared with norms for age peers (17-year-old boys) and norms for skeletal-age peers (13-year-old boys).

TABLE 30

GROWTH DATA

CASE C-XII (Hypogonadal Boy with Skeletal Deformities)

AGE (YR.–MO.)	WEIGHT (LB.)	STATURE		BI-CRIS-TAL (CM.)	SA (YR.–MO.)	PRED. HT. (IN.)
		In.	Cm.			
Birth	8.0	20.0				
1–0	28.0	31.0				
1–7	32.0	33.8				
2–9	36.0	36.5				
3–4	39.0	37.5				
3–11	41.0	39.0				
4–6	42.0	40.5				
6–0	45.0	42.5				
6–3	44.0	43.5				
7–8	50.0	45.5				
8–0	52.0	47.0				
8–3	55.0	48.5				
16–8	102.0	62.3	158.0	23.3	12–9	71.7
17–0	104.0	62.9				
17–5	105.0	63.7				
17–7	110.0	64.0				
18–0	113.0	64.5				
18–6	134.0	65.5				
18–10	131.0	66.5	168.9	25.2		
19–0	135.0	67.0			14–9	69.9
21–0	144.0	69.1	175.5	25.6	15–3	71.0
25–6	163.0	71.3	181.0	27.2	15–10	72.7

Skeletal Age versus Chronological Age

In order better to interpret this rather erratic behavior of the growth and growth-prediction curves, it seemed worthwhile to make a simple additional plot (Fig. 160) of skeletal age versus chronological age. From this it appears that after treatment began at age 16 years 8 months, skeletal age advanced relatively fast, thus accounting for the prediction drop—a kind of growth pattern which often follows the administration of thyroid or steroids. Later, the maturation rate remained steady, while growth continued.

Gradually, in this case, the problem shifted from the possibility of dwarfism to concern over evidence of increasing hormonal deficiency and osseous deformity, thus emphasizing the complexity of the constitutional factors involved.

Androgyny Profile

This graph illustrates the failure of differentiation which is the essence of the asexual build. There is some broadening of the trunk, but notable long-leggedness remains (Figs. 161, 162).

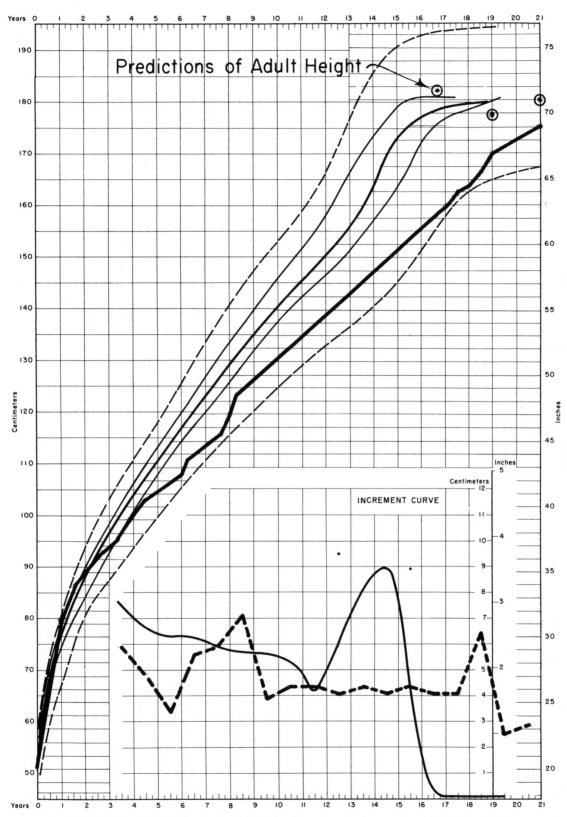

FIG. 159.—Curves of height by age for C-XII: absolute measures, increments, and height predictions

Hypogonadal Boy

Comment

Although the cardinal complaint with this boy was originally his short stature, the prediction was always for an adequate mature height. At a chronological age close to 17, his size was actually appropriate for his skeletal age; both were approximately at the 13-year level. His growth pattern therefore presents the obverse of that of the girl C-VI with her three-year speed-up in development.

In other ways, however, the outcome of this case was less favorable than that achieved by the girl. His short stature did not reflect an isolated deviation of tempo, as in her case, but was associated with many other serious congenital abnormalities.

Returning now to the comparison with the girls with traumatic castration (C-X and C-XI), the differences again can be attributed to the manifestations, in the boy, of constitutional anomalies associated with the disturbed developmental pattern. His evolution is similar to that of the untreated castrated girl, however, in that total linear growth proceeded according to ex-

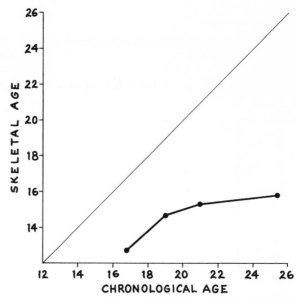

Fig. 160.—C-XII, skeletal age plotted against chronological age.

pectations, whereas his proportions showed the characteristic hypogonadal shift to relatively excessive leg growth.

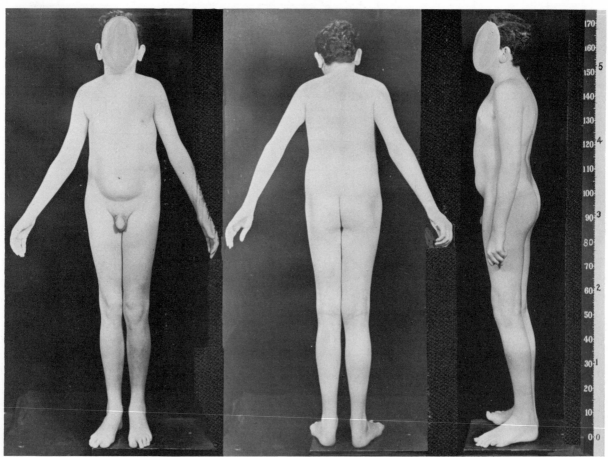

Fig. 161.—Three views of C-XII at 20 years 11 months

ANDROGYNIC PATTERNS OF BODY FORM: RATING PROFILE
Bayley-Bayer Standards*
17–18 Year Norms

Name	Sex Ⓜ F	Date	Age 21	Skeletal Age	Case Number CXII

ITEM	RATING				
("A" through "H" from rear-view photographs)	Hyper-masculine 1	Masculine 2	Intermediate, A-sexual, or Bi-sexual 3, 3a, 3b	Feminine 4	Hyper-feminine 5
I. A. **Surface modeling**	Exaggerated hardness of relief. ○	Strong muscle molding. Bone, vein and tendon prominences. ○	b. Muscular and fat. ● a. Little muscle or fat.	Smooth and soft, with little muscle. ○	Very soft, fat, no muscle. ○
II. **Trunk Contours** B. Shoulder girdle	Massive. ○	Appears wide, heavy and muscular. ○	b. Muscular and fat. ● a. Narrow, "bony."	Slight, soft and narrow. ○	Frail, softly fat. ○
C. Waist line	Marked torso narrowing to low waist: may have minimal indentation. ○	Slight indentation due to narrowing of torso. ○	b. Broad hip and shoulder; little indentation. ● a. Slight symmetrical high concavity.	Definite line accentuated by hip widening. ○	Marked indentation. ○
D. Hip flare	No widening. ○	Slight widening of hips from waist. ○	Intermediate ●	Flares into wide hips laterally and posteriorly. ○	Marked flare. ○
E. Buttocks	Very flat. ○	Flat and angular. ○	Intermediate. ●	Rounded and full. ○	Very broad and rounded. ○
III. **Leg Patterns** F. Thigh Form	Cylinder and/or bulging muscles. ○	Approaches cylinder. Lateral outline convex. ○	Intermediate. ●	Funnel, fat and rounded. Lateral outline concave. ○	Fat, wide-top funnel. ○
G. Interspace (whole leg)	Very open. ○	Open center above and below knees. ○	Intermediate. ○	Closed center except small space below knees. ●	Thighs and knees together, feet apart. ○
H. Muscle bulge (lower leg)	Strong bulge, no fat. ○	Prominent inner bulge of gastrocnemius. ○	b. Moderate muscle bulge. ○ a. No muscle bulge; spindly.	Slight inner bulge; shapely, smooth, outer curve. ●	Very little muscle, but smoothly rounded and outer curve. ○
J. Penis size	1 Very ○ 1.5 Large ○	2 Average ○	2.5 Small ○ 3 Very ●		
K. Breast size			3 Very ○ 3.5 Small ○	4 Average ○	4.5 Large ○ 5 Very ○
L. Body hair density	1 ○ Heavy on thighs, etc.	2 ○ Easily discernible	2.5 ● ○ Sparse.	○♀ Absent	
M. Pubic pattern	Disperse ○	Acuminate. ○	Sagittal ○ ●	Horizontal ○♀	
N. Bicristal ──── Index Biacromial 71	– ←68 69 ○	73 74 ●	76 77 ○	82 83 → + ○	
P. Strength (Kg) Grip (R+L)+Thrust +Pull	+ ←244 243 ○	186 185 ○	148 147 ○	110 109 → – ○	
Grip (R+L)	+ ←126 125 ○	95 94 ○	80 79 ○	59 58 → – ○	
Androgyny Score (Sum of "A"–"H") 25.5	8 ○ 12 13	19 20 ○	B ○ A ● 25 26	34 35 ○	40
Characteristic Description (Circle one)	**Hypermasculine**	**Masculine**	Intermediate Bisexual (Asexual) Disharmonious	**Feminine**	**Hyperfeminine**

Fig. 162.—Androgyny profile of C-XII at 21 years

Chapter 21

Female Pseudohermaphrodism

Pseudohermaphrodism is such a crucial developmental disturbance that every aspect of the constitution is affected by it. The case reports that follow are limited to an exposition of the somatic data. The two cases permit examination of striking androgynic contrasts in the patterns of body form as well as indicating some of the effects of the newer hormonal therapy.

It should be pointed out that despite the complete difference in etiology between these two cases of pseudohermaphrodism and the two with precocious menarche, their growth patterns show many points of similarity. In all these cases, the factor which dominates the growth picture is the too-early skeletal maturation.

CASE C-XIII (FEMALE PSEUDOHERMAPHRODITE)

Presenting Problem at 11 Years 6 Months

Masculine development in a child (Fig. 163, 164) who wished to be, and whose family considered her to be, a girl, despite the fact that there were the following masculine traits:

> Penis-like structure, well developed since birth
> Precocious growth of pubic and axillary hair since age 5
> Hair on chin and face, recently necessitating shaving

Complete clinical, laboratory, and psychological details and the complex interplay between them is reported elsewhere (Bayer, 1947). The presentation at hand deals only with the morphologic data.

Anthropometric Values and Deviation Charts

Illustrated in the deviation chart (Fig. 165) are the measures at 15 years 9 months, the first complete set available. However, some earlier (age 11 years 6 months) and later (age 18 years 4 months) measurements are recorded in the longitudinal growth data (Table 31) and warrant brief comment.

At 11 years 6 months: Measurements indicate that C-XIII's weight is heavy for a girl and would be considered heavier still for a boy. Stature is normal for either. Weight/stature ratio is normal for girls but would be much too large for boys. Sitting height/stature ratio is large, i.e., the child is very short-legged. This short-leggedness suggests early maturation and eventual short stature.

Age 15 years 9 months: By this time the divergence between male and female characteristics is more marked (see Figs. 164, 165). Stature is short for a girl; it is even shorter against the norms for boys. Bi-cristal is narrow for boys, more so for girls. The bi-acromial breadth is too broad for girls. Measurements relative to stature are too large for either girls or boys, considering her short stature. Bi-cristal/bi-acromial index is too small for either sex, but smaller for females.

Age 18 years 4 months: Measurements are not much changed, except that there has been some increase in stature, almost all of this being in trunk rather than leg length (Fig. 166). The bi-cristal diameter remains absolutely and relatively narrow.

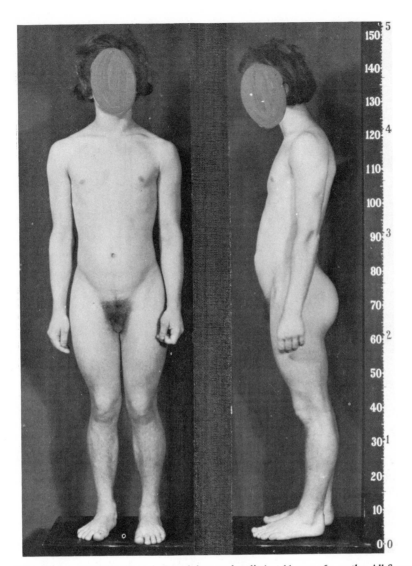

FIG. 163.—Views of C-XIII (Female Pseudohermaphrodite) at 11 years 6 months. All figures pertaining to this case, Figs. 163–68, are from Bayer, "Pseudohermaphrodism: A Psychosomatic Case Study," *Psychosomatic Medicine*, Vol. 9 (1947). Courtesy of Paul B. Hoeber, New York.

TABLE 31

GROWTH DATA
CASE C-XIII (Female Pseudohermaphrodite)

Age (Yr.–Mo.)	Weight (Kg.)	Stature (Cm.)	Bi-Cristal (Cm.)	SA (Mo.)	Pred. Ht. (In.)
11–6	51.3	149.9			
15–9	54.9	151.5	23.9	Adult	
18–4	59.4	152.1	24.2		

Androgyny

Examination of photos show divergencies from normal feminine build at all ages (Figs. 163, 164, 166).

In the anterior view at age 11 years 6 months, only the curve of buttock and thigh looks feminine. Masculine form is shown in the surface-modeling, shoulder width, waist line, and lower leg muscles. Absence of breasts and the presence of a hypertrophied clitoris, a sagittal pubic-hair pattern, facial hair, and diffuse body hair emphasize the masculinity. The large hands and feet also look boyish.

201

Female Pseudohermaphrodite

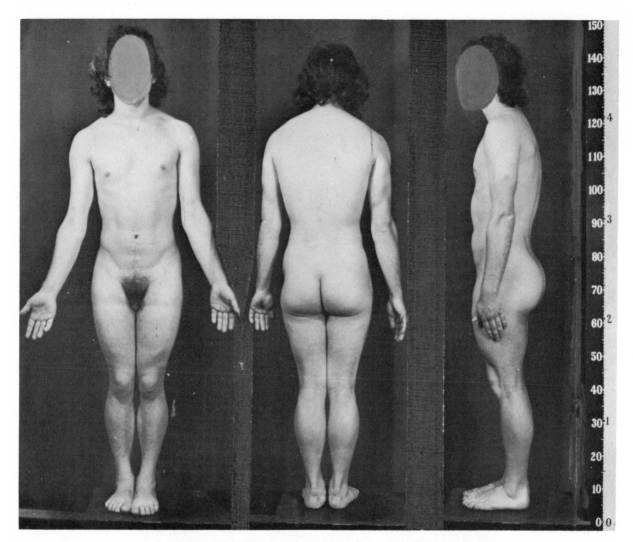

Fig. 164.—Three views of C-XIII at 15 years 9 months

By age 15 years 9 months, photographs record that the surface-modeling and shoulder girdle are now hypermasculine; the body and facial hair is more dense: the head hair is receding at the temples. There is no breast development, but the feminine curve of buttock and thigh is still more pronounced.

By age 18 years 4 months, hair recession at the temples has increased. The continuing hypermasculine trend in the upper body is curiously balanced by the development of a hyperfeminine thigh pattern. A fortuitous change in photographic technique suggests a softer surface modeling than actually existed. The androgynic pattern is shown on the accompanying androgynic rating profile, Figure 167.

These analyses imply abnormalities in all phases of sexual differentiation: the *direction* is bisexual; the *degree* is exaggerated in both directions; the *tempo* of maturation has been accelerated. This latter is evidenced by an "old look" at all three age levels, by the characteristic short-leggedness resulting from early epiphyseal closure, by a mature skeletal age at 15 years 9 months, and by the hair recession which, before 16 years of age, gives the appearance of a balding man. It should be mentioned that the abnormally small bicristal/bi-acromial, or trunk-breadth, index has been noted in reports of other pseudohermaphrodites.

Skeletal Age

Skeletal age was already adult at 15 years 9 months, thus confirming the other evidences of accelerated maturation.

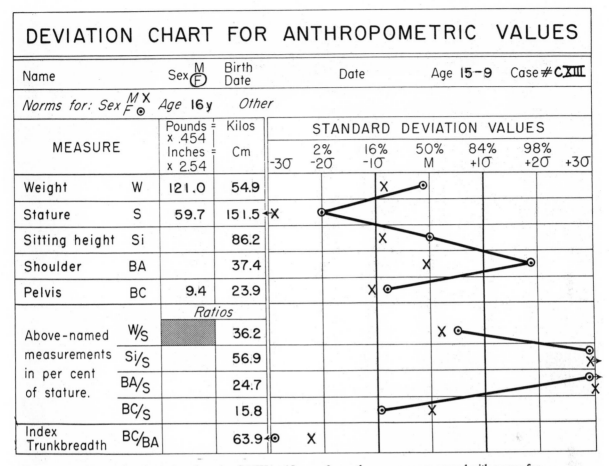

FIG. 165.—Deviation chart for C-XIII at 15 years 9 months; measures compared with norms for 16-year-old girls and norms for 16-year-old boys.

Graphic Growth Record of Height, Weight, and Bi-Cristal

Observations on this child began when the drama of accelerated growth and development was approaching its finale. The accompanying graph (Fig. 168) merely illustrates that, while growth in stature stopped prematurely, weight continued to increase. The narrow bi-cristal in this instance has no value for weight prediction.

Growth Diagnosis
Accelerated maturation
Bisexual body build

Clinical Diagnosis
Female pseudohermaphrodism
Gonads: female, atrophic

Comment

Treatment involved plastic surgery and subtotal removal of the right adrenal (at 18 years 7 months). Cortisone was not yet available during the period when this patient was under observation.

Comparison with Case C-XIV indicates that whereas the linear growth pattern is essentially similar, this patient showed no development of female secondary sex characters. Nevertheless, her basic body form is bisexual, showing some characteristics which are masculine, some feminine.

Female Pseudohermaphrodite

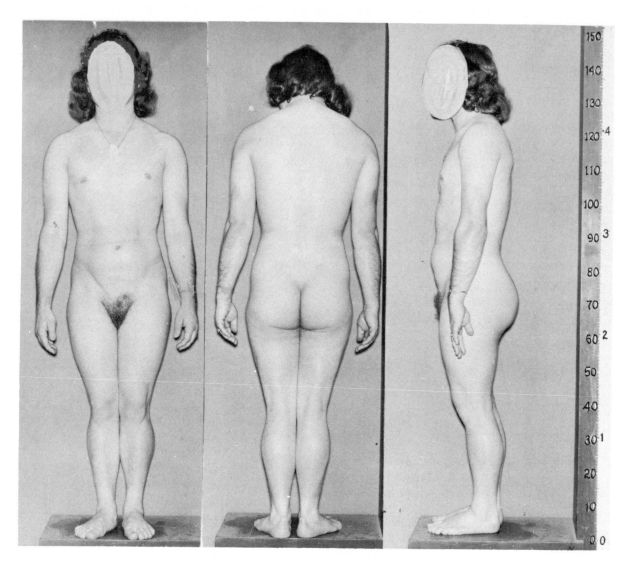

FIG. 166.—Three views of C-XIII at 18 years 4 months

ANDROGYNIC PATTERNS OF BODY FORM: RATING PROFILE
Bayley-Bayer Standards*
17–18 Year Norms

Name	Sex ⓜ/Ⓕ	Date	Age 18-4	Skeletal Age	Case Number C-XIII

ITEM	RATING				
("A" through "H" from rear-view photographs)	Hyper-masculine 1	Masculine 2	Intermediate, A-sexual, or Bi-sexual 3, 3a, 3b	Feminine 4	Hyper-feminine 5
I. A. **Surface modeling**	Exaggerated hardness of relief. ●	Strong muscle molding. Bone, vein and tendon ○ prominences.	b. Muscular and fat. ○ ○ a. Little muscle or fat.	Smooth and soft, with little muscle. ○	Very soft, fat, no muscle. ○
II. **Trunk Contours** B. Shoulder girdle	Massive. ●	Appears wide, heavy and muscular. ○	b. Muscular and fat. ○ a. Narrow, "bony."	Slight, soft and narrow. ○	Frail, softly fat. ○
C. Waist line	Marked torso narrowing to low waist: may have ○ minimal indentation.	Slight indentation due to narrowing of torso. ●	b. Broad hip and shoulder; little ○ indentation. a. Slight ○ symmetrical high concavity.	Definite line accentuated by hip widening. ○	Marked indentation. ○
D. Hip flare	No widening. ○	Slight widening of hips from waist. ●	Intermediate. ○	Flares into wide hips laterally and posteriorly. ○	Marked flare. ○
E. Buttocks	Very flat. ○	Flat and angular. ○	Intermediate. ●	Rounded and full. ○	Very broad and rounded. ○
III. **Leg Patterns** F. Thigh Form	Cylinder and/or bulging muscles. ○	Approaches cylinder. Lateral outline convex. ○	Intermediate. ○	Funnel, fat and rounded. Lateral outline concave. ●	Fat, wide-top funnel. ○
G. Interspace (whole leg)	Very open. ○	Open center above and below knees. ○	Intermediate. ○	Closed center except small space below knees. ○	Thighs and knees together, feet apart. ●
H. Muscle bulge (lower leg)	Strong bulge, no fat. ○	Prominent inner bulge of gastrocnemius. ●	b. Moderate muscle bulge. ○ a. No muscle bulge; spindly.	Slight inner bulge; shapely, smooth, outer curve. ○	Very little muscle, but smoothly rounded and outer curve.
J. Penis size	1 Very ○ 1.5 Large ○	2 Average ○	2.5 Small ● 3 Very ○		
K. Breast size		●	3 Very ○ 3.5 Small ○	4 Average ○	4.5 Large ○ 5 Very ○
L. Body hair density	1 ○ Heavy on thighs, etc.	Easily discernible ●	2.5 ○ Sparse.	(3) ○♂	○♀ Absent
M. Pubic pattern	Disperse ○ Acuminate. ●	Sagittal ○	○♂	Horizontal ○♀	
N. Bicristal / Biacromial Index **64**	— ←68 ● 69	73 ○ 74	76 ○ 77	82 ○ 83 → +	○
P. Strength (Kg) Grip (R+L)+Thrust +Pull	+←244 ○ 243	186 ○ 185	148 ○ 147	110 ○ 109 → —	○
Grip (R+L)	+←126 ○ 125	95 ○ 94	80 ○ 79	59 ○ 58 → —	○
Androgyny Score (Sum of "A"–"H") **20**	8 ○ 12 13	19 20	Ⓑ ○Ⓐ 25 26	34 35 ○	40
Characteristic Description (Circle one)	**Hypermasculine**	**Masculine**	**Intermediate** ⒷⒾⓈⓔⓧⓤⓐⓛ **Asexual** **Disharmonious**	**Feminine**	**Hyperfeminine**

Supplementary Criteria

Fig. 167.—Androgyny profile of C-XIII at 18 years 4 months

Female Pseudohermaphrodite

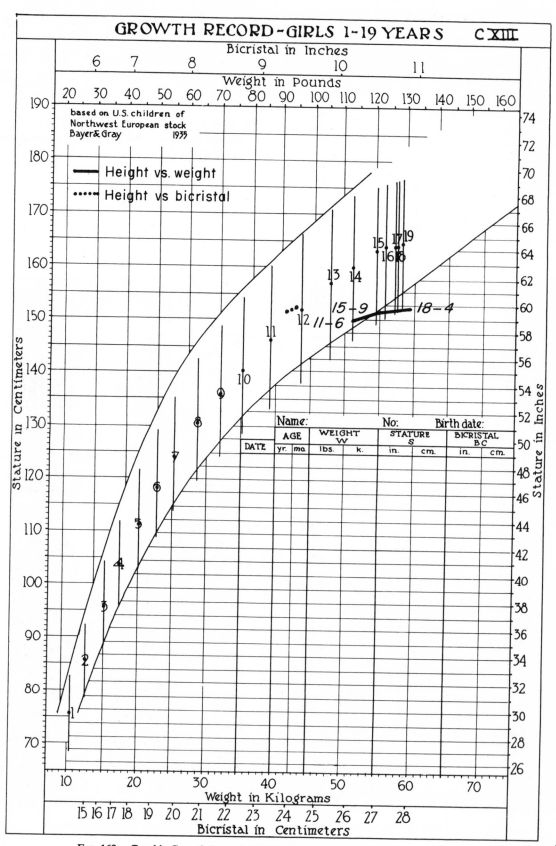

FIG. 168.—Graphic Growth Record, C-XIII: height vs. weight; height vs. bi-cristal

CASE C-XIV (FEMALE PSEUDOHERMAPHRODITE: SUPPRESSIVE THERAPY)

Presenting Problem at 6 Years 10 Months
  Large size
  Luxuriant pubic hair
  Overdeveloped clitoris

Anthropometric Values and Deviation Charts

Compared with her age and sex peers, this girl's measures are unusual only in that she is somewhat too tall and has a Si/S ratio that is too small. Since the sitting height itself is average, it is clear that the large stature and the small Si/S reflect overgrowth in the legs (Figs. 169, 170).

Because 7-year-old boys and girls are much alike, no significant difference in pattern is shown when this girl's measures are compared to norms for the opposite sex.

At 10 years 11 months (Figs. 171, 172) measurements plot somewhat differently. Compared to those of her chronological-age peers and sex peers, the length measures and ratios are normal, but there is a slight tendency for weight and breadth to be on the heavy side.

If now she is compared with her skeletal-age peers (15 years), the most significant finding is that she is too short in total stature and in sitting height for this 15-year level. This fits in with a small stature prediction.

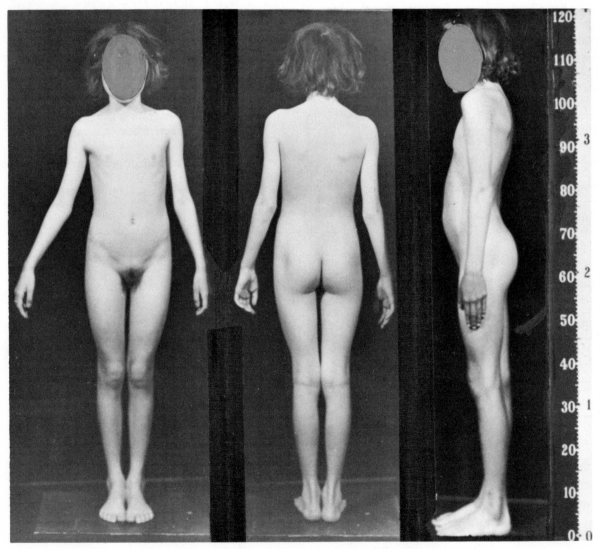

FIG. 169.—Three views of C-XIV (Female Pseudohermaphrodite: Suppressive Therapy) at 6 years 10 months.

Suppressive Therapy

Secondary Sex Characters

At the first examination (at 6 years 10 months), this girl had already reached breast stage II and hair stage III, i.e., she is close to a secondary sex level frequently found between the ages of 10 and 13 years and never normally found in such a young child.

Four years later, at 10 years 11 months, breast development has proceeded to the adult level, but the pubic pattern remains much as before.

Skeletal Age

At 6 years 10 months of age, C-XIV had a skeletal age of 11 years 6 months. Subsequent readings are shown in longitudinal growth data (Table 32), and in the accompanying graph (Fig. 173).

Skeletal maturation, when first documented, already has a lead of 4 years 8 months over the chronological age; four years later the lead is 4 years 2 months. The curve connecting the five observations shows that in the interval between the end points the skeletal maturation rate is temporarily retarded but later increases again.

Stature Prediction: 58.2 in. at CA 6 years 10 months.

Although C-XIV is tall for her age, the expectation is for eventual dwarfing.

TABLE 32

GROWTH DATA
CASE C-XIV (Female Pseudohemaphrodite with Suppressive Therapy)

AGE (YR.–MO.)	WEIGHT (KG.)	STATURE		BI-CRISTAL (CM.)	SA (YR.–MO.)	PRED. HT. (IN.)
		In.	Cm.			
Birth		19.0				
1–0		30.0				
6–2		49.5				
6–10	22.2	51.9	131.8	20.7	11–6	58.2
7–4		52.5	133.2		11–9	58.5
8–0		53.7	136.3		12–0	59.5
8–7		54.6			12–3	59.8
9–4	33.1	56.1		22.9		
9–5		56.2	142.6			
9–8		56.4	143.1			
9–9		56.7	144.0			13–3	59.4
10–0	38.1	57.1	144.9	23.8		
10–10		58.2			15–0	59.0
10–11	47.2	58.4	148.1	25.3		
14–1	49.4	59.4	150.9		16–0	59.8

Growth Diagnosis

Accelerated growth, especially in legs
Accelerated maturation
Bisexual characteristics

Clinical Diagnosis: Female pseudohermaphrodism

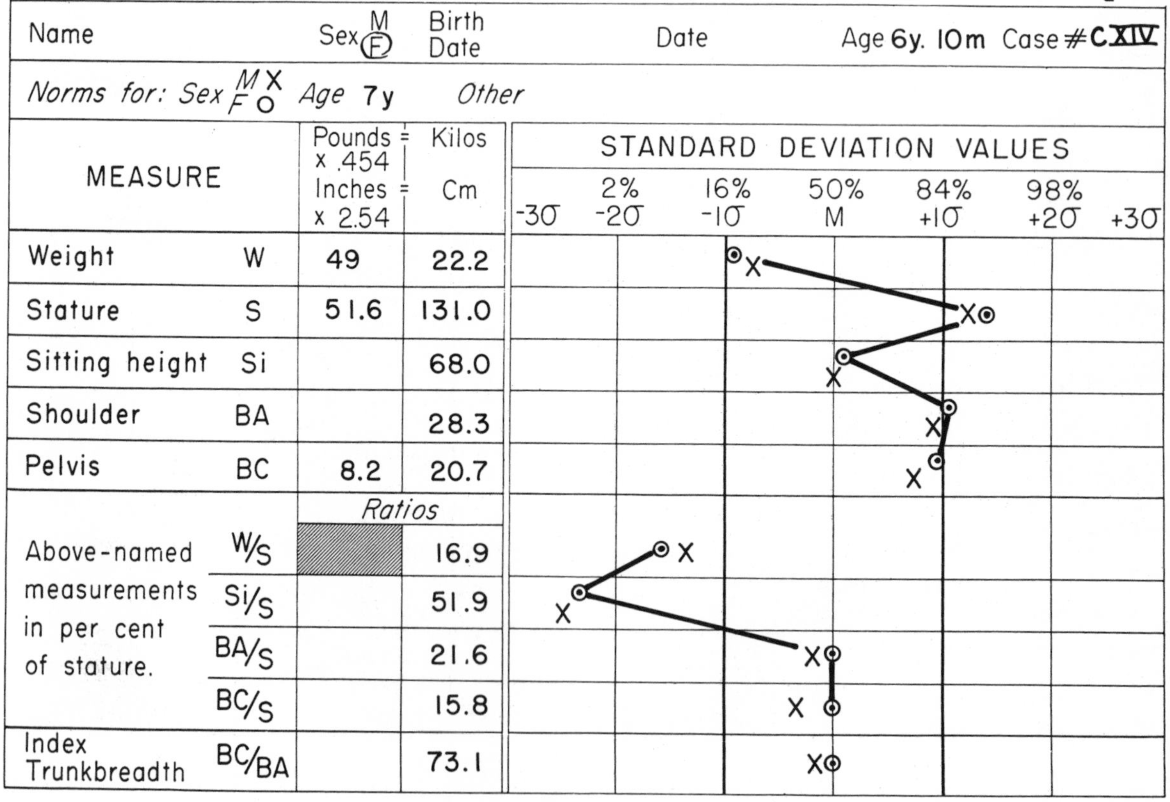

FIG. 170.—Deviation chart for C-XIV at 6 years 10 months; measures compared with norms for 7-year-old girls and norms for 7-year-old boys.

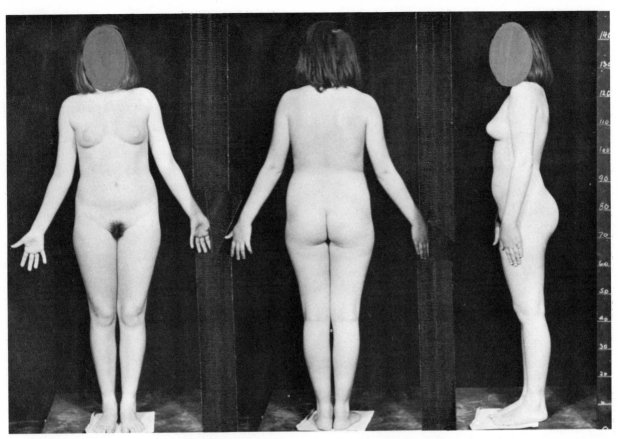

FIG. 171.—Three views of C-XIV at 10 years 11 months

Name		Sex (M/F)	Birth Date	Date		Age 10-11	Case # CXIV

Norms for: Sex (M/F) C. Age Peers 11 Other Skel. Age Peers 15 y □

MEASURE		Pounds = x .454 Inches = x 2.54	Kilos Cm	STANDARD DEVIATION VALUES						
				-3σ	2% -2σ	16% -1σ	50% M	84% $+1\sigma$	98% $+2\sigma$	$+3\sigma$
Weight	W	104.0	47.2			□		⊙		
Stature	S	58.4	148.1	□			⊙			
Sitting height	Si		77.0	□			⊙			
Shoulder	BA		33.4				□		⊙	
Pelvis	BC	10.0	25.3				□	⊙		
Above-named measurements in per cent of stature.		*Ratios*								
	W/S		31.9				□	⊙		
	Si/S		52.0				□⊙			
	BA/S		22.6						⊙□	
	BC/S		17.1					⊙ □		
Index Trunkbreadth	BC/BA		75.8			□ ⊙				

FIG. 172.—Deviation chart for C-XIV at 10 years 11 months; measures compared with norms for 11-year-old girls and norms for C-XIV's skeletal-age peers (15-year-old girls).

Suppressive Therapy

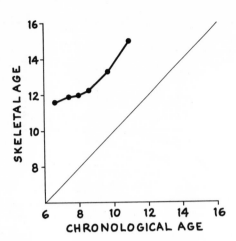

FIG. 173.—C-XIV, skeletal age plotted against chronological age.

This child has been continuously treated with cortisone, with the intention of securing optimal growth and optimal female differentiation. "Optimal growth" would involve enhanced linear growth relative to maturation.

The comparative data already shown in photos, anthropometric values, secondary sex characters, and skeletal development indicate that sexual differentiation has proceeded at an accelerated rate in the desired feminine direction, although certain masculine characteristics remain. Reference to graphs permit further evaluation of the growth trend.

Growth Curves of Height by Age

Combining historical with observational data, these growth curves (Fig. 174) show that there had been very rapid growth prior to the institution of treatment. It is not possible to say whether the slowing-down after the administration of cortisone is a response to treatment or reflects a decline after a premature adolescent spurt. The increment curve tends to parallel an adolescent curve and thus looks rather "autonomous."

The stature-prediction curve is the obverse of the bone-age curve, i.e., the slower the maturation, the greater the height potential. At 14 years C-XIV had achieved a skeletal age of 16 years and a stature of 59.4 in.—exactly the first height prediction made after the beginning of treatment but with 0.4 in. of potential growth remaining.

Graphic Growth Record of Height, Weight, and Bi-Cristal

This graph shows a dramatic change in the height-weight curve, from a point describing a tall slender girl to a point describing a girl of average height and lateral build. Since the bi-cristal breadth has been relatively broad throughout, the later heavier weights have gradually approached the weight prediction from build (Fig. 175).

Comment

On the basis of the foregoing data, it seems fair to credit the treatment program with a beneficent effect toward normal feminine differentiation, especially if comparison is made with the preceding Case XIII, who received no cortisone. Again, however, it is notable that the linear growth pattern and androgyny of body form are similar in the two cases, suggesting that the fundamental genetic and hormonal disturbance is deep and complex.

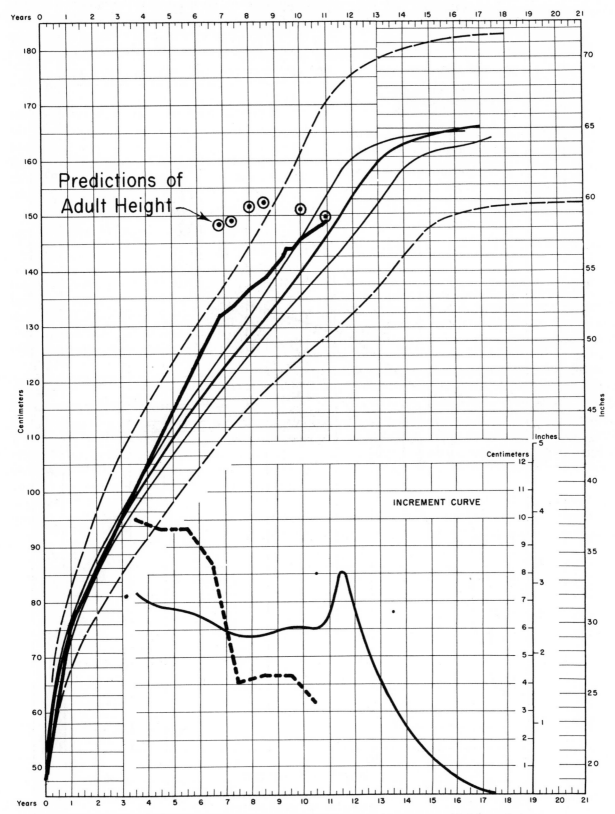

FIG. 174.—Curves of height by age for C-XIV: absolute measures, increments, and height predictions

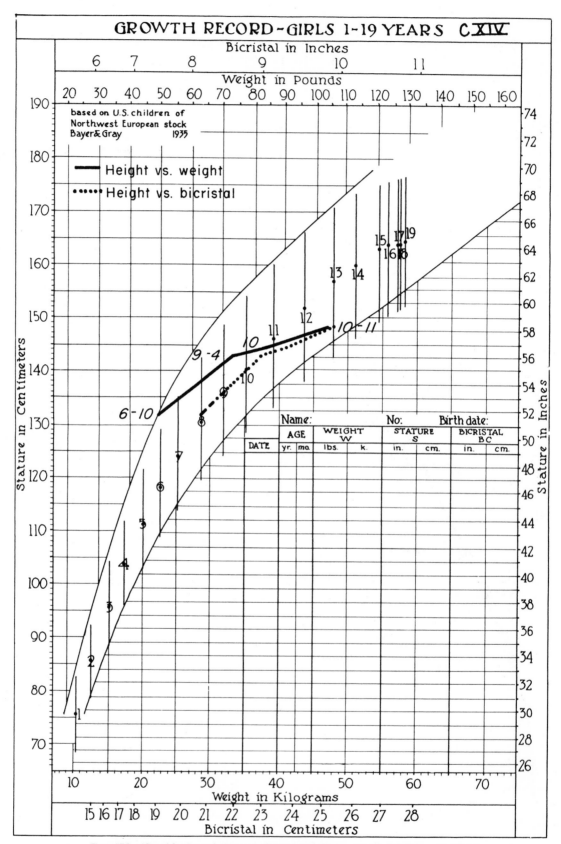

FIG. 175.—Graphic Growth Record, C-XIV: height vs. weight; height vs. bi-cristal

Appendixes

Appendix I
Anthropometric Values:
Means and Standard Deviations

Appendix II
Height-Prediction Tables

Appendix III
Converting Age into Decimal System

Appendix I

Anthropometric Values

ANTHROPOMETRIC VALUES FOR BOYS, AGE 1 (0.5–1.4 YEARS)*

	−3 S.D.	−2 S.D.	−1 S.D.	Mean	+1 S.D.	+2 S.D.	+3 S.D.	S.D.
Measures:								
Weight (W)...............	5.8	7.5	9.2	*10.9*	12.6	14.3	16.0	*1.7*
Stature (S)................	63.8	67.6	71.4	*75.2*	79.0	82.8	86.6	*3.8*
Sitting height (Si).........	43.0	44.8	46.6	*48.4*	50.2	52.0	53.8	*1.8*
Shoulder diameter (BA).....	....	....	....	....	....	....	....	....
Pelvic diameter (BC).......	....	....	....	....	....	....	....	....
Above measures, relative to stature:								
W/S....................	9.7	11.1	12.5	*13.9*	15.3	16.7	18.1	*1.4*
Si/S...................	59.0	60.6	62.2	*63.8*	65.4	67.0	68.6	*1.6*
BA/S..................	....	....	....	....	....	....	....	....
BC/S..................	....	....	....	....	....	....	....	....
Index:								
Trunk breadth (BC/BA)....	....	....	....	....	....	....	....	....

ANTHROPOMETRIC VALUES FOR BOYS, AGE 2 (1.5–2.4 YEARS)*

	−3 S.D.	−2 S.D.	−1 S.D.	Mean	+1 S.D.	+2 S.D.	+3 S.D.	S.D.
Measures:								
Weight (W)...............	8.6	10.2	11.8	*13.4*	15.0	16.6	18.2	*1.6*
Stature (S)................	*78.2*	82.0	85.8	*89.6*	93.4	97.2	101.0	*3.8*
Sitting height (Si).........	49.0	51.1	53.2	*55.3*	57.4	59.5	61.6	*2.1*
Shoulder diameter (BA)....	18.8	19.7	20.6	*21.5*	22.4	23.3	24.2	*0.9*
Pelvic diameter (BC).......	12.4	13.5	14.6	*15.7*	16.8	17.9	19.0	*1.1*
Above measures, relative to stature:								
W/S....................	10.8	12.0	13.2	*14.4*	15.6	16.8	18.0	*1.2*
Si/S...................	56.2	57.8	59.4	*61.0*	62.6	64.2	65.8	*1.6*
BA/S..................	22.2	22.8	23.4	*24.0*	24.6	25.2	25.8	*0.6*
BC/S..................	14.6	15.4	16.2	*17.0*	17.8	18.6	19.4	*0.8*
Index:								
Trunk breadth (BC/BA)....	61.1	64.1	67.1	*70.1*	73.1	76.1	79.1	*3.0*

ANTHROPOMETRIC VALUES FOR BOYS, AGE 3 (2.5–3.4 YEARS)*

	−3 S.D.	−2 S.D.	−1 S.D.	Mean	+1 S.D.	+2 S.D.	+3 S.D.	S.D.
Measures:								
Weight (W)...............	10.8	12.3	13.8	*15.3*	16.8	18.3	19.8	*1.5*
Stature (S)................	84.2	88.4	92.6	*96.8*	101.0	105.2	109.4	*4.2*
Sitting height (Si).........	50.4	52.8	55.2	*57.6*	60.0	62.4	64.8	*2.4*
Shoulder diameter (BA).....	19.3	20.4	21.5	*22.6*	23.7	24.8	25.9	*1.1*
Pelvic diameter (BC).......	12.9	13.9	14.9	*15.9*	16.9	17.9	18.9	*1.0*
Above measures relative to stature:								
W/S....................	12.4	13.5	14.6	*15.7*	16.8	17.9	19.0	*1.1*
Si/S...................	54.6	56.2	57.8	*59.4*	61.0	62.6	64.2	*1.6*
BA/S..................	20.5	21.5	22.5	*23.5*	24.5	25.5	26.5	*1.0*
BC/S..................	14.8	15.4	16.0	*16.6*	17.2	17.8	18.4	*0.6*
Index:								
Trunk breadth (BC/BA)....	61.3	64.4	67.5	*70.6*	73.7	76.8	79.9	*3.1*

* Means and standard deviations based on techniques and data of Gray and Ayres (1931). All measures according to the metric system.

ANTHROPOMETRIC VALUES FOR BOYS, AGE 4 (3.5–4.4 YEARS)*

	−3 S.D.	−2 S.D.	−1 S.D.	Mean	+1 S.D.	+2 S.D.	+3 S.D.	S.D.
Measures:								
Weight (W)...............	11.9	13.7	15.5	*17.3*	19.1	20.9	22.7	*1.8*
Stature (S)...............	90.6	95.3	100.0	*104.7*	109.4	114.1	118.8	*4.7*
Sitting height (Si).........	52.9	55.4	57.9	*60.4*	62.9	65.4	67.9	*2.5*
Shoulder diameter (BA).....	19.8	21.0	22.2	*23.4*	24.6	25.8	27.0	*1.2*
Pelvic diameter (BC).......	14.0	15.0	16.0	*17.0*	18.0	19.0	20.0	*1.0*
Above measures relative to stature:								
W/S....................	12.6	13.9	15.2	*16.5*	17.8	19.1	20.4	*1.3*
Si/S....................	53.0	54.6	56.2	*57.8*	59.4	61.0	62.6	*1.6*
BA/S....................	19.7	20.7	21.7	*22.7*	23.7	24.7	25.7	*1.0*
BC/S....................	14.6	15.2	15.8	*16.4*	17.0	17.6	18.2	*0.6*
Index:								
Trunk breadth (BC/BA)....	62.6	65.8	69.0	*72.2*	75.4	78.6	81.8	*3.2*

ANTHROPOMETRIC VALUES FOR BOYS, AGE 5 (4.5–5.4 YEARS)*

	−3 S.D.	−2 S.D.	−1 S.D.	Mean	+1 S.D.	+2 S.D.	+3 S.D.	S.D.
Measures:								
Weight (W)...............	12.7	15.0	17.3	*19.6*	21.9	24.2	26.5	*2.3*
Stature (S)...............	97.4	102.0	106.6	*111.2*	115.8	120.4	125.0	*4.6*
Sitting height (Si).........	55.6	58.0	60.4	*62.8*	65.2	67.6	70.0	*2.4*
Shoulder diameter (BA).....	21.2	22.4	23.6	*24.8*	26.0	27.2	28.4	*1.2*
Pelvic diameter (BC)......,	15.2	16.2	17.2	*18.2*	19.2	20.2	21.2	*1.0*
Above measures relative to stature:								
W/S....................	12.8	14.4	16.0	*17.6*	19.2	20.8	22.4	*1.6*
Si/S....................	51.8	53.1	55.0	*56.6*	58.2	59.8	61.4	*1.6*
BA/S....................	19.8	20.6	21.4	*22.2*	23.0	23.8	24.6	*0.8*
BC/S....................	14.6	15.2	15.8	*16.4*	17.0	17.6	18.2	*0.6*
Index:								
Trunk breadth (BC/BA)....	63.5	66.9	70.3	*73.7*	77.1	80.5	83.9	*3.4*

ANTHROPOMETRIC VALUES FOR BOYS, AGE 6 (5.5–6.4 YEARS)*

	−3 S.D.	−2 S.D.	−1 S.D.	Mean	+1 S.D.	+2 S.D.	+3 S.D.	S.D.
Measures:								
Weight (W)...............	13.8	16.6	19.4	*22.2*	25.0	27.8	30.6	*2.8*
Stature (S)...............	104.2	109.0	113.8	*118.6*	123.4	128.2	133.0	*4.8*
Sitting height (Si).........	58.0	60.6	63.2	*65.8*	68.4	71.0	73.6	*2.6*
Shoulder diameter (BA).....	22.6	23.7	24.8	*25.9*	27.0	28.2	29.3	*1.1*
Pelvic diameter (BC).......	16.2	17.2	18.2	*19.2*	20.2	21.2	22.2	*1.0*
Above measures relative to stature:								
W/S....................	12.9	14.8	16.7	*18.6*	20.5	22.4	24.3	*1.9*
Si/S....................	51.2	52.6	54.0	*55.4*	56.8	58.2	59.6	*1.4*
BA/S....................	19.5	20.3	21.1	*21.9*	22.7	23.5	24.3	*0.8*
BC/S....................	14.1	14.8	15.5	*16.2*	16.9	17.6	18.3	*0.7*
Index:								
Trunk breadth (BC/BA)....	63.9	67.3	70.7	*74.1*	77.5	80.9	84.3	*3.4*

* Means and standard deviations based on techniques and data of Gray and Ayres (1931). All measures according to the metric system.

Anthropometric Values

ANTHROPOMETRIC VALUES FOR BOYS, AGE 7 (6.5–7.4 YEARS)*

	−3 S.D.	−2 S.D.	−1 S.D.	Mean	−1 S.D.	+2 S.D.	+3 S.D.	S.D.
Measures:								
Weight (*W*)...............	14.4	17.8	21.2	*24.6*	28.0	31.4	34.8	*3.4*
Stature (*S*)...............	109.4	114.5	119.6	*124.7*	129.8	134.9	140.0	*5.1*
Sitting height (*Si*).........	60.2	62.8	65.4	*68.0*	70.6	73.2	75.8	*2.6*
Shoulder diameter (*BA*).....	73.2	74.5	75.8	*77.1*	78.4	79.7	81.0	*1.3*
Pelvic diameter (*BC*).......	16.7	17.8	18.9	*20.0*	21.1	22.2	23.3	*1.1*
Above measures, relative to stature:								
W/S....................	13.4	15.5	17.6	*19.7*	21.8	23.9	26.0	*2.1*
Si/S....................	51.2	52.3	53.4	*54.5*	55.6	56.7	57.8	*1.1*
BA/S....................	19.4	20.2	21.0	*21.8*	22.6	23.4	24.2	*0.8*
BC/S....................	13.2	14.8	15.4	*16.0*	16.6	17.2	17.8	*0.6*
Index:								
Trunk breadth (*BC/BA*)....	64.1	67.3	70.5	*73.7*	76.9	80.1	83.2	*3.2*

ANTHROPOMETRIC VALUES FOR BOYS, AGE 8 (7.5–8.4 YEARS)*

	−3 S.D.	−2 S.D.	−1 S.D.	Mean	+1 S.D.	+2 S.D.	+3 S.D.	S.D.
Measures:								
Weight (*W*)...............	15.9	19.9	23.9	*27.9*	31.9	35.9	39.9	*4.0*
Stature (*S*)...............	114.9	120.3	125.7	*131.1*	136.5	141.9	147.3	*5.4*
Sitting height (*Si*).........	62.1	64.9	67.7	*70.5*	73.3	76.1	78.9	*2.8*
Shoulder diameter (*BA*).....	24.0	25.4	26.8	*28.2*	29.6	31.0	32.4	*1.4*
Pelvic diameter (*BC*).......	17.6	18.7	19.8	*20.9*	22.0	23.1	24.2	*1.1*
Above measures, relative to stature:								
W/S....................	14.0	16.4	18.8	*21.2*	23.6	26.0	28.4	*2.4*
Si/S....................	50.8	51.8	52.8	*53.8*	54.8	55.8	56.8	*1.0*
BA/S....................	19.2	20.0	20.8	*21.6*	22.4	23.2	24.0	*0.8*
BC/S....................	14.2	14.8	15.4	*16.0*	16.6	17.2	17.8	*0.6*
Index:								
Trunk breadth (*BC/BA*)....	63.9	67.3	70.7	*74.1*	77.5	80.9	84.3	*3.4*

ANTHROPOMETRIC VALUES FOR BOYS, AGE 9 (8.5–9.4 YEARS)*

	−3 S.D.	−2 S.D.	−1 S.D.	Mean	+1 S.D.	+2 S.D.	+3 S.D.	S.D.
Measures:								
Weight (*W*)...............	16.8	21.5	26.2	*30.9*	35.6	40.3	45.0	*4.7*
Stature (*S*)...............	119.3	124.8	130.3	*135.8*	141.3	146.8	152.3	*5.5*
Sitting height (*Si*).........	63.6	66.4	69.2	*72.0*	74.8	77.6	80.4	*2.8*
Shoulder diameter (*BA*).....	25.0	26.4	27.8	*29.2*	30.6	32.0	33.4	*1.4*
Pelvic diameter (*BC*).......	18.2	19.3	20.4	*21.5*	22.6	23.7	24.8	*1.1*
Above measures, relative to stature:								
W/S....................	14.2	17.0	19.8	*22.6*	25.4	28.2	31.0	*2.8*
Si/S....................	50.0	51.1	52.2	*53.3*	54.4	55.5	56.6	*1.1*
BA/S....................	19.2	20.0	20.8	*21.6*	22.4	23.2	24.0	*0.8*
BC/S....................	14.1	14.7	15.3	*15.9*	16.5	17.1	17.7	*0.6*
Index:								
Trunk breadth (*BC/BA*)....	63.2	66.7	70.2	*73.7*	77.2	80.7	84.2	*3.5*

* Means and standard deviations based on techniques and data of Gray and Ayres (1931). All measures according to the metric system.

ANTHROPOMETRIC VALUES FOR BOYS, AGE 10 (9.5–10.4 YEARS)*

	−3 S.D.	−2 S.D.	−1 S.D.	Mean	+1 S.D.	+2 S.D.	+3 S.D.	S.D.
Measures:								
Weight (W)..............	18.6	23.9	29.2	*34.5*	39.8	45.1	50.4	*5.3*
Stature (S)...............	124.4	130.0	135.6	*141.2*	146.8	152.4	158.0	*5.6*
Sitting height (Si).........	66.1	68.9	71.7	*74.5*	77.3	80.1	82.9	*2.8*
Shoulder diameter (BA).....	26.9	28.0	29.1	*30.2*	31.3	32.4	33.5	*1.1*
Pelvic diameter (BC).......	18.9	20.0	21.1	*22.2*	23.3	24.4	25.5	*1.1*
Above measures, relative to stature:								
W/S....................	15.1	18.2	21.3	*24.4*	27.5	30.6	33.7	*3.1*
Si/S...................	49.2	50.4	51.6	*52.8*	54.0	55.2	56.4	*1.2*
BA/S..................	19.0	19.8	20.6	*21.4*	22.2	23.0	23.8	*0.8*
BC/S..................	14.1	14.7	15.3	*15.9*	16.5	17.1	17.7	*0.6*
Index:								
Trunk breadth (BC/BA)....	63.4	66.9	70.4	*73.9*	77.4	80.9	84.4	*3.5*

ANTHROPOMETRIC VALUES FOR BOYS, AGE 11 (10.5–11.4 YEARS)*

	−3 S.D.	−2 S.D.	−1 S.D.	Mean	+1 S.D.	+2 S.D.	+3 S.D.	S.D.
Measures:								
Weight (W)..............	20.2	26.0	31.8	*37.6*	43.4	49.2	55.0	*5.8*
Stature (S)...............	126.2	132.6	139.0	*145.4*	151.8	158.2	164.6	*6.4*
Sitting height (Si).........	67.0	70.0	73.0	*76.0*	79.0	82.0	85.0	*3.0*
Shoulder diameter (BA).....	26.6	28.1	29.6	*31.1*	32.6	34.1	35.6	*1.5*
Pelvic diameter (BC).......	19.4	20.6	21.8	*23.0*	24.2	25.4	26.6	*1.2*
Above measures, relative to stature:								
W/S....................	15.7	19.1	22.5	*25.9*	29.3	32.7	36.1	*3.4*
Si/S...................	48.4	49.7	51.0	*52.3*	53.6	54.9	56.2	*1.3*
BA/S..................	18.9	19.7	20.5	*21.3*	22.1	22.9	23.7	*0.8*
BC/S..................	14.1	14.7	15.3	*15.9*	16.5	17.1	17.7	*0.6*
Index:								
Trunk breadth (BC/BA)....	63.4	67.0	70.6	*74.2*	77.8	81.4	85.0	*3.6*

ANTHROPOMETRIC VALUES FOR BOYS, AGE 12 (11.5–12.4 YEARS)*

	−3 S.D.	−2 S.D.	−1 S.D.	Mean	+1 S.D.	+2 S.D.	+3 S.D.	S.D.
Measures:								
Weight (W)..............	20.9	27.5	34.1	*40.7*	47.3	53.9	60.5	*6.6*
Stature (S)...............	130.0	136.8	143.6	*150.4*	157.2	164.0	170.8	*6.8*
Sitting height (Si).........	67.7	71.0	74.3	*77.6*	80.9	84.2	87.5	*3.3*
Shoulder diameter (BA).....	26.5	28.3	30.1	*31.9*	33.7	35.5	37.3	*1.8*
Pelvic diameter (BC).......	19.7	21.0	22.3	*23.6*	24.9	26.2	27.5	*1.3*
Above measures, relative to stature:								
W/S....................	15.9	19.6	23.3	*27.0*	30.7	34.4	38.1	*3.7*
Si/S...................	47.8	49.1	50.4	*51.7*	53.0	54.3	55.6	*1.3*
BA/S..................	18.5	19.4	20.3	*21.2*	22.1	23.0	23.9	*0.9*
BC/S..................	14.0	14.6	15.2	*15.8*	16.4	17.0	17.6	*0.6*
Index:								
Trunk breadth (BC/BA)....	62.9	66.7	70.5	*74.3*	78.1	81.9	85.7	*3.8*

* Means and standard deviations based on techniques and data of Gray and Ayres (1931). All measures according to the metric system.

Anthropometric Values

ANTHROPOMETRIC VALUES FOR BOYS, AGE 13 (12.5–13.4 YEARS)*

	−3 S.D.	−2 S.D.	−1 S.D.	Mean	+1 S.D.	+2 S.D.	+3 S.D.	S.D.
Measures:								
Weight (W)..............	22.3	29.8	37.3	*44.8*	52.3	59.8	67.3	*7.5*
Stature (S)................	134.2	141.6	149.0	*156.4*	163.8	171.2	178.6	*7.4*
Sitting height (Si).........	69.6	73.2	76.8	*80.4*	84.0	87.6	91.2	*3.6*
Shoulder diameter (BA).....	27.3	29.2	31.1	*33.0*	34.9	36.8	38.7	*1.9*
Pelvic diameter (BC).......	20.4	21.8	23.2	*24.6*	26.0	27.4	28.8	*1.4*
Above measures, relative to stature:								
W/S....................	17.1	20.9	24.7	*28.5*	32.3	36.1	39.9	*3.8*
Si/S....................	47.8	49.0	50.2	*51.4*	52.6	53.8	55.0	*1.2*
BA/S....................	18.4	19.3	20.2	*21.1*	22.0	22.9	23.8	*0.9*
BC/S....................	14.0	14.6	15.2	*15.8*	16.4	17.0	17.6	*0.6*
Index:								
Trunk breadth (BC/BA)....	63.3	67.1	70.9	*74.7*	78.5	82.3	86.1	*3.8*

ANTHROPOMETRIC VALUES FOR BOYS, AGE 14 (13.5–14.4 YEARS)*

	−3 S.D.	−2 S.D.	−1 S.D.	Mean	+1 S.D.	+2 S.D.	+3 S.D.	S.D.
Measures:								
Weight (W)..............	24.4	32.7	41.0	*49.3*	57.6	65.9	74.2	*8.3*
Stature (S)................	139.6	147.2	154.8	*162.4*	170.0	177.6	185.2	*7.6*
Sitting height (Si).........	70.9	74.9	78.9	*82.9*	86.9	90.9	94.9	*4.0*
Shoulder diameter (BA).....	28.1	30.2	32.3	*34.4*	36.5	38.6	40.8	*2.1*
Pelvic diameter (BC).......	20.9	22.4	23.9	*25.4*	26.9	28.4	29.9	*1.5*
Above measures, relative to stature:								
W/S....................	20.7	24.7	28.7	*32.7*	36.7	40.7	44.7	*4.0*
Si/S....................	47.5	48.7	49.9	*51.1*	52.3	53.5	54.7	*1.2*
BA/S....................	18.2	19.2	20.2	*21.2*	22.2	23.2	24.2	*1.0*
BC/S....................	13.9	14.5	15.1	*15.7*	16.3	16.9	17.5	*0.6*
Index:								
Trunk breadth (BC/BA)....	62.6	66.4	70.2	*74.0*	77.8	81.6	85.4	*3.8*

ANTHROPOMETRIC VALUES FOR BOYS, AGE 15 (14.5–15.4 YEARS)*

	−3 S.D.	−2 S.D.	−1 S.D.	Mean	+1 S.D.	+2 S.D.	+3 S.D.	S.D.
Measures:								
Weight (W)..............	29.3	38.2	47.1	*56.0*	64.9	73.8	82.7	*8.9*
Stature (S)................	146.0	153.5	161.0	*168.5*	176.0	183.5	191.0	*7.5*
Sitting height (Si).........	73.7	77.9	82.1	*86.3*	90.5	94.7	98.9	*4.2*
Shoulder diameter (BA).....	29.6	31.8	34.0	*36.2*	38.4	40.6	42.8	*2.2*
Pelvic diameter (BC).......	21.8	23.4	25.0	*26.6*	28.2	29.8	31.4	*1.6*
Above measures, relative to stature:								
W/S....................	20.8	24.9	29.0	*33.1*	37.2	41.3	45.4	*4.1*
Si/S....................	47.3	48.6	49.9	*51.2*	52.5	53.8	55.1	*1.3*
BA/S....................	18.6	19.6	20.6	*21.6*	22.6	23.6	24.6	*1.0*
BC/S....................	13.7	14.4	15.1	*15.8*	16.5	17.2	17.9	*0.7*
Index:								
Trunk breadth (BC/BA)....	61.8	65.7	69.6	*73.5*	77.4	81.3	85.2	*3.9*

* Means and standard deviations based on techniques and data of Gray and Ayres (1931). All measures according to the metric system.

ANTHROPOMETRIC VALUES FOR BOYS, AGE 16 (15.5–16.4 YEARS)*

	−3 S.D.	−2 S.D.	−1 S.D.	Mean	+1 S.D.	+2 S.D.	+3 S.D.	S.D.
Measures:								
Weight (W)	33.9	42.8	51.7	*60.6*	69.5	78.4	87.3	*8.9*
Stature (S)	152.4	159.2	166.0	*172.8*	179.6	186.4	193.2	*6.8*
Sitting height (Si)	77.2	81.2	85.2	*89.2*	93.2	97.2	101.2	*4.0*
Shoulder diameter (BA)	31.2	33.3	35.4	*37.5*	39.6	41.7	43.8	*2.1*
Pelvic diameter (BC)	22.4	24.0	25.6	*27.2*	28.8	30.4	32.0	*1.6*
Above measures, relative to stature:								
W/S	22.2	26.5	30.8	*35.1*	39.4	43.7	48.0	*4.3*
Si/S	47.8	49.1	50.4	*51.7*	53.0	54.3	55.6	*1.3*
BA/S	18.7	19.7	20.7	*21.7*	22.7	23.7	24.7	*1.0*
BC/S	13.7	14.4	15.1	*15.8*	16.5	17.2	17.9	*0.7*
Index:								
Trunk breadth (BC/BA)	61.1	65.0	68.9	*72.8*	76.7	80.6	84.5	*3.9*

ANTHROPOMETRIC VALUES FOR BOYS, AGE 17 (16.5–17.4 YEARS)*

	−3 S.D.	−2 S.D.	−1 S.D.	Mean	+1 S.D.	+2 S.D.	+3 S.D.	S.D.
Measures:								
Weight (W)	37.9	46.7	55.5	*64.3*	73.1	81.9	90.7	*8.8*
Stature (S)	156.0	162.4	168.8	*175.2*	181.6	188.0	194.4	*6.4*
Sitting height (Si)	80.4	83.9	87.4	*90.9*	94.4	97.9	101.4	*3.5*
Shoulder diameter (BA)	32.9	34.8	36.7	*38.6*	40.5	42.4	44.3	*1.9*
Pelvic diameter (BC)	22.9	24.5	26.1	*27.7*	29.3	30.9	32.5	*1.6*
Above measures, relative to stature:								
W/S	23.1	27.6	32.1	*36.6*	41.1	45.6	50.1	*4.5*
Si/S	48.0	49.3	50.6	*51.9*	53.2	54.5	55.8	*1.3*
BA/S	19.1	20.1	21.1	*22.1*	23.1	24.1	25.1	*1.0*
BC/S	13.7	14.4	15.1	*15.8*	16.5	17.2	17.9	*0.7*
Index:								
Trunk breadth (BC/BA)	60.3	64.1	67.9	*71.7*	75.5	79.3	83.1	*3.8*

ANTHROPOMETRIC VALUES FOR BOYS, AGE 18 (17.5–18.4 YEARS)*

	−3 S.D.	−2 S.D.	−1 S.D.	Mean	+1 S.D.	+2 S.D.	+3 S.D.	S.D.
Measures:								
Weight (W)	38.5	47.7	56.9	*66.1*	75.3	84.5	93.7	*9.2*
Stature (S)	157.6	163.8	170.0	*176.2*	182.4	188.6	194.8	*6.2*
Sitting height (Si)	82.4	85.5	88.6	*91.7*	94.8	97.9	101.0	*3.1*
Shoulder diameter (BA)	33.7	35.5	37.3	*39.1*	40.9	42.7	44.5	*1.8*
Pelvic diameter (BC)	23.2	24.7	26.2	*27.7*	29.2	30.7	32.2	*1.5*
Above measures, relative to stature:								
W/S	23.6	28.2	32.8	*37.4*	42.0	46.6	51.2	*4.6*
Si/S	49.9	50.0	51.1	*52.2*	53.3	54.4	55.5	*1.1*
BA/S	19.2	20.2	21.2	*22.2*	23.2	24.2	25.2	*1.0*
BC/S	13.1	14.0	14.9	*15.8*	16.7	17.6	18.5	*0.9*
Index:								
Trunk breadth (BC/BA)	59.6	63.4	67.2	*71.0*	74.8	78.6	82.4	*3.8*

* Means and standard deviations based on techniques and data of Gray and Ayres (1931). All measures according to the metric system.

Appendix I

Anthropometric Values

ANTHROPOMETRIC VALUES FOR GIRLS, AGE 1 (0.5–1.4 YEARS)*

	−3 S.D.	−2 S.D.	−1 S.D.	Mean	+1 S.D.	+2 S.D.	+3 S.D.	S.D.
Measures:								
Weight (W)	7.2	8.2	9.2	*10.2*	11.2	12.2	13.2	*1.0*
Stature (S)	64.0	67.8	71.6	*75.4*	79.2	83.0	86.8	*3.8*
Sitting height (Si)	42.6	43.4	44.2	*45.0*	45.8	46.6	47.4	*0.8*
Shoulder diameter (BA)								
Pelvic diameter (BC)								
Above measures, relative to stature:								
W/S	9.9	11.2	12.5	*13.8*	15.1	16.4	17.7	*1.3*
Si/S	58.1	59.5	60.9	*62.3*	63.7	65.1	66.5	*1.4*
BA/S								
BC/S								
Index:								
Trunk breadth (BC/BA)								

ANTHROPOMETRIC VALUES FOR GIRLS, AGE 2 (1.5–2.4 YEARS)*

	−3 S.D.	−2 S.D.	−1 S.D.	Mean	+1 S.D.	+2 S.D.	+3 S.D.	S.D.
Measures:								
Weight W/S	8.6	9.9	11.2	*12.5*	13.8	15.1	16.4	*1.3*
Stature (S)	74.0	77.8	81.6	*85.4*	89.2	93.0	96.8	*3.8*
Sitting height (Si)	50.1	51.7	53.3	*54.9*	56.5	58.1	59.7	*1.6*
Shoulder diameter (BA)	19.6	20.2	20.8	*21.4*	22.0	22.6	23.2	*0.6*
Pelvic diameter (BC)	13.7	14.1	14.5	*14.9*	15.3	15.7	16.1	*0.4*
Above measures, relative to stature:								
W/S	10.1	11.5	12.9	*14.3*	15.7	17.1	18.5	*1.4*
Si/S	56.2	57.6	59.0	*60.4*	61.8	63.2	64.6	*1.4*
BA/S	22.8	23.9	24.0	*25.1*	26.2	27.3	28.4	*1.1*
BC/S	14.1	15.2	16.3	*17.4*	18.5	19.6	20.7	*1.1*
Index:								
Trunk breadth (BC/BA)	64.3	66.0	67.7	*69.4*	71.1	72.8	74.5	*1.7*

ANTHROPOMETRIC VALUES FOR GIRLS, AGE 3 (2.5–3.4 YEARS)*

	−3 S.D.	−2 S.D.	−1 S.D.	Mean	+1 S.D.	+2 S.D.	+3 S.D.	S.D.
Measures:								
Weight (W)	10.0	11.7	13.4	*15.1*	16.8	18.5	20.2	*1.7*
Stature (S)	84.2	88.1	92.0	*95.9*	99.8	103.7	107.6	*3.9*
Sitting height (Si)	50.6	52.6	54.6	*56.6*	58.6	60.6	62.6	*2.0*
Shoulder diameter (BA)	20.2	21.1	22.0	*22.9*	23.8	24.7	25.6	*0.9*
Pelvic diameter (BC)	14.5	15.1	15.7	*16.3*	16.9	17.5	18.1	*0.6*
Above measures, relative to stature:								
W/S	11.2	12.7	14.2	*15.7*	17.2	18.7	20.2	*1.5*
Si/S	54.4	55.8	57.2	*58.6*	60.0	61.4	62.8	*1.4*
BA/S	20.2	21.2	22.2	*23.2*	24.2	25.2	26.2	*1.0*
BC/S	14.4	15.2	16.0	*16.8*	17.6	18.4	19.2	*0.8*
Index:								
Trunk breadth (BC/BA)	64.3	66.7	69.1	*71.5*	73.9	76.3	78.7	*2.4*

* Means and standard deviations based on techniques and data of Gray and Ayres (1931). All measures according to the metric system.

220

ANTHROPOMETRIC VALUES FOR GIRLS, AGE 4 (3.5–4.4 YEARS)*

	−3 S.D.	−2 S.D.	−1 S.D.	Mean	+1 S.D.	+2 S.D.	+3 S.D.	S.D.
Measures:								
Weight (W)................	11.4	13.4	15.4	*17.4*	19.4	21.4	23.4	*2.0*
Stature (S)................	91.5	95.5	99.5	*103.5*	107.5	111.5	115.5	*4.0*
Sitting height (Si)..........	53.7	55.7	57.7	*59.7*	61.7	63.7	65.7	*2.0*
Shoulder diameter (BA).....	20.5	21.6	22.7	*23.8*	24.9	25.0	26.1	*1.1*
Pelvic diameter (BC)........	14.9	15.7	16.5	*17.3*	18.1	18.9	19.7	*0.8*
Above measures, relative to stature:								
W/S....................	12.1	13.6	15.1	*16.6*	18.1	19.6	21.1	*1.5*
Si/S....................	53.3	54.7	56.1	*57.5*	58.9	60.3	61.7	*1.4*
BA/S....................	20.2	21.1	22.0	*22.9*	23.8	24.7	25.6	*0.9*
BC/S....................	14.4	15.1	15.8	*16.5*	17.2	17.9	18.6	*0.7*
Index:								
Trunk breadth (BC/BA)....	62.0	65.5	69.0	*72.5*	76.0	79.5	83.0	*3.5*

ANTHROPOMETRIC VALUES FOR GIRLS, AGE 5 (4.5–5.4 YEARS)*

	−3 S.D.	−2 S.D.	−1 S.D.	Mean	+1 S.D.	+2 S.D.	+3 S.D.	S.D.
Measures:								
Weight (W)................	12.6	14.9	17.2	*19.5*	21.8	24.1	26.4	*2.3*
Stature (S)................	98.5	102.7	106.9	*111.1*	115.3	119.5	123.7	*4.2*
Sitting height (Si)..........	55.9	58.1	60.3	*62.5*	64.7	66.9	69.1	*2.2*
Shoulder diameter (BA).....	21.3	22.5	23.7	*24.9*	26.1	27.3	28.5	*1.2*
Pelvic diameter (BC)........	15.5	16.4	17.3	*18.2*	19.1	20.0	20.9	*0.9*
Above measures, relative to stature:								
W/S....................	12.7	14.3	15.9	*17.5*	19.1	20.7	22.3	*1.6*
Si/S....................	51.9	53.3	54.7	*56.1*	57.5	58.9	60.3	*1.4*
BA/S....................	19.5	20.4	21.3	*22.2*	23.1	24.0	24.9	*0.9*
BC/S....................	14.3	15.0	15.7	*16.4*	17.1	17.8	18.5	*0.7*
Index:								
Trunk breadth (BC/BA)....	63.3	66.8	70.3	*73.8*	77.3	80.8	84.3	*3.5*

ANTHROPOMETRIC VALUES FOR GIRLS, AGE 6 (5.5–6.4 YEARS)*

	−3 S.D.	−2 S.D.	−1 S.D.	Mean	+1 S.D.	+2 S.D.	+3 S.D.	S.D.
Measures:								
Weight (W)................	14.0	16.8	19.6	*22.4*	25.2	28.0	30.8	*2.8*
Stature (S)................	104.6	109.1	113.6	*118.1*	122.6	127.1	131.6	*4.5*
Sitting height (Si)..........	58.5	60.8	63.1	*65.4*	67.7	70.0	72.3	*2.3*
Shoulder diameter (BA).....	21.5	22.9	24.3	*25.7*	27.1	28.5	29.9	*1.4*
Pelvic diameter (BC)........	16.7	17.8	18.9	*19.0*	20.1	21.2	22.3	*1.1*
Above measures, relative to stature:								
W/S....................	13.3	15.2	17.1	*19.0*	20.9	22.8	24.7	*1.9*
Si/S....................	51.7	53.0	54.3	*55.6*	56.9	58.2	59.5	*1.3*
BA/S....................	18.7	19.7	20.7	*21.7*	22.7	23.7	24.7	*1.0*
BC/S....................	13.6	14.4	15.2	*16.0*	16.8	17.6	18.4	*0.8*
Index:								
Trunk breadth (BC/BA)....	62.2	66.2	70.2	*74.2*	78.2	82.2	86.2	*4.0*

* Means and standard deviations based on techniques and data of Gray and Ayres (1931). All measures according to the metric system.

Appendix I

Anthropometric Values

ANTHROPOMETRIC VALUES FOR GIRLS, AGE 7 (6.5–7.4 YEARS)*

	−3 S.D.	−2 S.D.	−1 S.D.	Mean	+1 S.D.	+2 S.D.	+3 S.D.	S.D.
Measures:								
Weight (W)	15.2	18.5	21.8	*25.1*	28.4	31.7	35.0	*3.3*
Stature (S)	109.4	114.3	119.2	*124.1*	129.0	133.9	138.8	*4.9*
Sitting height (Si)	60.4	62.9	65.4	*67.9*	70.4	72.9	75.4	*2.5*
Shoulder diameter (BA)	22.2	27.7	25.2	*26.7*	28.2	29.7	31.2	*1.5*
Pelvic diameter (BC)	16.0	17.2	18.4	*19.6*	20.8	22.0	23.2	*1.2*
Above measures, relative to stature:								
W/S	13.9	16.0	18.1	*20.2*	22.3	24.4	26.6	*2.1*
Si/S	50.9	52.2	53.5	*54.8*	56.1	57.4	58.7	*1.3*
BA/S	18.6	19.6	20.6	*21.6*	22.6	23.6	24.6	*1.0*
BC/S	13.1	14.0	14.9	*15.8*	16.7	17.6	18.5	*0.9*
Index:								
Trunk breadth (BC/BA)	60.2	64.6	69.0	*73.4*	77.8	82.2	86.6	*4.4*

ANTHROPOMETRIC VALUES FOR GIRLS, AGE 8 (7.5–8.4 YEARS)*

	−3 S.D.	−2 S.D.	−1 S.D.	Mean	+1 S.D.	+2 S.D.	+3 S.D.	S.D.
Measures:								
Weight (W)	15.0	19.3	23.6	*27.9*	32.2	36.5	40.8	*4.3*
Stature (S)	114.5	119.9	125.3	*130.7*	136.1	141.5	146.9	*5.4*
Sitting height (Si)	62.5	65.1	67.7	*70.3*	72.9	75.5	78.1	*2.6*
Shoulder diameter (BA)	23.1	24.7	26.3	*27.9*	29.5	31.1	32.7	*1.6*
Pelvic diameter (BC)	16.6	18.0	19.4	*20.8*	22.2	23.6	25.0	*1.4*
Above measures, relative to stature:								
W/S	14.3	16.8	19.3	*21.8*	24.3	26.8	29.3	*2.5*
Si/S	49.7	51.0	52.3	*53.6*	54.9	56.2	57.5	*1.3*
BA/S	18.2	19.2	20.2	*21.2*	22.2	23.2	24.2	*1.0*
BC/S	13.2	14.1	15.0	*15.9*	16.8	17.7	18.6	*0.9*
Index:								
Trunk breadth (BC/BA)	61.7	66.0	70.3	*74.6*	78.9	83.2	87.5	*4.3*

ANTHROPOMETRIC VALUES FOR GIRLS, AGE 9 (8.5–9.4 YEARS)*

	−3 S.D.	−2 S.D.	−1 S.D.	Mean	+1 S.D.	+2 S.D.	+3 S.D.	S.D.
Measures:								
Weight (W)	16.2	21.4	26.6	*31.8*	37.0	42.2	47.4	*5.2*
Stature (S)	118.2	124.1	130.0	*135.9*	141.8	147.7	153.6	*5.9*
Sitting height (Si)	64.0	66.8	69.6	*72.4*	75.2	78.0	80.8	*2.8*
Shoulder diameter (BA)	23.9	25.5	27.1	*28.7*	30.3	31.9	33.5	*1.6*
Pelvic diameter (BC)	17.0	18.5	20.0	*21.5*	23.0	24.5	26.0	*1.5*
Above measures, relative to stature:								
W/S	14.1	17.2	20.3	*23.4*	26.5	29.6	32.7	*3.1*
Si/S	49.1	50.5	51.9	*53.3*	54.7	56.1	57.5	*1.4*
BA/S	18.2	19.2	20.2	*21.2*	22.2	23.2	24.2	*1.0*
BC/S	13.4	14.2	15.0	*15.8*	16.6	17.4	18.2	*0.8*
Index:								
Trunk breadth (BC/BA)	62.3	66.5	70.7	*74.9*	79.1	83.3	87.5	*4.2*

* Means and standard deviations based on techniques and data of Gray and Ayres (1931). All measures according to the metric system.

ANTHROPOMETRIC VALUES FOR GIRLS, AGE 10 (9.5–10.4 YEARS)*

	−3 S.D.	−2 S.D.	−1 S.D.	Mean	+1 S.D.	+2 S.D.	+3 S.D.	S.D.
Measures:								
Weight (W)..............	16.6	22.8	29.0	*35.2*	41.4	47.6	53.8	*6.2*
Stature (S)...............	121.5	127.7	133.9	*140.1*	146.3	152.5	158.7	*6.2*
Sitting height (Si)..........	64.5	67.6	70.7	*73.8*	76.9	80.0	83.1	*3.1*
Shoulder diameter (BA).....	24.8	26.0	28.0	*29.6*	31.2	32.8	34.4	*1.6*
Pelvic diameter (BC).......	17.5	19.1	20.7	*22.3*	23.9	25.5	27.1	*1.6*
Above measures, relative to stature:								
W/S....................	14.0	17.7	21.4	*25.1*	28.8	32.5	36.2	*3.7*
Si/S...................	48.9	50.2	51.5	*52.8*	54.1	55.4	56.7	*1.3*
BA/S..................	18.2	19.2	20.2	*21.2*	22.2	23.2	24.2	*1.0*
BC/S..................	12.9	13.9	14.9	*15.9*	16.9	17.9	18.9	*1.0*
Index:								
Trunk breadth (BC/BA)....	62.8	67.0	71.2	*75.4*	79.6	83.8	88.0	*4.2*

ANTHROPOMETRIC VALUES FOR GIRLS, AGE 11 (10.5–11.4 YEARS)*

	−3 S.D.	−2 S.D.	−1 S.D.	Mean	+1 S.D.	+2 S.D.	+3 S.D.	S.D.
Measures:								
Weight (W)..............	17.5	24.7	31.9	*39.1*	46.3	53.5	60.7	*7.2*
Stature (S)...............	125.4	132.3	139.2	*146.1*	153.0	159.9	166.8	*6.9*
Sitting height (Si)	65.6	69.1	72.6	*76.1*	79.6	83.1	86.6	*3.5*
Shoulder diameter (BA).....	25.4	27.2	29.0	*30.8*	32.6	34.4	36.2	*1.8*
Pelvic diameter (BC).......	17.6	19.5	21.4	*23.3*	25.2	27.1	29.0	*1.9*
Above measures, relative to stature:								
W/S....................	14.4	18.5	22.6	*26.7*	30.8	34.9	39.0	*4.1*
Si/S...................	48.6	49.8	51.0	*52.2*	53.4	54.6	55.8	*1.2*
BA/S..................	18.4	19.3	20.2	*21.1*	22.0	22.9	23.8	*0.9*
BC/S..................	13.0	14.0	15.0	*16.0*	17.0	18.0	19.0	*1.0*
Index:								
Trunk breadth (BC/BA)....	62.3	66.8	71.3	*75.8*	80.3	84.8	89.3	*4.5*

ANTHROPOMETRIC VALUES FOR GIRLS, AGE 12 (11.5–12.4 YEARS)*

	−3 S.D.	−2 S.D.	−1 S.D.	Mean	+1 S.D.	+2 S.D.	+3 S.D.	S.D.
Measures:								
Weight (W)..............	19.7	27.7	35.7	*43.7*	51.7	59.7	67.7	*8.0*
Stature (S)...............	130.4	137.7	145.0	*152.0*	159.3	166.6	173.9	*7.3*
Sitting height (Si)..........	67.6	71.3	75.0	*78.7*	82.4	86.1	89.8	*3.7*
Shoulder diameter (BA).....	26.2	28.1	30.0	*31.9*	33.8	35.7	37.6	*1.9*
Pelvic diameter (BC).......	18.4	20.4	22.4	*24.4*	26.4	28.4	30.4	*2.0*
Above measures, relative to stature:								
W/S....................	16.2	20.4	24.6	*28.8*	33.0	37.2	41.4	*4.2*
Si/S...................	48.3	49.5	50.7	*51.9*	53.1	54.3	55.5	*1.2*
BA/S..................	18.3	19.2	20.1	*21.0*	21.9	22.8	23.7	*0.9*
BC/S..................	13.1	14.1	15.1	*16.1*	17.1	18.1	19.1	*1.0*
Index:								
Trunk breadth (BC/BA)....	62.0	66.8	71.6	*76.4*	81.2	86.0	90.8	*4.8*

* Means and standard deviations based on techniques and data of Gray and Ayres (1931). All measures according to the metric system.

Anthropometric Values

ANTHROPOMETRIC VALUES FOR GIRLS, AGE 13 (12.5–13.4 YEARS)*

	−3 S.D.	−2 S.D.	−1 S.D.	Mean	+1 S.D.	+2 S.D.	+3 S.D.	S.D.
Measures:								
Weight (W)	23.3	31.5	39.7	*47.9*	56.1	64.3	72.5	*8.2*
Stature (S)	135.5	142.8	150.0	*157.2*	164.4	171.6	178.8	*7.2*
Sitting height (Si)	70.3	74.0	77.7	*81.4*	85.1	88.8	92.5	*3.7*
Shoulder diameter (BA)	26.7	28.8	30.9	*33.0*	35.1	37.2	39.3	*2.1*
Pelvic diameter (BC)	20.2	22.0	23.8	*25.6*	27.4	29.2	31.0	*1.8*
Above measures, relative to stature:								
W/S	17.1	21.5	25.9	*30.3*	34.7	39.1	43.5	*4.4*
Si/S	27.9	49.2	50.5	*51.8*	53.1	54.4	55.7	*1.3*
BA/S	18.3	19.2	20.1	*21.0*	21.9	22.8	23.7	*0.9*
BC/S	13.0	14.1	15.2	*16.3*	17.4	18.5	19.6	*1.1*
Index:								
Trunk breadth (BC/BA)	62.7	67.7	72.7	*77.7*	82.7	87.7	92.7	*5.0*

ANTHROPOMETRIC VALUES FOR GIRLS, AGE 14 (13.5–14.4 YEARS)*

	−3 S.D.	−2 S.D.	−1 S.D.	Mean	+1 S.D.	+2 S.D.	+3 S.D.	S.D.
Measures:								
Weight (W)	26.7	34.7	42.7	*50.7*	58.7	66.7	74.7	*8.0*
Stature (S)	140.0	146.7	153.4	*160.1*	166.8	173.5	180.2	*6.7*
Sitting height (Si)	73.2	76.6	80.0	*83.4*	86.8	90.2	93.6	*3.4*
Shoulder diameter (BA)	28.1	29.9	31.7	*33.5*	35.3	37.1	38.9	*1.8*
Pelvic diameter (BC)	19.8	21.9	24.0	*26.1*	28.3	30.4	32.5	*2.1*
Above measures, relative to stature:								
W/S	18.7	23.0	27.3	*31.6*	35.9	40.2	44.5	*4.3*
Si/S	48.2	49.5	50.8	*52.1*	53.4	54.7	56.0	*1.3*
BA/S	18.0	19.0	20.0	*21.0*	22.0	23.0	24.0	*1.0*
BC/S	11.7	12.9	14.1	*16.3*	17.5	18.7	19.9	*1.2*
Index:								
Trunk breadth (BC/BA)	62.3	67.5	72.7	*77.9*	83.1	88.3	93.5	*5.2*

ANTHROPOMETRIC VALUES FOR GIRLS, AGE 15 (14.5–15.4 YEARS)*

	−3 S.D.	−2 S.D.	−1 S.D.	Mean	+1 S.D.	+2 S.D.	+3 S.D.	S.D.
Measures:								
Weight (W)	31.1	38.9	46.7	*54.5*	62.3	70.1	77.9	*7.8*
Stature (S)	145.0	151.0	157.0	*163.0*	169.0	175.0	181.0	*6.0*
Sitting height (Si)	76.0	79.1	82.2	*85.3*	88.4	91.5	94.6	*3.1*
Shoulder diameter (BA)	29.0	30.7	32.4	*34.1*	35.8	37.5	39.2	*1.7*
Pelvic diameter (BC)	20.9	22.9	24.9	*26.9*	28.9	30.9	32.9	*2.0*
Above measures, relative to stature:								
W/S	20.5	24.8	29.1	*33.4*	37.7	42.0	46.3	*4.3*
Si/S	48.5	49.8	51.1	*52.4*	53.7	55.0	56.3	*1.3*
BA/S	18.3	19.2	20.1	*21.0*	21.9	22.8	23.7	*0.9*
BC/S	13.2	14.3	15.4	*16.5*	17.6	18.7	19.8	*1.1*
Index:								
Trunk breadth (BC/BA)	63.5	68.5	73.5	*78.5*	83.5	88.5	93.5	*5.0*

* Means and standard deviations based on techniques and data of Gray and Ayres (1931). All measures according to the metric system.

ANTHROPOMETRIC VALUES FOR GIRLS, AGE 16 (15.5–16.4 YEARS)*

	−3 S.D.	−2 S.D.	−1 S.D.	Mean	+1 S.D.	+2 S.D.	+3 S.D.	S.D.
Measures:								
Weight (W)	33.2	40.7	48.2	*55.7*	63.2	70.7	78.2	*7.5*
Stature (S)	145.8	151.5	157.2	*162.9*	168.6	174.3	180.0	*5.7*
Sitting height (Si)	76.9	80.0	83.1	*86.2*	89.3	92.4	95.5	*3.1*
Shoulder diameter (BA)	29.2	30.9	32.6	*34.3*	36.0	37.7	39.4	*1.7*
Pelvic diameter (BC)	21.5	23.4	25.3	*27.2*	29.1	31.0	32.9	*1.9*
Above measures, relative to stature:								
W/S	21.5	25.7	29.9	*34.1*	38.3	42.5	46.7	*4.2*
Si/S	48.7	50.1	51.5	*52.9*	54.3	55.7	57.1	*1.4*
BA/S	18.3	19.2	20.1	*21.0*	21.9	22.8	23.7	*0.9*
BC/S	13.7	14.7	15.7	*16.7*	17.7	18.7	19.7	*1.0*
Index:								
Trunk breadth (BC/BA)	65.2	70.0	74.8	*79.6*	84.4	89.2	94.0	*4.8*

ANTHROPOMETRIC VALUES FOR GIRLS, AGE 17 (16.5–17.4 YEARS)*

	−3 S.D.	−2 S.D.	−1 S.D.	Mean	+1 S.D.	+2 S.D.	+3 S.D.	S.D.
Measures:								
Weight (W)	36.3	43.2	50.1	*57.0*	63.9	70.8	77.7	*6.9*
Stature (S)	147.7	153.1	158.5	*163.9*	169.3	174.7	180.1	*5.4*
Sitting height (Si)	77.4	80.5	83.6	*86.7*	89.8	92.9	96.0	*3.1*
Shoulder diameter (BA)	29.2	31.0	32.8	*34.6*	36.4	38.2	40.0	*1.8*
Pelvic diameter (BC)	21.8	23.7	25.6	*27.5*	29.4	31.3	33.2	*1.9*
Above measures, relative to stature:								
W/S	23.4	27.2	31.0	*34.8*	38.6	42.4	46.2	*3.8*
Si/S	48.8	50.2	51.6	*53.0*	54.4	55.8	57.2	*1.4*
BA/S	18.2	19.2	20.2	*21.2*	22.2	23.2	24.2	*1.0*
BC/S	13.7	14.7	15.7	*16.7*	17.7	18.7	19.7	*1.0*
Index:								
Trunk breadth (BC/BA)	65.5	70.1	74.7	*79.3*	83.9	88.5	93.1	*4.6*

ANTHROPOMETRIC VALUES FOR GIRLS, AGE 18 (17.5–18.4 YEARS)*

	−3 S.D.	−2 S.D.	−1 S.D.	Mean	+1 S.D.	+2 S.D.	+3 S.D.	S.D.
Measures:								
Weight (W)	38.5	44.8	51.1	*57.4*	63.7	70.0	76.3	*6.3*
Stature (S)	148.4	153.5	158.6	*163.7*	168.8	173.9	179.0	*5.1*
Sitting height (Si)	77.2	80.3	83.4	*86.5*	89.6	92.7	95.8	*3.1*
Shoulder diameter (BA)	29.1	31.0	32.9	*34.8*	36.7	38.6	40.5	*1.9*
Pelvic diameter (BC)	22.3	24.1	25.9	*27.7*	29.5	31.3	33.1	*1.8*
Above measures, relative to stature:								
W/S	24.3	27.9	31.5	*35.1*	38.7	42.3	45.9	*3.6*
Si/S	48.1	49.7	51.3	*52.9*	54.5	56.1	57.7	*1.6*
BA/S	18.9	19.0	20.1	*21.2*	22.3	23.4	24.5	*1.1*
BC/S	13.7	14.8	15.9	*17.0*	18.1	19.2	20.3	*1.1*
Index:								
Trunk breadth (BC/BA)	66.0	70.6	75.2	*79.8*	84.4	89.0	93.6	*4.6*

* Means and standard deviations based on techniques and data of Gray and Ayres (1931). All measures according to the metric system.

Height-Prediction Tables

AVERAGE BOYS

PERCENTAGES AND ESTIMATED MATURE HEIGHTS FOR BOYS WITH SKELETAL AGES WITHIN
ONE YEAR OF THEIR CHRONOLOGICAL AGES

Skeletal Ages 7 Through 12 Years

Skeletal Age	7-0	7-3	7-6	7-9	8-0	8-3	8-6	8-9	9-0	9-3	9-6	9-9	10-0	10-3	10-6	10-9	11-0	11-3	11-6	11-9	12-0	12-3	12-6	12-9
% of Mature Height	69.5	70.2	70.9	71.6	72.3	73.1	73.9	74.6	75.2	76.1	76.9	77.7	78.4	79.1	79.5	80.0	80.4	81.2	81.8	82.7	83.4	84.3	85.3	86.3
Ht. (inches)																								
42	60.4																							
43	61.9	61.3	60.6	60.1																				
44	63.3	62.7	62.1	61.5	60.9	60.2																		
45	64.7	64.1	63.5	62.8	62.2	61.6	60.9	60.3																
46	66.2	65.5	64.9	64.2	63.6	62.9	62.2	61.7	61.2	60.4														
47	67.6	67.0	66.3	65.6	65.0	64.3	63.6	63.0	62.5	61.8	61.1	60.5												
48	69.1	68.4	67.7	67.0	66.4	65.7	65.0	64.3	63.8	63.1	62.4	61.8	61.2	60.7	60.4	60.0								
49	70.5	69.8	69.1	68.4	67.8	67.0	66.3	65.7	65.2	64.4	63.7	63.1	62.5	61.9	61.6	61.3	60.9	60.3						
50	71.9	71.2	70.5	69.8	69.2	68.4	67.7	67.0	66.5	65.7	65.0	64.4	63.8	63.2	62.9	62.5	62.2	61.6	61.1	60.5				
51	73.4	72.6	71.9	71.2	70.5	69.8	69.0	68.4	67.8	67.0	66.3	65.6	65.1	64.5	64.2	63.8	63.4	62.8	62.3	61.7	61.1	60.5	59.8	
52	74.8	74.1	73.3	72.6	71.9	71.1	70.4	69.7	69.1	68.3	67.6	66.9	66.3	65.7	65.4	65.0	64.7	64.0	63.6	62.9	62.3	61.7	61.0	60.3
53	76.3	75.5	74.8	74.0	73.3	72.5	71.7	71.0	70.5	69.6	68.9	68.2	67.6	67.0	66.7	66.3	65.9	65.3	64.8	64.1	63.5	62.9	62.1	61.4
54	77.7	76.9	76.2	75.4	74.7	73.9	73.1	72.4	71.8	71.0	70.2	69.5	68.9	68.3	67.9	67.5	67.2	66.5	66.0	65.3	64.7	64.1	63.3	62.6
55	79.1	78.3	77.6	76.8	76.1	75.2	74.4	73.7	73.1	72.3	71.5	70.8	70.2	69.5	69.2	68.8	68.4	67.7	67.2	66.5	65.9	65.2	64.5	63.7
56	80.6	79.8	79.0	78.2	77.5	76.6	75.8	75.1	74.5	73.6	72.8	72.1	71.4	70.8	70.4	70.0	69.7	69.0	68.5	67.7	67.1	66.4	65.6	64.9
57			80.4	79.6	78.8	78.0	77.1	76.4	75.8	74.9	74.1	73.4	72.7	72.1	71.7	71.3	70.9	70.2	69.7	68.9	68.3	67.6	66.8	66.0
58					80.2	79.3	78.5	77.7	77.1	76.2	75.4	74.6	74.0	73.3	73.0	72.5	72.1	71.4	70.9	70.1	69.5	68.8	68.0	67.2
59						80.7	79.8	79.1	78.5	77.5	76.7	75.9	75.3	74.6	74.2	73.8	73.4	72.7	72.1	71.3	70.7	70.0	69.2	68.4
60								80.4	79.8	78.8	78.0	77.2	76.5	75.9	75.5	75.0	74.6	73.9	73.3	72.6	71.9	71.2	70.3	69.5
61										80.2	79.3	78.5	77.8	77.1	76.7	76.3	75.9	75.1	74.6	73.8	73.1	72.4	71.5	70.7
62											80.6	79.8	79.1	78.4	78.0	77.5	77.1	76.4	75.8	75.0	74.3	73.5	72.7	71.8
63													80.4	79.6	79.2	78.8	78.4	77.6	77.0	76.2	75.5	74.7	73.9	73.0
64														80.9	80.5	80.0	79.6	78.8	78.2	77.4	76.7	75.9	75.0	74.2
65																	80.8	80.0	79.5	78.6	77.9	77.1	76.2	75.3
66																			80.7	79.8	79.1	78.3	77.4	76.5
67																					80.3	79.5	78.5	77.6
68																						80.7	79.7	78.8
69																							80.9	80.0

AVERAGE BOYS

PERCENTAGES AND ESTIMATED MATURE HEIGHTS FOR BOYS WITH SKELETAL AGES WITHIN
ONE YEAR OF THEIR CHRONOLOGICAL AGES

Skeletal Ages 13 Years to Maturity

Skeletal Age	13-0	13-3	13-6	13-9	14-0	14-3	14-6	14-9	15-0	15-3	15-6	15-9	16-0	16-3	16-6	16-9	17-0	17-3	17-6	17-9	18-0	18-3	18-6
% of Mature Height	87.6	89.0	90.2	91.4	92.7	93.8	94.8	95.8	96.8	97.3	97.6	98.0	98.2	98.5	98.7	98.9	99.1	99.3	99.4	99.5	99.6	99.8	100.0
Ht. (inches)																							
53	60.5																						
54	61.6	60.7																					
55	62.8	61.8	61.0	60.2																			
56	63.9	62.9	62.1	61.3	60.4																		
57	65.1	64.0	63.2	62.4	61.5	60.8	60.1																
58	66.2	65.2	64.3	63.5	62.6	61.8	61.2	60.5															
59	67.4	66.3	65.4	64.6	63.6	62.9	62.2	61.6	61.0	60.6	60.5	60.2	60.1										
60	68.5	67.4	66.5	65.6	64.7	64.0	63.3	62.6	62.0	61.7	61.5	61.2	61.1	60.9	60.8	60.7	60.5	60.4	60.4	60.3	60.2	60.1	60.0
61	69.6	68.5	67.6	66.7	65.8	65.0	64.3	63.7	63.0	62.7	62.5	62.2	62.1	61.9	61.8	61.7	61.6	61.4	61.4	61.3	61.2	61.1	61.0
62	70.8	69.7	68.7	67.8	66.9	66.1	65.4	64.7	64.1	63.7	63.5	63.3	63.1	62.9	62.8	62.7	62.6	62.4	62.4	62.3	62.2	62.1	62.0
63	71.9	70.8	69.8	68.9	68.0	67.2	66.5	65.8	65.1	64.7	64.5	64.3	64.2	64.0	63.8	63.7	63.6	63.4	63.4	63.3	63.3	63.1	63.0
64	73.1	71.9	71.0	70.0	69.0	68.2	67.5	66.8	66.1	65.8	65.6	65.3	65.2	65.0	64.8	64.7	64.6	64.4	64.4	64.3	64.3	64.1	64.0
65	74.2	73.0	72.1	71.1	70.1	69.3	68.6	67.8	67.2	66.8	66.6	66.3	66.2	66.0	65.9	65.7	65.6	65.5	65.4	65.3	65.3	65.1	65.0
66	75.3	74.2	73.2	72.2	71.2	70.4	69.6	68.9	68.2	67.8	67.6	67.3	67.2	67.0	66.9	66.7	66.6	66.5	66.4	66.3	66.3	66.1	66.0
67	76.5	75.3	74.3	73.3	72.3	71.4	70.7	69.9	69.2	68.9	68.6	68.4	68.2	68.0	67.9	67.7	67.6	67.5	67.4	67.3	67.3	67.1	67.0
68	77.6	76.4	75.4	74.4	73.4	72.5	71.7	71.0	70.3	69.9	69.7	69.4	69.2	69.0	68.9	68.8	68.6	68.5	68.4	68.3	68.3	68.1	68.0
69	78.8	77.5	76.5	75.5	74.4	73.6	72.8	72.0	71.3	70.9	70.7	70.4	70.3	70.0	69.9	69.8	69.6	69.5	69.4	69.3	69.3	69.1	69.0
70	79.9	78.7	77.6	76.6	75.5	74.6	73.8	73.1	72.3	71.9	71.7	71.4	71.3	71.1	70.9	70.8	70.6	70.5	70.4	70.4	70.3	70.1	70.0
71		79.8	78.7	77.7	76.6	75.7	74.9	74.1	73.4	73.0	72.7	72.4	72.3	72.1	71.9	71.8	71.6	71.5	71.4	71.4	71.3	71.1	71.0
72		80.9	79.8	78.8	77.7	76.8	75.9	75.2	74.4	74.0	73.8	73.5	73.3	73.1	73.0	72.8	72.7	72.5	72.4	72.4	72.3	72.1	72.0
73			80.9	79.9	78.7	77.8	77.0	76.2	75.4	75.0	74.8	74.5	74.3	74.1	74.0	73.8	73.7	73.5	73.4	73.4	73.3	73.1	73.0
74					79.8	78.9	78.1	77.2	76.4	76.0	75.8	75.5	75.4	75.1	75.0	74.8	74.7	74.5	74.4	74.4	74.3	74.1	74.0
75					80.9	80.0	79.1	78.3	77.5	77.1	76.8	76.5	76.4	76.1	76.0	75.8	75.7	75.5	75.5	75.4	75.3	75.2	75.0
76							80.2	79.3	78.5	78.1	77.9	77.6	77.4	77.2	77.0	76.8	76.7	76.5	76.5	76.4	76.3	76.2	76.0
77								80.4	79.5	79.1	78.9	78.6	78.4	78.2	78.0	77.9	77.7	77.5	77.5	77.4	77.3	77.2	77.0
78									80.6	80.2	79.9	79.6	79.4	79.2	79.0	78.9	78.7	78.5	78.5	78.4	78.3	78.2	78.0

ACCELERATED BOYS

PERCENTAGES AND ESTIMATED MATURE HEIGHTS FOR BOYS WITH SKELETAL AGES ONE YEAR
OR MORE ADVANCED OVER THEIR CHRONOLOGICAL AGES

Skeletal Ages 7 Through 11 Years

Skeletal Age	7-0	7-3	7-6	7-9	8-0	8-3	8-6	8-9	9-0	9-3	9-6	9-9	10-0	10-3	10-6	10-9	11-0	11-3	11-6	11-9
% of Mature Height	67.0	67.6	68.3	68.9	69.6	70.3	70.9	71.5	72.0	72.8	73.4	74.1	74.7	75.3	75.8	76.3	76.7	77.6	78.6	80.0
Ht. (inches)																				
41	61.2	60.7	60.0																	
42	62.7	62.1	61.5	61.0	60.3															
43	64.2	63.6	63.0	62.4	61.8	61.2	60.6	60.1												
44	65.7	65.1	64.4	63.9	63.2	62.6	62.1	61.5	61.1	60.4										
45	67.2	66.6	65.9	65.3	64.7	64.0	63.5	62.9	62.5	61.8	61.3	60.7	60.2							
46	68.7	68.0	67.3	66.8	66.1	65.4	64.9	64.3	63.9	63.2	62.7	62.1	61.6	61.1	60.7	60.3	60.0			
47	70.1	69.5	68.8	68.2	67.5	66.9	66.3	65.7	65.3	64.6	64.0	63.4	62.9	62.4	62.0	61.6	61.3	60.6		
48	71.6	71.0	70.3	69.7	69.0	68.3	67.7	67.1	66.7	65.9	65.4	64.8	64.3	63.7	63.3	62.9	62.6	61.9	61.1	60.0
49	73.1	72.5	71.7	71.1	70.4	69.7	69.1	68.5	68.1	67.3	66.8	66.1	65.6	65.1	64.6	64.2	63.9	63.1	62.3	61.3
50	74.6	74.0	73.2	72.6	71.8	71.1	70.5	69.9	69.4	68.7	68.1	67.5	66.9	66.4	66.0	65.5	65.2	64.4	63.6	62.5
51	76.2	75.4	74.7	74.0	73.3	72.5	71.9	71.3	70.8	70.1	69.5	68.8	68.3	67.7	67.3	66.8	66.5	65.7	64.9	63.8
52	77.6	76.9	76.1	75.5	74.7	74.0	73.3	72.7	72.2	71.4	70.8	70.2	69.6	69.1	68.6	68.2	67.8	67.0	66.2	65.0
53	79.1	78.4	77.6	76.9	76.2	75.4	74.8	74.1	73.6	72.8	72.2	71.5	71.0	70.4	69.9	69.5	69.1	68.3	67.4	66.3
54	80.6	79.9	79.1	78.4	77.6	76.8	76.2	75.5	75.0	74.2	73.6	72.9	72.3	71.7	71.2	70.8	70.4	69.6	68.7	67.5
55			80.5	79.8	79.0	78.2	77.6	76.9	76.4	75.5	74.9	74.2	73.6	73.0	72.6	72.1	71.7	70.9	70.0	68.8
56					80.5	79.7	79.0	78.3	77.8	76.9	76.3	75.6	75.0	74.4	73.9	73.4	73.0	72.2	71.2	70.0
57							80.4	79.7	79.2	78.3	77.7	76.9	76.3	75.7	75.2	74.7	74.3	73.5	72.5	71.3
58									80.6	79.7	79.0	78.3	77.6	77.0	76.5	76.0	75.6	74.7	73.8	72.5
59											80.4	79.6	79.0	78.4	77.8	77.3	76.9	76.0	75.1	73.8
60													80.3	79.7	79.2	78.6	78.2	77.3	76.3	75.0
61															80.5	79.9	79.5	78.6	77.6	76.3
62																81.3	80.8	79.9	78.9	77.5
63																			80.2	78.8
64																				80.0

ACCELERATED BOYS

PERCENTAGES AND ESTIMATED MATURE HEIGHTS FOR BOYS WITH SKELETAL AGES ONE YEAR
OR MORE ADVANCED OVER THEIR CHRONOLOGICAL AGES

Skeletal Ages 12 Through 17 Years

Skeletal Age	12-0	12-3	12-6	12-9	13.0	13-3	13-6	13-9	14-0	14-3	14-6	14-9	15-0	15-3	15-6	15-9	16-0	16-3	16-6	16-9	17-0
% of Mature Height	80.9	81.8	82.8	83.9	85.0	86.3	87.5	89.0	90.5	91.8	93.0	94.3	95.8	96.7	97.1	97.6	98.0	98.3	98.5	98.8	99.0
Ht. (inches)																					
49	60.6																				
50	61.8	61.1	60.4																		
51	63.0	62.3	61.6	60.8	60.0																
52	64.3	63.6	62.8	62.0	61.2	60.3															
53	65.5	64.8	64.0	63.2	62.4	61.4	60.6														
54	66.7	66.0	65.2	64.4	63.5	62.6	61.7	60.7													
55	68.0	67.2	66.4	65.6	64.7	63.7	62.9	61.8	60.8												
56	69.2	68.5	67.6	66.7	65.9	64.9	64.0	62.9	61.9	61.0	60.2										
57	70.5	69.7	68.8	67.9	67.1	66.0	65.1	64.0	63.0	62.1	61.3	60.4									
58	71.7	70.9	70.0	69.1	68.2	67.2	66.3	65.2	64.1	63.2	62.4	61.5	60.5	60.0							
59	72.9	72.1	71.3	70.3	69.4	68.4	67.4	66.3	65.2	64.3	63.4	62.6	61.6	61.0	60.8	60.5	60.2	60.0			
60	74.2	73.4	72.5	71.5	70.6	69.5	68.6	67.4	66.3	65.4	64.5	63.6	62.6	62.0	61.8	61.5	61.2	61.0	60.9	60.7	60.6
61	75.4	74.6	73.7	72.7	71.8	70.7	69.7	68.5	67.4	66.4	65.6	64.7	63.7	63.1	62.8	62.5	62.2	62.1	61.9	61.7	61.6
62	76.6	75.8	74.9	73.9	72.9	71.8	70.9	69.7	68.5	67.5	66.7	65.7	64.7	64.1	63.9	63.5	63.3	63.1	62.9	62.8	62.6
63	77.9	77.0	76.1	75.1	74.1	73.0	72.0	70.8	69.6	68.6	67.7	66.8	65.8	65.1	64.9	64.5	64.3	64.1	64.0	63.8	63.6
64	79.1	78.2	77.3	76.3	75.3	74.2	73.1	71.9	70.7	69.7	68.8	67.9	66.8	66.2	65.9	65.6	65.3	65.1	65.0	64.8	64.6
65	80.3	79.5	78.5	77.5	76.5	75.3	74.3	73.0	71.8	70.8	69.9	68.9	67.8	67.2	66.9	66.6	66.3	66.1	66.0	65.8	65.7
66		80.7	79.7	78.7	77.6	76.5	75.4	74.2	72.9	71.9	71.0	70.0	68.9	68.3	68.0	67.6	67.3	67.1	67.0	66.8	66.7
67			80.9	79.9	78.8	77.6	76.6	75.3	74.0	73.0	72.0	71.1	69.9	69.3	69.0	68.6	68.4	68.2	68.0	67.8	67.7
68				80.0	78.8	77.7	76.4	75.1	74.1	73.1	72.1	71.0	70.3	70.0	69.7	69.4	69.2	69.0	68.8	68.7	
69					80.0	78.9	77.5	76.2	75.2	74.2	73.2	72.0	71.4	71.1	70.7	70.4	70.2	70.0	69.8	69.7	
70						80.0	78.7	77.3	76.3	75.3	74.2	73.1	72.4	72.1	71.7	71.4	71.2	71.1	70.8	70.7	
71							79.8	78.5	77.3	76.3	75.3	74.1	73.4	73.1	72.7	72.4	72.2	72.1	71.9	71.7	
72							80.9	79.6	78.4	77.4	76.4	75.2	74.5	74.2	73.8	73.5	73.2	73.1	72.9	72.7	
73								80.7	79.5	78.5	77.4	76.2	75.5	75.2	74.8	74.5	74.3	74.1	73.9	73.7	
74									80.6	79.6	78.5	77.2	76.5	76.2	75.8	75.5	75.3	75.1	74.9	74.7	
75										80.6	79.6	79.5	78.3	77.6	77.2	76.8	76.5	76.3	76.1	75.9	75.8
76											80.6	79.3	78.6	78.3	77.9	77.6	77.3	77.2	76.9	76.8	
77												80.4	79.6	79.3	78.9	78.6	78.3	78.2	77.9	77.8	
78												80.7	80.3	79.9	79.6	79.3	79.2	78.9	78.8		

Appendix II

Height-Prediction Tables

RETARDED BOYS

PERCENTAGES AND ESTIMATED MATURE HEIGHTS FOR BOYS WITH SKELETAL AGES ONE YEAR
OR MORE RETARDED FOR THEIR CHRONOLOGICAL AGES

Skeletal Ages 6 Through 13 Years

Skeletal Age	**6-0**	6-3	6-6	6-9	**7-0**	7-3	7-6	7-9	**8-0**	8-3	8-6	8-9	**9-0**	9-3	9-6	9-9	**10-0**	10-3	10-6	10-9	**11-0**	11-3	11-6	11-9	12-0	12-3	**12-6**	12-9	13-0
% of Mature Height	68.0	69.0	70.0	70.9	71.8	72.8	73.8	74.7	75.6	76.5	77.3	77.9	78.6	79.4	80.0	80.7	81.2	81.6	81.9	82.1	82.3	82.7	83.2	83.9	84.5	85.2	86.0	86.9	88.0
Ht. (inches)																													
41	60.3																												
42	61.8	60.9	60.0																										
43	63.2	62.3	61.4	60.6																									
44	64.7	63.8	62.9	62.1	61.3	60.4																							
45	66.2	65.2	64.3	63.5	62.7	61.8	61.0	60.2																					
46	67.6	66.7	65.7	64.9	64.1	63.2	62.3	61.6	60.8	60.1																			
47	69.1	68.1	67.1	66.3	65.5	64.6	63.7	62.9	62.2	61.4	60.8	60.3																	
48	70.6	69.6	68.6	67.7	66.9	65.9	65.0	64.3	63.5	62.7	62.1	61.6	61.1	60.5	60.0														
49	72.1	71.0	70.0	69.1	68.3	67.3	66.4	65.6	64.8	64.1	63.4	62.9	62.3	61.7	61.3	60.7	60.3	60.0											
50	73.5	72.5	71.4	70.5	69.6	68.7	67.8	66.9	66.1	65.4	64.7	64.2	63.6	63.0	62.5	62.0	61.6	61.3	61.1	60.9	60.8	60.5	60.1						
51	75.0	73.9	72.9	71.9	71.0	70.1	69.1	68.3	67.5	66.7	66.0	65.5	64.9	64.2	63.8	63.2	62.8	62.5	62.3	62.1	62.0	61.7	61.3	60.8	60.4				
52	76.5	75.4	74.3	73.3	72.4	71.4	70.5	69.6	68.8	68.0	67.3	66.8	66.2	65.5	65.0	64.4	64.0	63.7	63.5	63.3	63.2	62.9	62.5	62.0	61.5	61.0	60.5		
53	77.9	76.8	75.7	74.8	73.8	72.8	71.8	71.0	70.1	69.3	68.6	68.0	67.4	66.8	66.3	65.7	65.3	65.0	64.7	64.6	64.4	64.1	63.7	63.2	62.7	62.2	61.6	61.0	60.2
54	79.4	78.3	77.1	76.2	75.2	74.2	73.2	72.3	71.4	70.6	69.9	69.3	68.7	68.0	67.5	66.9	66.5	66.2	65.9	65.8	65.6	65.3	64.9	64.4	63.9	63.4	62.8	62.1	61.4
55	80.9	79.7	78.6	77.6	76.6	75.5	74.5	73.6	72.8	71.9	71.2	70.6	70.0	69.3	68.8	68.2	67.7	67.4	67.2	67.0	66.8	66.5	66.1	65.6	65.1	64.6	64.0	63.3	62.5
56			80.0	79.0	78.0	76.9	75.9	75.0	74.1	73.2	72.4	71.9	71.2	70.5	70.0	69.4	69.0	68.6	68.4	68.2	68.0	67.7	67.3	66.7	66.3	65.7	65.1	64.4	63.6
57				80.4	79.4	78.3	77.2	76.3	75.4	74.5	73.7	73.2	72.5	71.8	71.3	70.6	70.2	69.9	69.6	69.4	69.3	68.9	68.5	67.9	67.5	66.9	66.3	65.6	64.8
58					80.8	79.7	78.6	77.6	76.7	75.8	75.0	74.5	73.8	73.0	72.5	71.9	71.4	71.1	70.8	70.6	70.5	70.1	69.7	69.1	68.6	68.1	67.4	66.7	65.9
59							79.9	79.0	78.0	77.1	76.3	75.7	75.1	74.3	73.8	73.1	72.7	72.3	72.0	71.9	71.7	71.3	70.9	70.3	69.8	69.2	68.6	67.9	67.0
60								80.3	79.4	78.4	77.6	77.0	76.3	75.6	75.0	74.4	73.9	73.5	73.3	73.1	72.9	72.6	72.1	71.5	71.0	70.4	69.8	69.0	68.2
61									80.7	79.7	78.9	78.3	77.6	76.8	76.3	75.6	75.1	74.8	74.5	74.3	74.1	73.8	73.3	72.7	72.2	71.6	70.9	70.2	69.3
62											80.2	79.6	78.9	78.1	77.5	76.8	76.4	76.0	75.7	75.5	75.3	75.0	74.5	73.9	73.4	72.8	72.1	71.3	70.5
63												80.9	80.2	79.3	78.8	78.1	77.6	77.2	76.9	76.7	76.5	76.2	75.7	75.1	74.6	73.9	73.3	72.5	71.6
64														80.6	80.0	79.3	78.8	78.4	78.1	78.0	77.8	77.4	76.9	76.3	75.7	75.1	74.4	73.6	72.7
65																80.5	80.0	79.7	79.4	79.2	79.0	78.6	78.1	77.5	76.9	76.3	75.6	74.8	73.9
66																		80.9	80.6	80.4	80.2	79.8	79.3	78.7	78.1	77.5	76.7	75.9	75.0
67																							80.5	79.9	79.3	78.6	77.9	77.1	76.1

NOTE: For predicting mature height of retarded boys older than 13 years, the second table of this Appendix, for average boys with skeletal ages from 13 years to maturity, is adequate; the figures for retarded boys and for average boys are very similar for this age range. For discussion, see text, page 45.

228

AVERAGE GIRLS

PERCENTAGES AND ESTIMATED MATURE HEIGHTS FOR GIRLS WITH SKELETAL AGES WITHIN
ONE YEAR OF THEIR CHRONOLOGICAL AGES

Skeletal Ages 6 Through 11 Years

Skeletal Age	6-0	6-3	6-6	6-10	7-0	7-3	7-6	7-10	8-0	8-3	8-6	8-10	9-0	9-3	9-6	9-9	10-0	10-3	10-6	10-9	11-0	11-3	11-6	11-9
% of Mature Height	72.0	72.9	73.8	75.1	75.7	76.5	77.2	78.2	79.0	80.1	81.0	82.1	82.7	83.6	84.4	85.3	86.2	87.4	88.4	89.6	90.6	91.0	91.4	91.8
Ht. (inches)																								
37	51.4																							
38	52.8	52.1	51.5																					
39	54.2	53.5	52.8	52.0	51.5	51.0																		
40	55.6	54.9	54.2	53.3	52.8	52.3	51.8	51.2																
41	56.9	56.2	55.6	54.6	54.2	53.6	53.1	52.4	51.9	51.2														
42	58.3	57.6	56.9	55.9	55.5	54.9	54.4	53.7	53.2	52.4	51.9	51.2												
43	59.7	59.0	58.3	57.3	56.8	56.2	55.7	55.0	54.4	53.7	53.1	52.4	52.0	51.4										
44	61.1	60.4	59.6	58.6	58.1	57.5	57.0	56.3	55.7	54.9	54.3	53.6	53.2	52.6	52.1	51.6	51.0							
45	62.5	61.7	61.0	59.9	59.4	58.8	58.3	57.5	57.0	56.2	55.6	54.8	54.4	53.8	53.3	52.8	52.2	51.5						
46	63.9	63.1	62.3	61.3	60.8	60.1	59.6	58.8	58.2	57.4	56.8	56.0	55.6	55.0	54.5	53.9	53.4	52.6	52.0	51.3				
47	65.3	64.5	63.7	62.6	62.1	61.4	60.9	60.1	59.5	58.7	58.0	57.2	56.8	56.2	55.7	55.1	54.5	53.8	53.2	52.5	51.9	51.6	51.4	51.2
48	66.7	65.8	65.0	63.9	63.4	62.7	62.2	61.4	60.8	59.9	59.3	58.5	58.0	57.4	56.9	56.3	55.7	54.9	54.3	53.6	53.0	52.7	52.5	52.3
49	68.1	67.2	66.4	65.2	64.7	64.1	63.5	62.7	62.0	61.2	60.5	59.7	59.3	58.6	58.1	57.4	56.8	56.1	55.4	54.7	54.1	53.8	53.6	53.4
50	69.4	68.6	67.8	66.6	66.1	65.4	64.8	63.9	63.3	62.4	61.7	60.9	60.5	59.8	59.2	58.6	58.0	57.2	56.6	55.8	55.2	54.9	54.7	54.5
51	70.8	70.0	69.1	67.9	67.4	66.7	66.1	65.2	64.6	63.7	63.0	62.1	61.7	61.0	60.4	59.8	59.2	58.4	57.7	56.9	56.3	56.0	55.8	55.6
52	72.2	71.3	70.5	69.2	68.7	68.0	67.4	66.5	65.8	64.9	64.2	63.3	62.9	62.2	61.6	61.0	60.3	59.5	58.8	58.0	57.4	57.1	56.9	56.6
53	73.6	72.7	71.8	70.6	70.0	69.3	68.7	67.8	67.1	66.2	65.4	64.6	64.1	63.4	62.8	62.1	61.5	60.6	60.0	59.2	58.5	58.2	58.0	57.7
54		74.1	73.2	71.9	71.3	70.6	69.9	69.1	68.4	67.4	66.7	65.8	65.3	64.6	64.0	63.3	62.6	61.8	61.1	60.3	59.6	59.3	59.1	58.8
55			74.5	73.2	72.7	71.9	71.2	70.3	69.6	68.7	67.9	67.0	66.5	65.8	65.2	64.5	63.8	62.9	62.2	61.4	60.7	60.4	60.2	59.9
56				74.6	74.0	73.2	72.5	71.6	70.9	69.9	69.1	68.2	67.7	67.0	66.4	65.7	65.0	64.1	63.3	62.5	61.8	61.5	61.3	61.0
57					74.5	73.8	72.9	72.2	71.2	70.4	69.4	68.9	68.2	67.5	66.8	66.1	65.2	64.5	63.6	62.9	62.6	62.4	62.1	
58								74.2	73.4	72.4	71.6	70.6	70.1	69.4	68.7	68.0	67.3	66.4	65.6	64.7	64.0	63.7	63.5	63.2
59									74.7	73.7	72.8	71.9	71.3	70.6	69.9	69.2	68.4	67.5	66.7	65.8	65.1	64.8	64.6	64.3
60										74.9	74.1	73.1	72.6	71.8	71.1	70.3	69.6	68.7	67.9	67.0	66.2	65.9	65.6	65.4
61												74.3	73.8	73.0	72.3	71.5	70.8	69.8	69.0	68.1	67.3	67.0	66.7	66.4
62														74.2	73.5	72.7	71.9	70.9	70.1	69.2	68.4	68.1	67.8	67.5
63															74.6	73.9	73.1	72.1	71.3	70.3	69.5	69.2	68.9	68.6
64																	74.2	73.2	72.4	71.4	70.6	70.3	70.0	69.7
65																		74.4	73.5	72.5	71.7	71.4	71.1	70.8
66																			74.7	73.7	72.9	72.5	72.2	71.9
67																				74.8	74.0	73.6	73.3	73.0
68																						74.7	74.4	74.1

AVERAGE GIRLS

PERCENTAGES AND ESTIMATED MATURE HEIGHTS FOR GIRLS WITH SKELETAL AGES WITHIN
ONE YEAR OF THEIR CHRONOLOGICAL AGES

Skeletal Ages 12 Through 18 Years

Skeletal Age	12-0	12-3	12-6	12-9	13-0	13-3	13-6	13-9	14-0	14-3	14-6	14-9	15-0	15-3	15-6	15-9	16-0	16-3	16-6	16-9	17-0	17-6	18-0
% of Mature Height	92.2	93.2	94.1	95.0	95.8	96.7	97.4	97.8	98.0	98.3	98.6	98.8	99.0	99.1	99.3	99.4	99.6	99.6	99.7	99.8	99.9	99.95	100.0
Ht. (inches)																							
47	51.0																						
48	52.1	51.5	51.0																				
49	53.1	52.6	52.1	51.6	51.1																		
50	54.2	53.6	53.1	52.6	52.2	51.7	51.3	51.1	51.0														
51	55.3	54.7	54.2	53.7	53.2	52.7	52.4	52.1	52.0	51.9	51.7	51.6	51.5	51.5	51.4	51.3	51.2	51.2	51.2	51.1	51.1	51.0	51.0
52	56.4	55.8	55.3	54.7	54.3	53.8	53.4	53.2	53.1	52.9	52.7	52.6	52.5	52.5	52.4	52.3	52.2	52.2	52.2	52.1	52.1	52.0	52.0
53	57.5	56.9	56.3	55.8	55.3	54.8	54.4	54.2	54.1	53.9	53.8	53.6	53.5	53.5	53.4	53.3	53.2	53.2	53.2	53.1	53.1	53.0	53.0
54	58.6	57.9	57.4	56.8	56.4	55.8	55.4	55.2	55.1	54.9	54.8	54.7	54.5	54.5	54.4	54.3	54.2	54.2	54.2	54.1	54.1	54.0	54.0
55	59.7	59.0	58.4	57.9	57.4	56.9	56.5	56.2	56.1	56.0	55.8	55.7	55.5	55.5	55.3	55.2	55.2	55.2	55.2	55.1	55.1	55.0	55.0
56	60.7	60.1	59.5	58.9	58.5	57.9	57.5	57.3	57.1	57.0	56.8	56.7	56.6	56.5	56.4	56.3	56.2	56.2	56.2	56.1	56.1	56.0	56.0
57	61.8	61.2	60.6	60.0	59.5	58.9	58.5	58.3	58.2	58.0	57.8	57.7	57.6	57.5	57.4	57.3	57.2	57.2	57.2	57.1	57.1	57.0	57.0
58	62.9	62.2	61.6	61.1	60.5	60.0	59.5	59.3	59.2	59.0	58.8	58.7	58.6	58.5	58.3	58.2	58.2	58.2	58.2	58.1	58.1	58.0	58.0
59	64.0	63.3	62.7	62.1	61.6	61.0	60.6	60.3	60.2	60.0	59.8	59.7	59.6	59.5	59.4	59.4	59.2	59.2	59.2	59.1	59.1	59.0	59.0
60	65.1	64.4	63.8	63.2	62.6	62.0	61.6	61.3	61.2	61.0	60.9	60.7	60.6	60.5	60.4	60.4	60.2	60.2	60.2	60.1	60.1	60.0	60.0
61	66.2	65.5	64.8	64.2	63.7	63.1	62.6	62.4	62.2	62.1	61.9	61.7	61.6	61.6	61.4	61.4	61.2	61.2	61.2	61.1	61.1	61.0	61.0
62	67.2	66.5	65.9	65.3	64.7	64.1	63.6	63.4	63.3	63.1	62.9	62.8	62.6	62.6	62.4	62.4	62.2	62.2	62.2	62.1	62.1	62.0	62.0
63	68.3	67.6	67.0	66.3	65.8	65.1	64.7	64.4	64.3	64.1	63.9	63.8	63.6	63.6	63.4	63.4	63.3	63.3	63.2	63.1	63.1	63.0	63.0
64	69.4	68.7	68.0	67.4	66.8	66.2	65.7	65.4	65.3	65.1	64.9	64.8	64.6	64.6	64.4	64.4	64.3	64.3	64.2	64.1	64.1	64.0	64.0
65	70.5	69.7	69.1	68.4	67.8	67.2	66.7	66.5	66.3	66.1	65.9	65.8	65.7	65.6	65.5	65.4	65.3	65.3	65.2	65.1	65.1	65.0	65.0
66	71.6	70.8	70.1	69.5	68.9	68.3	67.8	67.5	67.3	67.1	66.9	66.8	66.7	66.6	66.5	66.4	66.3	66.3	66.2	66.1	66.1	66.0	66.0
67	72.7	71.9	71.2	70.5	69.9	69.3	68.8	68.5	68.4	68.2	68.0	67.8	67.7	67.6	67.5	67.4	67.3	67.3	67.2	67.1	67.1	67.0	67.0
68	73.8	73.0	72.3	71.6	71.0	70.3	69.8	69.5	69.4	69.2	69.0	68.8	68.7	68.6	68.5	68.4	68.3	68.3	68.2	68.1	68.1	68.0	68.0
69	74.8	74.0	73.3	72.6	72.0	71.4	70.8	70.6	70.4	70.2	70.0	69.8	69.7	69.6	69.5	69.4	69.3	69.3	69.2	69.1	69.1	69.0	69.0
70			74.3	73.7	73.1	72.4	71.9	71.6	71.4	71.2	71.0	70.8	70.7	70.6	70.5	70.4	70.3	70.3	70.2	70.1	70.1	70.0	70.0
71				74.7	74.1	73.4	72.9	72.6	72.4	72.2	72.0	71.9	71.7	71.6	71.5	71.4	71.3	71.3	71.2	71.1	71.1	71.0	71.0
72						74.5	73.9	73.6	73.5	73.2	73.0	72.9	72.7	72.7	72.5	72.4	72.3	72.3	72.2	72.1	72.1	72.0	72.0
73							74.9	74.6	74.5	74.3	74.0	73.9	73.7	73.7	73.5	73.4	73.3	73.3	73.2	73.1	73.1	73.0	73.0
74												74.9	74.7	74.7	74.5	74.4	74.3	74.3	74.2	74.1	74.1	74.0	74.0

Height-Prediction Tables

ACCELERATED GIRLS

PERCENTAGES AND ESTIMATED MATURE HEIGHTS FOR GIRLS WITH SKELETAL AGES ONE YEAR
OR MORE ADVANCED OVER THEIR CHRONOLOGICAL AGES

Skeletal Ages 7 Through 11 Years

Skeletal Age	7-0	7-3	7-6	7-10	8-0	8-3	8-6	8-10	9-0	9-3	9-6	9-9	10-0	10-3	10-6	10-9	11-0	11-3	11-6	11-9
% of Mature Height	71.2	72.2	73.2	74.2	75.0	76.0	77.1	78.4	79.0	80.0	80.9	81.9	82.8	84.1	85.6	87.0	88.3	88.7	89.1	89.7
Ht. (inches)																				
37		52.0	51.2																	
38	53.4	52.6	51.9	51.2																
39	54.8	54.0	53.3	52.6	52.0	51.3														
40	56.2	55.4	54.6	53.9	53.3	52.6	51.9	51.0												
41	57.6	56.8	56.0	55.3	54.7	53.9	53.2	52.3	51.9	51.3										
42	59.0	58.2	57.4	56.6	56.0	55.3	54.5	53.6	53.2	52.5	51.9	51.3								
43	60.4	59.6	58.7	58.0	57.3	56.6	55.8	54.8	54.4	53.8	53.2	52.5	51.9	51.1						
44	61.8	60.9	60.1	59.3	58.7	57.9	57.1	56.1	55.7	55.0	54.4	53.7	53.1	52.3	51.4					
45	63.2	62.3	61.5	60.6	60.0	59.2	58.4	57.4	57.0	56.3	55.6	54.9	54.3	53.5	52.6	51.7	51.0			
46	64.6	63.7	62.8	62.0	61.3	60.5	59.7	58.7	58.2	57.5	56.9	56.2	55.6	54.7	53.7	52.9	52.1	51.9	51.6	51.3
47	66.0	65.1	64.2	63.3	62.7	61.8	61.0	59.9	59.5	58.8	58.1	57.4	56.8	55.9	54.9	54.0	53.2	53.0	52.7	52.4
48	67.4	66.5	65.6	64.7	64.0	63.2	62.3	61.2	60.8	60.0	59.3	58.6	58.0	57.1	56.1	55.2	54.4	54.1	53.9	53.5
49	68.8	67.9	66.9	66.0	65.3	64.5	63.6	62.5	62.0	61.3	60.6	59.8	59.2	58.3	57.2	56.3	55.5	55.2	55.0	54.6
50	70.2	69.3	68.3	67.4	66.7	65.8	64.9	63.8	63.3	62.5	61.8	61.1	60.4	59.5	58.4	57.5	56.6	56.4	56.1	55.7
51	71.6	70.6	69.7	68.7	68.0	67.1	66.1	65.1	64.6	63.8	63.0	62.3	61.6	60.6	59.6	58.6	57.8	57.5	57.2	56.9
52	73.0	72.0	71.0	70.1	69.3	68.4	67.4	66.3	65.8	65.0	64.3	63.5	62.8	61.8	60.7	59.8	58.9	58.6	58.4	58.0
53	74.4	73.4	72.4	71.4	70.7	69.7	68.7	67.6	67.1	66.3	65.5	64.7	64.0	63.0	61.9	60.9	60.0	59.8	59.5	59.1
54		74.8	73.8	72.8	72.0	71.1	70.0	68.9	68.4	67.5	66.7	65.9	65.2	64.2	63.1	62.1	61.2	60.9	60.6	60.2
55				74.1	73.3	72.4	71.3	70.2	69.6	68.8	68.0	67.2	66.4	65.4	64.3	63.2	62.3	62.0	61.7	61.3
56					74.7	73.7	72.6	71.4	70.9	70.0	69.2	68.4	67.6	66.6	65.4	64.4	63.4	63.1	62.8	62.4
57							73.9	72.7	72.2	71.3	70.5	69.6	68.8	67.8	66.6	65.5	64.6	64.3	64.0	63.5
58								74.0	73.4	72.5	71.7	70.8	70.0	69.0	67.8	66.7	65.7	65.4	65.1	64.7
59									74.7	73.8	72.9	72.0	71.3	70.2	68.9	67.8	66.8	66.5	66.2	65.8
60											74.2	73.3	72.5	71.3	70.1	69.0	68.0	67.6	67.3	66.9
61												74.5	73.7	72.5	71.3	70.1	69.1	68.8	68.5	68.0
62													74.9	73.7	72.4	71.3	70.2	69.9	69.6	69.1
63														74.9	73.6	72.4	71.3	71.0	70.7	70.2
64															74.8	73.6	72.4	72.2	71.8	71.3
65																74.7	73.6	73.3	72.9	72.5
66																	74.7	74.4	74.1	73.6
67																				74.7

ACCELERATED GIRLS

PERCENTAGES AND ESTIMATED MATURE HEIGHTS FOR GIRLS WITH SKELETAL AGES ONE YEAR
OR MORE ADVANCED OVER THEIR CHRONOLOGICAL AGES

Skeletal Ages 12 Through 17 Years

Skeletal Age	12-0	12-3	12-6	12-9	13-0	13-3	13-6	13-9	14-0	14-3	14-6	14-9	15-0	15-3	15-6	15-9	16-0	16-3	16-6	16-9	17-0	17-6
% of Mature Height	90.1	91.3	92.4	93.5	94.5	95.5	96.3	96.8	97.2	97.7	98.0	98.3	98.6	98.8	99.0	99.2	99.3	99.4	99.5	99.7	99.8	99.95
Ht. (inches)																						
46	51.1																					
47	52.2	51.5																				
48	53.3	52.6	51.9	51.3																		
49	54.4	53.7	53.0	52.4	51.9	51.3	50.9															
50	55.5	54.8	54.1	53.5	52.9	52.4	51.9	51.7	51.4	51.2	51.0											
51	56.6	55.9	55.2	54.5	54.0	53.4	53.0	52.7	52.5	52.2	52.0	51.9	51.7	51.6	51.5	51.4	51.4	51.3	51.3	51.2	51.1	51.0
52	57.7	57.0	56.3	55.6	55.0	54.5	54.0	53.7	53.5	53.2	53.1	52.9	52.7	52.6	52.5	52.4	52.4	52.3	52.3	52.2	52.1	52.0
53	58.8	58.1	57.4	56.7	56.1	55.5	55.0	54.8	54.5	54.2	54.1	53.9	53.8	53.6	53.5	53.4	53.4	53.3	53.3	53.2	53.1	53.0
54	59.9	59.1	58.4	57.8	57.1	56.5	56.1	55.8	55.6	55.3	55.1	54.9	54.8	54.7	54.5	54.4	54.4	54.3	54.3	54.2	54.1	54.0
55	61.0	60.2	59.5	58.8	58.2	57.6	57.1	56.8	56.6	56.3	56.1	56.0	55.8	55.7	55.5	55.4	55.4	55.3	55.3	55.2	55.1	55.0
56	62.2	61.3	60.6	59.9	59.3	58.6	58.2	57.9	57.6	57.3	57.1	57.0	56.8	56.7	56.5	56.5	56.4	56.3	56.3	56.2	56.1	56.0
57	63.3	62.4	61.7	61.0	60.3	59.7	59.2	58.9	58.6	58.3	58.2	58.0	57.8	57.7	57.6	57.5	57.4	57.3	57.3	57.2	57.1	57.0
58	64.4	63.5	62.8	62.0	61.4	60.7	60.2	59.9	59.7	59.4	59.2	59.0	58.8	58.7	58.6	58.5	58.4	58.3	58.3	58.2	58.1	58.0
59	65.5	64.6	63.9	63.1	62.4	61.8	61.3	61.0	60.7	60.4	60.2	60.0	59.8	59.7	59.6	59.5	59.4	59.4	59.3	59.2	59.1	59.0
60	66.6	65.7	64.9	64.2	63.5	62.8	62.3	62.0	61.7	61.4	61.2	61.0	60.9	60.7	60.6	60.5	60.4	60.4	60.3	60.2	60.1	60.0
61	67.7	66.8	66.0	65.2	64.6	63.9	63.3	63.0	62.8	62.4	62.2	62.1	61.9	61.7	61.6	61.5	61.4	61.4	61.3	61.2	61.1	61.0
62	68.8	67.9	67.1	66.3	65.6	64.9	64.4	64.0	63.8	63.5	63.3	63.1	62.9	62.8	62.6	62.5	62.4	62.4	62.3	62.2	62.1	62.0
63	69.9	69.0	68.2	67.4	66.7	66.0	65.4	65.1	64.8	64.5	64.3	64.1	63.9	63.8	63.6	63.5	63.4	63.4	63.3	63.2	63.1	63.0
64	71.0	70.1	69.3	68.4	67.7	67.0	66.5	66.1	65.8	65.5	65.3	65.1	64.9	64.8	64.6	64.5	64.4	64.4	64.3	64.2	64.1	64.0
65	72.1	71.2	70.3	69.5	68.8	68.1	67.5	67.1	66.9	66.5	66.3	66.1	65.9	65.8	65.7	65.5	65.5	65.4	65.3	65.2	65.1	65.0
66	73.3	72.3	71.4	70.6	69.8	69.1	68.5	68.2	67.9	67.6	67.3	67.1	66.9	66.8	66.7	66.5	66.5	66.4	66.3	66.2	66.1	66.0
67	74.4	73.4	72.5	71.7	70.9	70.2	69.6	69.2	68.9	68.6	68.4	68.2	68.0	67.8	67.7	67.5	67.5	67.4	67.3	67.2	67.1	67.0
68		74.5	73.6	72.7	72.0	71.2	70.6	70.2	70.0	69.6	69.4	69.2	69.0	68.8	68.7	68.6	68.5	68.4	68.3	68.2	68.1	68.0
69			74.7	73.8	73.0	72.3	71.7	71.3	71.0	70.6	70.4	70.2	70.0	69.8	69.7	69.6	69.5	69.4	69.3	69.2	69.1	69.0
70				74.9	74.1	73.3	72.7	72.3	72.0	71.6	71.4	71.2	71.0	70.8	70.7	70.6	70.5	70.4	70.3	70.2	70.1	70.0
71						74.3	73.7	73.3	73.0	72.7	72.4	72.2	72.0	71.9	71.7	71.6	71.5	71.4	71.4	71.2	71.1	71.0
72							74.8	74.4	74.1	73.7	73.5	73.2	73.0	72.9	72.7	72.6	72.5	72.4	72.4	72.2	72.1	72.0
73										74.7	74.5	74.3	74.0	73.9	73.7	73.6	73.5	734.	73.4	73.2	73.1	73.0
74														74.9	74.4	74.6	74.5	74.4	74.4	74.2	74.1	74.0

RETARDED GIRLS

PERCENTAGES AND ESTIMATED MATURE HEIGHTS FOR GIRLS WITH SKELETAL AGES ONE YEAR
OR MORE RETARDED FOR THEIR CHRONOLOGICAL AGES

Skeletal Ages 6 Through 11 Years

Skeletal Age	6-0	6-3	6-6	6-10	7-0	7-3	7-6	7-10	8-0	8-3	8-6	8-10	9-0	9-3	9-6	9-9	10-0	10-3	10-6	10-9	11-0	11-3	11-6	11-9
% of Mature Height	73.3	74.2	75.1	76.3	77.0	77.9	78.8	79.7	80.4	81.3	82.3	83.6	84.1	85.1	85.8	86.6	87.4	88.4	89.6	90.7	91.8	92.2	92.6	92.9
Ht. (inches)																								
38	51.8	51.2																						
39	53.2	52.6	51.9	51.1																				
40	54.6	53.9	53.3	52.4	51.9	51.3																		
41	55.9	55.3	54.6	53.7	53.2	52.6	52.0	51.4																
42	57.3	56.6	55.9	55.0	54.5	53.9	53.3	52.7	52.2	51.7	51.0													
43	58.7	58.0	57.3	56.4	55.8	55.2	54.6	54.0	53.5	52.9	52.2	51.4	51.1											
44	60.0	59.3	58.6	57.7	57.1	56.5	55.8	55.2	54.7	54.1	53.5	52.6	52.3	51.7	51.3									
45	61.4	60.6	59.9	59.0	58.4	57.8	57.1	56.5	56.0	55.4	54.7	53.8	53.5	52.9	52.4	52.0	51.5							
46	62.8	62.0	61.3	60.3	59.7	59.1	58.4	57.7	57.2	56.6	55.9	55.0	54.7	54.1	53.6	53.1	52.6	52.0	51.3					
47	64.1	63.3	62.6	61.6	61.0	60.3	59.6	59.0	58.5	57.8	57.1	56.2	55.9	55.2	54.8	54.3	53.8	53.2	52.5	51.8	51.2	51.0		
48	65.5	64.7	63.9	62.9	62.3	61.6	60.9	60.2	59.7	59.0	58.3	57.4	57.1	56.4	55.9	55.4	54.9	54.3	53.6	52.9	52.3	52.1	51.8	51.7
49	66.9	66.0	65.2	64.2	63.6	62.9	62.2	61.5	60.9	60.3	59.5	58.6	58.3	57.6	57.1	56.6	56.1	55.4	54.7	54.0	53.4	53.1	52.9	52.7
50	68.2	67.4	66.6	65.5	64.9	64.2	63.5	62.7	62.2	61.5	60.8	59.8	59.5	58.8	58.3	57.7	57.2	56.6	55.8	55.1	54.5	54.2	54.0	53.8
51	69.6	68.7	67.9	66.8	66.2	65.5	64.7	64.0	63.4	62.7	62.0	61.0	60.6	59.9	59.4	58.9	58.4	57.7	56.9	56.2	55.6	55.3	55.1	54.9
52	70.9	70.1	69.2	68.2	67.5	66.8	66.0	65.2	64.7	64.0	63.2	62.2	61.8	61.1	60.6	60.0	59.5	58.8	58.0	57.3	56.6	56.4	56.2	56.0
53	72.3	71.4	70.6	69.5	68.8	68.0	67.3	66.5	65.9	65.2	64.4	63.4	63.0	62.3	61.8	61.2	60.6	60.0	59.2	58.4	57.7	57.5	57.2	57.1
54	73.7	72.8	71.9	70.8	70.1	69.3	68.5	67.8	67.2	66.4	65.6	64.6	64.2	63.5	62.9	62.4	61.8	61.1	60.3	59.5	58.8	58.6	58.3	58.1
55		74.1	73.2	72.1	71.4	70.6	69.8	69.0	68.4	67.7	66.8	65.8	65.4	64.6	64.1	63.5	62.9	62.2	61.4	60.6	59.9	59.7	59.4	59.2
56			74.6	73.4	72.7	71.9	71.1	70.3	69.7	68.9	68.0	67.0	66.6	65.8	65.3	64.7	64.1	63.3	62.5	61.7	61.0	60.7	60.5	60.3
57				74.7	74.0	73.2	72.3	71.5	70.9	70.1	69.3	68.2	67.8	67.0	66.4	65.8	65.2	64.5	63.6	62.8	62.1	61.8	61.6	61.4
58					74.5	73.6	72.8	72.1	71.3	70.5	69.4	69.0	68.2	67.6	67.0	66.4	65.6	64.7	63.9	63.2	62.9	62.6	62.4	
59						74.9	74.0	73.4	72.6	71.7	70.6	70.2	69.3	68.8	68.1	67.5	66.7	65.8	65.0	64.3	64.0	63.7	63.5	
60							74.6	73.8	72.9	71.8	71.3	70.5	69.9	69.3	68.7	67.9	67.0	66.2	65.4	65.1	64.8	64.6		
61								74.1	73.0	72.5	71.7	71.1	70.4	69.8	69.0	68.1	67.3	66.4	66.2	65.9	65.7			
62									74.2	73.7	72.9	72.3	71.6	70.9	70.1	69.2	68.4	67.5	67.2	67.0	66.7			
63										74.7	74.0	73.4	72.7	72.1	71.3	70.3	69.5	68.6	68.3	68.0	67.8			
64											74.6	73.9	73.2	72.4	71.4	70.6	69.7	69.4	69.1	68.9				
65												74.4	73.5	72.5	71.7	70.8	70.5	70.2	70.0					
66													74.7	73.7	72.8	71.9	71.6	71.3	71.0					
67														74.8	73.9	73.0	72.7	72.4	72.1					
68															74.1	73.8	73.4	73.2						
69																74.8	74.5	74.3						

RETARDED GIRLS

PERCENTAGES AND ESTIMATED MATURE HEIGHTS FOR GIRLS WITH SKELETAL AGES ONE YEAR
OR MORE RETARDED FOR THEIR CHRONOLOGICAL AGES

Skeletal Ages 12 Through 17 Years

Skeletal Age	12-0	12-3	12-6	12-9	13-0	13-3	13-6	13-9	14-0	14-3	14-6	14-9	15-0	15-3	15-6	15-9	16-0	16-3	16-6	16-9	17-0
% of Mature Height	93.2	94.2	94.9	95.7	96.4	97.1	97.7	98.1	98.3	98.6	98.9	99.2	99.4	99.5	99.6	99.7	99.8	99.9	99.9	99.95	100.0
Ht. (inches)																					
48	51.5	51.0																			
49	52.6	52.0	51.6	51.2																	
50	53.6	53.1	52.7	52.2	51.9	51.5	51.2	51.0													
51	54.7	54.1	53.7	53.3	52.9	52.5	52.2	52.0	51.9	51.7	51.6	51.4	51.3	51.3	51.2	51.2	51.1	51.1	51.1	51.0	51.0
52	55.8	55.2	54.8	54.3	53.9	53.6	53.2	53.0	52.9	52.7	52.6	52.4	52.3	52.3	52.2	52.2	52.1	52.1	52.1	52.0	52.0
53	56.9	56.3	55.8	55.4	55.0	54.6	54.2	54.0	53.9	53.8	53.6	53.4	53.3	53.3	53.2	53.2	53.1	53.1	53.1	53.0	53.0
54	57.9	57.3	56.9	56.4	56.0	55.6	55.3	55.0	54.9	54.8	54.6	54.4	54.3	54.3	54.2	54.2	54.1	54.1	54.1	54.0	54.0
55	59.0	58.4	58.0	57.5	57.1	56.6	56.3	56.1	56.0	55.8	55.6	55.4	55.3	55.3	55.2	55.2	55.1	55.1	55.1	55.0	55.0
56	60.1	59.4	59.0	58.5	58.1	57.7	57.3	57.1	57.0	56.8	56.6	56.5	56.3	56.3	56.2	56.2	56.1	56.1	56.1	56.0	56.0
57	61.2	60.5	60.1	59.6	59.1	58.7	58.3	58.1	58.0	57.8	57.6	57.5	57.3	57.3	57.2	57.2	57.1	57.1	57.1	57.0	57.0
58	62.2	61.6	61.1	60.6	60.2	59.7	59.4	59.1	59.0	58.8	58.6	58.5	58.3	58.3	58.2	58.2	58.1	58.1	58.1	58.0	58.0
59	63.3	62.6	62.2	61.7	61.2	60.8	60.4	60.1	60.0	59.8	59.7	59.5	59.4	59.3	59.2	59.2	59.1	59.1	59.1	59.0	59.0
60	64.4	63.7	63.2	62.7	62.2	61.8	61.4	61.2	61.0	60.9	60.7	60.5	60.4	60.3	60.2	60.2	60.1	60.1	60.1	60.0	60.0
61	65.5	64.8	64.3	63.7	63.3	62.8	62.4	62.2	62.1	61.9	61.7	61.5	61.4	61.3	61.2	61.2	61.1	61.1	61.1	61.0	61.0
62	66.5	65.8	65.3	64.8	64.3	63.9	63.5	63.2	63.1	62.9	62.7	62.5	62.4	62.3	62.2	62.2	62.1	62.1	62.1	62.0	62.0
63	67.6	66.9	66.4	65.8	65.3	64.9	64.5	64.2	64.1	63.9	63.7	63.5	63.4	63.3	63.3	63.2	63.1	63.1	63.1	63.0	63.0
64	68.7	67.9	67.4	66.9	66.4	65.9	65.5	65.2	65.1	64.9	64.7	64.5	64.4	64.3	64.3	64.2	64.1	64.1	64.1	64.0	64.0
65	69.7	69.0	68.5	67.9	67.4	66.9	66.5	66.3	66.1	65.9	65.7	65.5	65.4	65.3	65.3	65.2	65.1	65.1	65.1	65.0	65.0
66	70.8	70.1	69.5	69.0	68.5	68.0	67.6	67.3	67.1	66.9	66.7	66.5	66.4	66.3	66.3	66.2	66.1	66.1	66.1	66.0	66.0
67	71.9	71.1	70.6	70.0	69.5	69.0	68.6	68.3	68.2	68.0	67.7	67.5	67.4	67.3	67.3	67.2	67.1	67.1	67.1	67.0	67.0
68	73.0	72.2	71.7	71.1	70.5	70.0	69.6	69.3	69.2	69.0	68.8	68.6	68.4	68.3	68.3	68.2	68.1	68.1	68.1	68.0	68.0
69	74.0	73.2	72.7	72.1	71.6	71.1	70.6	70.3	70.2	70.0	69.8	69.6	69.4	69.3	69.3	69.2	69.1	69.1	69.1	69.0	69.0
70		74.3	73.8	73.1	72.6	72.1	71.6	71.4	71.2	71.0	70.8	70.6	70.4	70.4	70.3	70.2	70.1	70.1	70.1	70.0	70.0
71			74.8	74.2	73.6	73.1	72.7	72.4	72.2	72.0	71.8	71.6	71.4	71.4	71.3	71.2	71.1	71.1	71.1	71.0	71.0
72				74.7	74.2	73.7	73.4	73.3	73.0	72.8	72.6	72.4	72.4	72.3	72.2	72.1	72.1	72.1	72.0	72.0
73					74.7	74.4	74.3	74.0	73.8	73.6	73.4	73.4	73.3	73.2	73.1	73.1	73.1	73.0	73.0
74									74.8	74.6	74.4	74.4	74.3	74.2	74.1	74.1	74.1	74.0	74.0

Converting Age into Decimal System

To quote Pearl and Miner (1932), who prepared the table presented here: "Standard calendar divisions of time constitute a minor nuisance to statisticians. Months are neither equal in length nor simple fractions of a year. Weeks go only unevenly into months. The most satisfactory way of dealing with . . . elapsed time appears to us to be to express the time between any two calendar dates in terms of years and decimal fractions of a year."

In determining growth rate, for example, one factor is the length of time between two given sets of observations. This involves subtracting the age of a patient at the beginning of the period from the age at the end. For this purpose it would be extremely awkward to manipulate two figures like "9 years 2 months 5 days" and "9 years 8 months 9 days." The only feasible unit would be number of days, and this could only be derived by actual count of intervening dates. But the operation becomes simple once the ages under consideration are converted into the decimal system by use of the Pearl and Miner Table for Ascertaining Elapsed Time in Years and Decimals of a Year between Any Two Dates.

Let us say that the patient referred to above was

ELAPSED TIME EXPRESSED IN DECIMALS OF A YEAR*

a—fraction of year since January 1
b—fraction of year remaining

a	JAN	b	a	FEB.	b	a	MARCH	b	a	APRIL	b	a	MAY	b	a	JUNE	b
0	1	1.000	.085	1	.915	.162	1	.838	.247	1	.753	.329	1	.671	414	1	.586
.003	2	.997	.088	2	.912	.164	2	.836	.249	2	.751	.332	2	.668	.416	2	.584
.005	3	.995	.090	3	.910	.167	3	.833	.252	3	.748	.334	3	.666	.419	3	.581
.008	4	.992	.093	4	.907	.170	4	.830	.255	4	.745	.337	4	.663	.422	4	.578
.011	5	.989	.096	5	.904	.173	5	.827	.258	5	.742	.340	5	.660	.425	5	.575
.014	6	.986	.099	6	.901	.175	6	.825	.260	6	.740	.342	6	.658	.427	6	.573
.016	7	.984	.101	7	.899	.178	7	.822	.263	7	.737	.345	7	.655	.430	7	.570
.019	8	.981	.104	8	.896	.181	8	.819	.266	8	.734	.348	8	.652	.433	8	.567
.022	9	.978	.107	9	.893	.184	9	.816	.268	9	.732	.351	9	.649	.436	9	.564
.025	10	.975	.110	10	.890	.186	10	.814	.271	10	.729	.353	10	.647	.438	10	.562
.027	11	.973	.112	11	.888	.189	11	.811	.274	11	.726	.356	11	.644	.441	11	.559
.030	12	.970	.115	12	.885	.192	12	.808	.277	12	.723	.359	12	.641	.444	12	.556
.033	13	.967	.118	13	.882	.195	13	.805	.279	13	.721	.362	13	.638	.447	13	.553
.036	14	.964	.121	14	.879	.197	14	.803	.282	14	.718	.364	14	.636	.449	14	.551
.038	15	.962	.123	15	.877	.200	15	.800	.285	15	.715	.367	15	.633	.452	15	.548
.041	16	.959	.126	16	.874	.203	16	.797	.288	16	.712	.370	16	.630	.455	16	.545
.044	17	.956	.129	17	.871	.205	17	.795	.290	17	.710	.373	17	.627	.458	17	.542
.047	18	.953	.132	18	.868	.208	18	.792	.293	18	.707	.375	18	.625	.460	18	.540
.049	19	.951	.134	19	.866	.211	19	.789	.296	19	.704	.378	19	.622	.463	19	.537
.052	20	.948	.137	20	.863	.214	20	.786	.299	20	.701	.381	20	.619	.466	20	.534
.055	21	.945	.140	21	.860	.216	21	.784	.301	21	.699	.384	21	.616	.468	21	.532
.058	22	.942	.142	22	.858	.219	22	.781	.304	22	.696	.386	22	.614	.471	22	.529
.060	23	.940	.145	23	.855	.222	23	.778	.307	23	.693	.389	23	.611	.474	23	.526
.063	24	.937	.148	24	.852	.225	24	.775	.310	24	.690	.392	24	.608	.477	24	.523
.066	25	.934	.151	25	.849	.227	25	.773	.312	25	.688	.395	25	.605	.479	25	.521
.068	26	.932	.153	26	.847	.230	26	.770	.315	26	.685	.397	26	.603	.482	26	.518
.071	27	.929	.156	27	.844	.233	27	.767	.318	27	.682	.400	27	.600	.485	27	.515
.074	28	.926	.159	28	.841	.236	28	.764	.321	28	.679	.403	28	.597	.488	28	.512
.077	29	.923	.162	29	.838	.238	29	.762	.323	29	.677	.405	29	.595	.490	29	.510
.079	30	.921				.241	30	.759	.326	30	.674	.408	30	.592	.493	30	.507
.082	31	.918				.244	31	.756				.411	31	.589			

* Calculated by Pearl and Miner (1932).

born on June 3, 1949, and was first examined on August 8, 1958. His nine years of life are obvious. To determine the additional fraction of a year, we use column a of the table. Subtracting the reading opposite June 3 (.419) from August 8 (.600), we arrive at .181. The patient is 9.181 years old.

If the patient's birthday comes at a later point in the calendar year than the observation, column b also comes into use. Suppose the second examination were made on February 12, 1959. He has then completed nine years and about two-thirds of a year. To obtain his exact decimal age in this case, we add the b reading

of June 3 (.581)—the fraction of a year from that date to the following December 31—and the a reading of February 12 (.115)—the fraction of a year from January 1 to February 12. Since .581 plus .115 equals .696, the patient is 9.696 years of age.

The elapsed time between the two observations is 9.696 years minus 9.181 years or .515 years.

The Pearl and Miner table may obviously be used to convert any period of elapsed time into decimals. We have merely expressed our examples in terms of the patient's age at time of examinations, since our principal need for it is in making growth-rate calculations.

ELAPSED TIME EXPRESSED IN DECIMALS OF A YEAR (*Continued*)

a—fraction of year since January 1
b—fraction of year remaining

a	JULY	b	a	AUG.	b	a	SEPT.	b	a	OCT.	b	a	NOV.	b	a	DEC.	b
.496	1	.504	.581	1	.419	.666	1	.334	.748	1	.252	.833	1	.167	.915	1	.085
.499	2	.501	.584	2	.416	.668	2	.332	.751	2	.249	.836	2	.164	.918	2	.082
.501	3	.499	.586	3	.414	.671	3	.329	.753	3	.247	.838	3	.162	.921	3	.079
.504	4	.496	.589	4	.411	.674	4	.326	.756	4	.244	.841	4	.159	.923	4	.077
.507	5	.493	.592	5	.408	.677	5	.323	.759	5	.241	.844	5	.156	.926	5	.074
.510	6	.490	.595	6	.405	.679	6	.321	.762	6	.238	.847	6	.153	.929	6	.071
.512	7	.488	.597	7	.403	.682	7	.318	.764	7	.236	.849	7	.151	.932	7	.068
.515	8	.485	.600	8	.400	.685	8	.315	.767	8	.233	.852	8	.148	.934	8	.066
.518	9	.482	.603	9	.397	.688	9	.312	.770	9	.230	.855	9	.145	.937	9	.063
.521	10	.479	.605	10	.395	.690	10	.310	.773	10	.227	.858	10	.142	.940	10	.060
.523	11	.477	.608	11	.392	.693	11	.307	.775	11	.225	.860	11	.140	.942	11	.058
.526	12	.474	.611	12	.389	.696	12	.304	.778	12	.222	.863	12	.137	.945	12	.055
.529	13	.471	.614	13	.386	.699	13	.301	.781	13	.219	.866	13	.134	.948	13	.052
.532	14	.468	.616	14	.384	.701	14	.299	.784	14	.216	.868	14	.132	.951	14	.049
.534	15	.466	.619	15	.381	.704	15	.296	.786	15	.214	.871	15	.129	.953	15	.047
.537	16	.463	.622	16	.378	.707	16	.293	.789	16	.211	.874	16	.126	.956	16	.044
.540	17	.460	.625	17	.375	.710	17	.290	.792	17	.208	.877	17	.123	.959	17	.041
.542	18	.458	.627	18	.373	.712	18	.288	.795	18	.205	.879	18	.121	.962	18	.038
.545	19	.455	.630	19	.370	.715	19	.285	.797	19	.203	.882	19	.118	.964	19	.036
.548	20	.452	.633	20	.367	.718	20	.282	.800	20	.200	.885	20	.115	.967	20	.033
.551	21	.449	.636	21	.364	.721	21	.279	.803	21	.197	.888	21	.112	.970	21	.030
.553	22	.447	.638	22	.362	.723	22	.277	.805	22	.195	.890	22	.110	.973	22	.027
.556	23	.444	.641	23	.359	.726	23	.274	.808	23	.192	.893	23	.107	.975	23	.025
.559	24	.441	.644	24	.356	.729	24	.271	.811	24	.189	.896	24	.104	.978	24	.022
.562	25	.438	.647	25	.353	.731	25	.269	.814	25	.186	.899	25	.101	.981	25	.019
.564	26	.436	.649	26	.351	.734	26	.266	.816	26	.184	.901	26	.099	.984	26	.016
.567	27	.433	.652	27	.348	.737	27	.263	.819	27	.181	.904	27	.096	.986	27	.014
.570	28	.430	.655	28	.345	.740	28	.260	.822	28	.178	.907	28	.093	.989	28	.011
.573	29	.427	.658	29	.342	.742	29	.258	.825	29	.175	.910	29	.090	.992	29	.008
.575	30	.425	.660	30	.340	.745	30	.255	.827	30	.173	.912	30	.088	.995	30	.005
.578	31	.422	.663	31	.337				.830	31	.170				.997	31	.003

Bibliography

BALDWIN, BIRD T. 1921. *The Physical Growth of Children from Birth to Maturity.* ("The University of Iowa Studies in Child Welfare," Vol. I, No. 1.) Iowa City, Iowa.

BAYER, LEONA M. 1939. "Build in Relation to Menstrual Disorders and Obesity," *Endocrinology,* 24:260–68.

———. 1940a. "Build Variations in Adolescent Girls," *J. Pediat.,* 17:331–44.

———. 1940b. "Weight and Menses in Adolescent Girls, with Special Reference to Build," *J. Pediat.,* 17:345–54.

———. 1947. "Pseudohermaphrodism: A Psychosomatic Case Study," *Psychosomatic Med.,* 9:246–55.

———. 1956. "Growth Following Castration in Two Adolescent Girls," *J. Am. Med. Women's Assoc.,* 11:1–10.

BAYER, LEONA M., and BAYLEY, NANCY. 1949. "Stature Prediction in Stature Control," *Stanford Med. Bull.,* 7:130–36.

———. 1953. "Growth and Maturation of a Girl with Idiopathic Precocious Puberty," *Stanford Med. Bull.,* 11:241–52.

BAYER, LEONA M., and GRAY, H. 1935. "Plotting of a Graphic Record of Growth for Children Aged from One to Nineteen Years," *Am. J. Dis. Child.,* 50:1408–17.

BAYER, LEONA M., and KOETS, PETER. 1951. "Relation of 17-Ketosteroid Excretion to the Completeness of the Virilizing Syndrome," *Am. J. Med. Sciences,* 222:13–17.

BAYER, LEONA M., and REICHARD, SUZANNE. 1951. "Androgyny, Weight, and Personality," *Psychosomatic Med.,* 13:358–74.

BAYLEY, NANCY. 1943a. "Skeletal Maturing in Adolescence as a Basis for Determining Percentage of Completed Growth," *Child Devel.,* 14:1–46.

———. 1943b. "Size and Body Build of Adolescents in Relation to Rate of Skeletal Maturing," *Child Devel.,* 14:47–90.

———. 1946. "Tables for Predicting Adult Height from Skeletal Age and Present Height," *J. Pediat.,* 28:49–64.

———. 1956a. "Growth Curves of Height and Weight by Age for Boys and Girls, Scaled According to Physical Maturity," *J. Pediat.,* 48:187–94.

———. 1956b. "Individual Patterns of Development," *Child Devel.,* 27:1–21.

BAYLEY, NANCY, and BAYER, LEONA M. 1946. "The Assessment of Somatic Androgyny," *Am. J. Phys. Anthrop.,* N.S., 4:433–62.

BAYLEY, NANCY, and PINNEAU, SAMUEL R. 1952. "Tables for Predicting Adult Height from Skeletal Age: Revised for Use with the Greulich-Pyle Hand Standards," *J. Pediat.,* 40:423–41.

BEHNKE, A. R., GUTTENTAG, O. E., and BRODSKY, C. 1957a. *Quantification of Body Configuration in Geometrical Terms.* (United States Naval Radiological Defense Laboratory Technical Report 204.)

BEHNKE, A. R., and SIRI, W. E. 1957b. *The Estimation of Lean Body Weight from Anthropometric and X-Ray Measurements.* (United States Naval Radiological Defense Laboratory Technical Report 203.)

BRODY, SAMUEL. 1927. *Growth and Development. III. Growth Rates: Their Evaluation and Significance.* (Missouri Agr. Expt. Sta. Res. Bull. No. 97.) Columbia, Mo.

BRUCH, HILDE. 1939. "The Fröhlich Syndrome: Report of the Original Case." (Translation and Abstract in English.) *Am. J. Dis. Child.,* 58:1282–89.

BUEHL, C. C., and PYLE, S. I. 1942. "The Use of Age at First Appearance of Three Ossification Centers in Determining the Skeletal Status of Children," *J. Pediat.,* 21:335–42.

CATTELL, PSYCHE. 1934. "Preliminary Report on the Measurement of the Hand and Wrist," *Human Biol.,* 6:454–71.

DRAPER, GEORGE. 1941. "The Mosaic of Androgyny," *New England Med. J.,* 225:393–401.

DRAPER, G., DUPERTUIS, C. W., and CAUGHEY, J. L., JR. 1944. *Human Constitution in Clinical Medicine.* New York: Paul B. Hoeber, Inc.

DUPERTUIS, C. W., ATKINSON, W. B., and ELFTMAN, H. 1945. "Sex Differences in Pubic Hair Distribution," *Human Biol.,* 17:137–42.

EICHORN, DOROTHY H. 1955. "A Comparison of Laboratory Determinations and Wetzel Grid Estimates of Basal Metabolism among Adolescents," *J. Pediat.,* 46:146–55.

ERIKSON, ERIK HOMBURGER. 1950. *Childhood and Society.* New York: W. W. Norton & Co.

FISHER, R. A. 1936. *Statistical Methods for Research Workers.* Edinburgh and London: Oliver & Boyd.

FLORY, CHARLES D. 1936. *Osseous Development in the Hand as an Index of Skeletal Development.* ("Society for Research in Child Development Monographs," Vol. I, No. 3.) Chicago.

FRÖHLICH, ALFRED. 1901. "Ein Fall von Tumor der Hypophysis cerebri ohne Acromegalie," *Wien. Klin. Rund.,* 15:883–86, 906–8.

GALLAGHER, J. ROSWELL, and GALLAGHER, C. D. 1953. "Some Comments on Growth and Development in Adolescence," *Yale J. Biol. Med.,* 25:334–48.

GAVAN, J. A., WASHBURN, S. L., and LEWIS, P. H. 1952. "Photography: An Anthropometric Tool," *Am. J. Phys. Anthrop.,* N.S., 10:331–54.

GLUECK, SHELDON, and GLUECK, ELEANOR. 1956. *Physique and Delinquency.* New York: Harper & Bros.

GRAY, H. 1922. "Sitting Height and Stem Length in Private School Boys," *Am. J. Dis. Child.,* 23:406–18.

———. 1928. "Weight Prediction from Stature and Pelvic Breadth Is Better than from Stature and Age," *J. Clin. Invest.,* 6:27–28.

GRAY, H. 1948. "Prediction of Adult Stature," *Child Devel.*, **19**:167–75.

GRAY, H., and AYRES, J. G. 1931. *Growth in Private School Children*. Chicago: University of Chicago Press.

GREULICH, W. W., DORFMAN, R. I., CATCHPOLE, H. R., SOLOMON, C. I., and CULOTTA, C. S., 1942. *Somatic and Endocrine Studies of Puberal and Adolescent Boys*. ("Society for Research in Child Development Monographs," Vol. VII, No. 3.) Chicago.

GREULICH, W. W., and PYLE, S. I. 1950. *Radiographic Atlas of Skeletal Development of the Hand and Wrist*. Stanford University: Stanford University Press.

———. 1959. *Radiographic Atlas of Skeletal Development of the Hand and Wrist*. 2d ed. Stanford University: Stanford University Press.

HATHAWAY, MILICENT L. 1957. *Heights and Weights of Children and Youth in the United States*. (Home Economics Research Report No. 2.) Washington, D.C.: United States Dept. of Agriculture.

HOLT, L. EMMETT, JR., and MCINTOSH, RUSTIN. 1953. *Pediatrics*. New York: Appleton-Century-Crofts, Inc.

JONES, HAROLD E. 1949. *Motor Performance and Growth*. ("University of California Publications in Child Development," No. 1.) Berkeley: University of California Press.

JONES, MARY COVER, and BAYLEY, NANCY. 1950. "Physical Maturing among Boys as Related to Behavior," *J. Educ. Psych.*, **41**:129–48.

KRETSCHMER, E. 1925. *Physique and Character*. New York: Harcourt, Brace & Co.

MACY, ICIE G., and KELLY, HARRIET J. 1957. *Chemical Anthropology*. Chicago: University of Chicago Press.

MARTIN, RUDOLPH. 1928. *Lehrbuch der Anthropologie*, Vol. I. 2d ed. Jena: Fischer.

MUSSEN, P. H., and JONES, M. C. 1957. "Self-conceptions, Motivations, and Interpersonal Attitudes of Late- and Early-Maturing Boys," *Child Devel.*, **28**:243–56.

NELSON, WALDO E. 1954. *Textbook of Pediatrics*. Philadelphia: W. B. Saunders Co.

NICOLSON, ARLINE B., and HANLEY, CHARLES. 1953. "Indices of Physiological Maturity: Derivation and Interrelationships," *Child Devel.*, **24**:1–38.

PEARL, RAYMOND, and MINER, JOHN R. 1932. "A Table for Ascertaining Elapsed Time in Years and Decimals of a Year between Any Two Dates," *Quart. Bull. of the Milbank Mem. Fund*, **10**:151–54.

PYLE, S. I., and HOERR, N. L. 1955. *Radiographic Atlas of Skeletal Development of the Knee*. Springfield, Ill.: Charles C Thomas.

REYNOLDS, E. L., and WINES, J. V. 1948. "Individual Differences in Physical Changes Associated with Adolescence in Girls," *Am. J. Dis. Child.*, **75**:329–50.

SHELDON, W. H., STEVENS, S. S., and TUCKER, W. B. 1940. *The Varieties of Human Physique*. New York: Harper & Bros.

STOCKARD, C. R. 1931. *The Physical Basis of Personality*. New York: W. W. Norton & Co.

STOLZ, HERBERT ROWELL, and STOLZ, LOIS MEEK. 1951. *Somatic Development of Adolescent Boys*. New York: Macmillan Co.

THAYER, W. S. 1919. "Osler, the Teacher," *Bull. of the Johns Hopkins Hospital*, **30**:198.

TODD, T. W. 1930. "The Roentgenographic Appraisement of Skeletal Differentiation," *Child Devel.*, **1**:298–310.

———. 1937. *Atlas of Skeletal Maturation*. St. Louis: C. V. Mosby Co.

WETZEL, NORMAN C. 1946. "Use of the Grid Technic as a Guide to the Treatment of Disease Causing Growth Failure in Children." Chap. 1 in *Pediatric Progress*, H. R. LITCHFIELD and L. H. DEMBO, eds. New York: Grune & Stratton, Inc.

WILKINS, LAWSON. 1957. *The Diagnosis and Treatment of Endocrine Disorders in Childhood and Adolescence*. Springfield, Ill.: Charles C Thomas.

WOLFF, EUGENE. 1933. *Anatomy for Artists*. 2d ed. New York: Macmillan Co.

Index